Walk the Walk, Talk the Talk

Published in 2016 by Forget-Me-Nots, Canterbury
Made and printed by NXP Europe, Tunbridge Wells

Front cover image copyright © Rosemary Oliver
Back cover image copyright © Jen Holland Photography

ISBN 978-0-9930742-1-9

Dedication

Whilst many of the chapters in this book are dedicated to specific individuals or groups of people who have played a significant role in my story, the most important person in my story is the one to whom this whole book is dedicated, that is my wife Rosemary.

Rosemary...

We live our love and life together
We care for each other together
We laugh, shed a tear and share our stories and thoughts together
We walk the walk and talk the talk together.

Foreword by Richard Madeley

Picture this: a man in late middle age, with dementia.

A man who has been dealing with his dementia for a long time – six or seven years; probably longer than that. (Those early symptoms were so easily brushed aside, weren't they? So comfortably explained away, even smiled at.)

What do you see? How might such a man appear, after all this time? A frail, uncertain, person? Someone standing on the fringes of the life he once led? Probably confused, afraid, fearful...

You could hardly be more wrong. Keith Oliver, who was diagnosed with dementia in 2010 aged 55 could hardly represent a stronger, crisper, more vibrant challenge to the stereotype of a man with dementia.

I know Keith. I've met him several times since I became an ambassador for Alzheimer's Society. We usually bump into each other at one of the Society's hallmark annual events – because if I'm hosting them, he's often one of the key speakers – and I'm always relieved he's on the programme. It'll be ten minutes when I can relax.

Yes, Keith has dementia. But he is no wavering, timorous recluse. He makes confident, funny, breezy and brave speeches. He gives his audience genuine insight into the condition - and not so much as how to live with it, but how to live with it WELL.

This is Keith's latest book. *Walk the Walk, Talk the Talk* rests on a formula that I, as a journalist by training, am deeply familiar with: 'How, What, When, Where, Who?' The fundamentals of any breaking news story: their core structure. Be the first to find the answers to these one-word questions, and you'll have your scoop.

Keith says he uses the mantra to organise his wider thoughts and decisions, but specifically he used it in planning and writing this wonderful book. He's been giving talks and lectures since 2011 on how to manage dementia (to large audiences who are expecting to see a diminished figure but end up deciding they'd rather like him as their MP, or failing that to see him as a regular contributor on *Question Time*).

Keith says now that he remembers not so much what the people he meets (such as myself) *say:* more how they make him *feel*.

I can think of worse ways to catalogue one's encounters with others.

Recent research has shown that regular exercise, such as a daily brisk walk, is highly effective in combating the advance of dementia. Keith writes that his habitual walking not only helps in this way, but is also hugely important in stimulating his thoughts, and inspiring him when it comes to writing. Many authors report the same effect: I have written three novels and when stuck on a plotline, a good walk often clears the mental blockage.

Walk the Walk, Talk the Talk is an essential companion for anyone who has been diagnosed with dementia, or those close to them.

And for the rest of us? It's a damn good read.

Richard Madeley, Alzheimer's Society Ambassador

Introduction from Reinhard Guss
Kent & Medway NHS and Social Care Partnership Trust (KMPT)

It is a tremendous pleasure to be asked to contribute to introducing the book that for several years now I have felt that Keith should be writing. From discussions of the concept to seeing examples of the content I am sure it will make a significant contribution to a body of literature that is still far too small: the first-hand accounts of people living well with dementia. Keith provides an impressive example of what can be achieved in the wake of an early diagnosis. I particularly like the way that the voices of people living with dementia are featured, and woven in amongst the contributions from the astonishing range of professionals working in the dementia field with whom Keith has been collaborating.

Over five and a half years since first meeting Keith following his diagnosis of Young Onset Alzheimer's disease, being asked to contribute to his book is a very special pleasure in a number of different but intertwined ways, broadly falling into personal and professional aspects. Perhaps not too surprisingly, since we both live in the small city of Canterbury, I had heard about Keith long before we met in person. I had even seen him in the distance at one of the school fetes of his primary school, where my sister-in-law was teaching. Thus, I had also heard about changes and difficulties at Keith's work. His case formed a part of a discussion around his test results at our monthly East Kent peer supervision meeting of clinical psychologists involved in the neuropsychological assessment of suspected dementia. For the clinician, these early factors in our collaboration emphasized the importance of thinking about boundaries, and ethical issues at the overlap between the professional and the personal in the different aspects of our relationships with people with a dementia diagnosis.

At the time I had changed posts within Kent, and had just re- joined the national committee of FPOP, the British Psychological Society's Faculty for the Psychology of Older People, keen to develop usefulness and awareness of psychological approaches in dementia. In my previous Medway post I had been working with an active group of younger people with dementia who, just prior to the publication of the first English Dementia Strategy, had become involved in peer support and public awareness raising. I was missing them, and having retained my trust role of Yong Onset Dementia Lead, I was looking for ways to increase the involvement of people with dementia further into decision making, training, service evaluation and development. This is when I happened upon an article in a local newspaper where Keith spoke candidly about the reason for his early retirement, and I hoped that making contact could be the starting point for East Kent Dementia Involvement.

In our early meetings we explored ways of collaborating, found common interests, discussed our aims and expectations, what support was needed and how to understand and define our relationship. Keith's term of the 'professional friends' has stuck from those times, and formed a helpful reference point for us, and for many of my subsequent relationships in the world of dementia service user involvement. Of course, questions of what this means surface for us both at times, and we revisit every so often. While Tom Kitwood's concept of relating and supporting personhood seems more appropriate here than the focus on clear boundaries from my psychotherapy training, it continues to feel like somewhat uncharted territory.

Keith's eagerness to explore new experiences, and his willingness and capacity to reflect on them make working with him so rewarding and educational for the Psychologist, whilst his warmth, openness, positivity and encouragement make time spent with him so enjoyable personally, and for such a wide range of people. Along with his ability to engage with varied audiences, no doubt honed in his teaching days, and his skill in operating and functioning in committee settings, which he will have practiced and perfected as a headmaster and education adviser, Keith has accumulated a rapidly increasing portfolio of local, regional and national roles, as well as a media and publishing profile.

Our joint study during the first year of how involvement works, looking into what helped, what hindered and what made things worthwhile, listed already over forty separate activities! It is good to know that the dos and don'ts we developed form this work with the help of Ian Asquith during his placement year, did not only serve as a presentation at our first Alzheimer's Disease International conference, but continue to be useful to Keith, and to others doing similar work.

Particular highlights of working with Keith have been the development of the role of Kent and Medway Partnership Trust Dementia Service User Envoy, forming a framework for involvement work in our local NHS trust, and founding, co-chairing and supporting the East Kent Forget Me Nots. Since then, Keith has provided one of the most inspirational examples of making best use of life-long skills, while managing the impact of progressive cognitive disability, well evidenced by his branching out into work with a whole range of organisations, quite independently of our initial joint work.

It has been a real pleasure to meet up with Keith, and to continue our mutual collaboration on groups like the National Young Onset Dementia Steering Group; to catch up at the fringes of the IDEAL Advisory Group; or to discuss more than the forthcoming agenda while travelling on the train to the DAA's board meeting. At first, not everyone was as confident in our endeavours as we were, but I think we can safely say that we have proved some of the more downbeat predictions of our early work together quite wrong, and I am looking forward to continuing our professional friendship for many years to come.

Reinhard Guss, KMPT Acting Head of Older People's Psychology - East Kent

Introduction from Lisa Bogue
formerly of the Alzheimer's Society

Growing up I had very little experience of dementia, other than a frightening visit to a care home as a Brownie and my friend's lovely grandmother who lost the ability to care for her family and herself, but continued to beautifully articulate love and affection. During a year out from my degree in graphic design I worked in a nursing home for people with advanced dementia. With no training, and little support from colleagues due to their capacity, I cared for the residents and supported them with their day-to-day life. Caring for the residents taught me about dementia and the unjust challenges it imposes upon everyone affected, about the inadequate infrastructure in society to support people with dementia and those close to them, and ultimately the residents themselves taught me the importance of love and kindness.

Inspired by the residents, I focused my final year degree work on dementia. I researched how people with dementia can be involved in design as a way to help alleviate some of the symptoms that are associated with dementia, but not necessarily caused by the disease. Upon graduating I wasn't sure exactly what I wanted to do, other than knowing it had to be something that made a difference for people affected by dementia, and I joined the Alzheimer's Society. After a year working in an admin job at the Society, I was processing a new role being advertised; it was all about enabling people affected by dementia to have their voice heard and I realised that was exactly what I wanted to do.

Keith and I first met over two years ago on a video call for my interview for the Engagement and Participation role. I was in the US visiting family and nervously delivered a presentation about the benefits of involving people affected by dementia in our work. Despite the Atlantic Ocean and a slight delay on the line between us, Keith put me at ease by asking why I wanted the job. The next time we met, I'd had a call from reception that there was a visitor for me. Assuming they'd called the wrong person as I never had visitors, I popped out to be greeted by a beaming big friendly giant whose face and voice I recognised from the video call interview. We chatted about the interview and the job, and learning that I had impressed Keith gave me so much confidence.

Since then, supported by Keith, my skills and abilities have continued to grow. Together we've co-delivered ten workshops that Keith helped to design, training staff and volunteers to meaningfully involve people affected by dementia. Together we have reached around 175 staff and volunteers and helped to give them the skills and confidence to support people affected by dementia to have their voice heard.

Keith has been instrumental in my development; in practical ways he connected me to colleagues I wouldn't otherwise know, made me aware of fantastic external projects and continued to motivate me when there were more challenges than successes. But he has gone far beyond developing me in my career; Keith has been like a fairy godfather to me. His helpful words, willingness to share his own experiences and person-centred approach have been an enduring magic wand that has gradually transformed me into a much more confident and content person.

Keith's drive to share his experiences of living with dementia continues to make an immeasurable impact on making life better for people affected by dementia now and in the future. I hope that he continues to inspire others affected by dementia to also realise how much expertise they have, how much they can offer and how good it can feel to have their voice heard.

Lisa Bogue, written when in post as the Engagement and Participation Officer for the Greater London Region at Alzheimer's Society (at time of writing, Senior Patient Involvement Officer at Cancer Research UK)

Introduction by Nada Savitch
Innovations in Dementia

Keith has taught me so much about life, relationships – and yes - living with dementia. Keith is a natural teacher as well as a trained one. He leads by example and always boosts people's wellbeing and confidence. He has such an encouraging way with people, I wish he had been my boss – he must have been a wonderful person to work for.

I guess the main lesson Keith has taught me is that people with dementia are the best advocates for people with dementia.

I first met Keith when the DEEP network was just beginning. His involvement personifies the principles of DEEP. As one person with dementia he makes a difference, as part of the Forget Me Nots group in Kent he can influence more, but as part of a collective voice of 50 different groups across the UK he will really get things changed.

Keith was instrumental in starting Forget Me Nots. He realised that although his role as Dementia Envoy was important, he was just one man. He knew that there were other people with dementia who also wanted their voices heard, and so encouraged the development of the Kent Forget Me Nots.

When I met Keith, I realised we were on the right track developing DEEP as a UK-wide network of dementia voices. He explained to me that people with dementia are more than their emotional stories – that they can contribute real insight into the development of services, policy and practice. I was so honoured when he agreed to launch the first set of DEEP guidelines at the DAA in November 2013.

My background is in the provision of information – both as a librarian and in developing information-based websites. I believe that knowledge is power. Information is key to understanding and making sense of the world. I have often heard Keith say the same.

I'm one of the directors of Innovations in Dementia, a social enterprise that works with people with dementia and tries to promote what people with dementia can do. Innovations in Dementia facilitates the DEEP network of groups of people with dementia across the UK who want to influence policy and practice.

Dementia affects people's ability to process information. It is difficult to work out who or what to trust. That is why involving people with dementia in supporting other people with dementia is so important. I have seen the effect on others when a person with dementia like Keith is honest and open about his dementia. How just by talking about his struggles (not being 'bullet-proof') he can reduce the shame, stigma and confusion that so many people with dementia feel.

But it is also important that people hoping to support people with dementia have the correct information. That is why people like Keith, groups like Forget Me Nots and initiatives like DEEP can make a difference. It is only by truly listening to people with dementia that we can even begin to understand what living with dementia is like. It is only by beginning to spread that knowledge that we can improve the lives of people with dementia.

I'm grateful for this opportunity to thank you, Keith.

Nada Savitch, Innovations in Dementia

Introduction from a friend and member of the editorial team of Walk the Walk, Talk the Talk

I first met Keith Oliver at Café Solo, the cosy cafe that lies halfway between our homes. We'd been put in touch through a friend, and I knew only that he wanted to write down some stories of his life experiences within a group setting, and that he had dementia. I wasn't sure what to expect.

I discovered that Keith's vision was one of a creative, stimulating environment where people of all ages could connect and benefit together. He constantly sought to release people's potential – and this is what he did for me: when we met I was deeply uncertain of my capabilities in leading a group of this kind. Keith wasn't put off by my lack of confidence or experience – in fact, in retrospect I can see clearly how he gently pushed me to believe that I could achieve something meaningful and lasting.

We went on to set up the life writing course at Canterbury's Beaney Library, which resulted in the book, *Welcome to our World*.

Keith's heart to see others reach their potential is something that's had a tremendous effect on me. T.S. Eliot famously said, 'Only those who will risk going too far can possibly find out how far one can go.' Keith Oliver is someone who is brave enough to take risks to pursue his hopes, dreams and visions. This book is another example! So many people talk about what they dream of doing: actively pursuing your dreams takes immense courage, and positive action. The brilliant thing I've noticed with Keith is that his dreams are never selfish: he's always searching out ways to encourage others to become all that they are capable of being (hence his inclusion of so many other voices, including mine, in this book!)

I didn't know much about dementia from a medical point of view when I first met Keith, but he quickly made me realise that my medical understanding was not the key here: people with dementia are, first and foremost, *people*. People with interests, passions, histories and stories to tell. People to value and respect, with their own characters and unique perspectives on the world.

It has been my privilege to get to know Keith and to meet and write with him and others with a diagnosis of dementia. Their determination to live well and to contribute positively to their communities inspires me continually to value life in the present tense, and to embrace its challenges with hope, enthusiasm, persistence and friends.

Liz Jennings is an author and writing tutor living in Canterbury

Contents

Part One:

Walk the Walk

Judging a book by its cover

We are both at times guilty of judging a book by its cover whether it is a real book or a metaphorical one, and are always pleased to be proved wrong in this hasty assessment, especially if the reality is better than the expectation. Whilst this phrase only appears here, it is central to much of this book and we hope the reader comes away from it at the end with a greater insight into Keith the person as well as a better understanding of dementia.

When we initially spoke about artwork for the book, Keith's idea was for me to create some pen and ink drawings to support the writing. I wasn't sure about this as I do not feel that I am a proficient enough artist. Keen to draw and paint, yes - but I am a less confident person than he often presents me as. Giving thought to the idea and his usual encouragement led me to say yes. I should have guessed he would then ask for more, after all his name is 'Oliver!' The next conversation we had on the subject centred on him asking me to design and paint the front cover. 'But I've never done anything like this before,' was my way of trying to say no and hope he would drop the idea. No chance. His approach was to ask the how, what, where type questions and from this my interest grew and I was hooked!

The cover of Walk the Walk, Talk the Talk is based on a variety of imagery - some obvious, some subtle - and we hope that as you progress through the book you will see the purpose of each part of the picture.

The background shows the view through an open door which, as former colleagues and pupils of Keith will recognise, is the way he used to work both literally and figuratively. It was also central to our conversation on the first day that Alzheimer's was suggested as the diagnosis we were both going to live with in the future. We discussed less than an hour after the initial diagnosis how we would cope; the one door closing, one door opening was Keith's approach, from which we have both tried to take strength since then.

The swan represents his self-image of how he looks on the surface; below the surface is often very different for both the swan and Keith. Good days for both Keith and me are days when the sun shines in our minds, hence the sun shining brightly in the picture. We spent ages talking about the footprints and possibly using speech bubbles, and the relevance to incorporating them in the design was the biggest challenge. The bubbles were thankfully dropped and the footprints changed significantly but retained.

Now that it is finished we like the cover, and think, for us, it works well. We sincerely hope you like it as well, and that it helps you in coming with us on our journey; a journey which like all journeys has a beginning, a middle and an end. Thank you for joining us so that we can talk to you on our way, and so that we don't walk alone.

Rosemary and Keith Oliver
Canterbury, September 2016

With A Little Help from My Friends

The emotions that Joe Cocker put into singing this song at the legendary Woodstock Music Festival in 1969 stayed with me long after I saw the film of it as a wide-eyed 17-year-old. Friendships are an emotional shared experience, and they so enrich our lives. I am extremely fortunate that since being diagnosed with dementia a large number of caring, thoughtful and compassionate people have come into my life and so enriched it. I have often said openly that the best thing about having dementia has been the amazing people I have met since being diagnosed, and this is honest and accurate. Many of these new friends are what one would refer to as 'professional friends,' and if that helps keep the friendship workable for us both then I will certainly sign up to that.

Elsewhere in this book I write about friends from my student days and from my time as a head teacher, and I think I was friendly towards colleagues. There was always the need for a little distance, and thus the role could at times be quite a lonely path to travel. I think that is another reason why I am so pleased that a number of friendships have been formed with professionals who care. The Kitwood flower means so much to me and I would wish to see

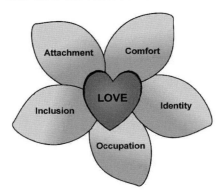

it mean as much to everyone, not only in the world of dementia but more generally.

(*The Kitwood Flower from* Dementia Reconsidered – the person comes first, *Kitwood, T. 1997, Open University Press, pp81- 84*)

I want to express my sincere, heartfelt thanks to the family and friends who, without hesitation, said 'yes' when asked to write a piece for this book and then they, too, walked the walk by putting this into action and sending me some moving and wonderful pieces which I now share with you. Each contribution adds to the story. Each person's honesty shines through. When considering this idea, I was extremely wary of it being seen as fishing for compliments or an ego boost. Nothing could have been further from my mind; as the seventy people who have contributed will vouch, that simply isn't me.

Understandably my long term memory is quite good but the short term needs memory aids for it to function. My memory aid here are the friends and family who have written. Some memories we shared I do remember, others I have forgotten. Some came back with your help - others have remained elusive. (My father who often slipped into spoonerisms without realising would say 'Our Keith has a photogenic memory.' We all knew what he meant, and no one argued with this within our family.)

They say every dark cloud has a silver lining; this is as true for me as it is for the amazing people I have either known from before being diagnosed or who have entered my life since. I wanted to share the story and the opportunity to contribute to my story as these people do every day outside of the book. *Welcome to our World* was a team project with two leaders, whilst this is more of a solo project it works best I feel when seen as a collaboration.

Whether the friend has known me for one year or forty years, they each know I am loyally committed to our friendship and that I will walk the extra mile for my family and friends. I hope that by reading this you will know me better, and that not only old friendships will become even more cherished in the time remaining, but new ones will be built and given opportunity to blossom and bloom. Thank you.

Keith Oliver, Canterbury, September 2016

Walk the Walk, Talk the Talk

Those that know me won't be surprised to hear that when considering writing a book of this sort I was hesitant at first and then, once I had thought deeply about the project and made it clear in my mind which direction to go in, I set out with what could be considered as drive, enthusiasm, energy, and yes, bloody-mindedness!

Structure for me is now crucial in all I do, and often I build this around these key words: how, what, where, when, who... These provide such a useful framework to any problem solving or planning challenge, and I try and encourage others I meet and speak with to do the same. I will refer back to this as the story unfolds.

Using these five key words resulted in me thinking of a plan for the book. I wanted to utilise the body of talks I have delivered since 2011 to a range of audiences about the challenges alongside strategies for trying to live well with dementia. I do like talking, but also I like to listen and I have learnt an awful lot from listening to talks and conversations with professionals and others affected by dementia at meetings and conferences. I want to continue to engage with other people and remain inter-dependant rather than just independent for as long as possible. Often I will say I now no longer remember the bulk of what people say to me but I do remember how they made me feel. One can learn as much from listening, talking and engaging emotionally as one can cognitively.

When first being asked to deliver talks I recognised that I was something of a rarity for the audience (still am on some occasions!) I quickly realised that I challenged the stereotypical image of a person with dementia, as the majority of the audience would see this being a much older, frailer person with more impaired function than this bloke in front of them. From early on I was determined to give the audiences a real sense of the person beyond the dementia. I am so pleased that this approach has been taken on board by others who share this pathway and who also seek to raise awareness and influence through engaging with health and social care professionals and the public generally.

Alongside this I have attended four life writing courses over the past three years and have enjoyed, through great teaching from April Doyle, Liz Jennings and Nicky Thompson, the opportunity to re-visit past events and thoughts, to reflect upon them and to then write about them in a memoir format. This book gives me the opportunity to record and share with you some of these events and thoughts.

The third element to the book, and all are equally important to me, are the thoughts and memories of a range of family and friends. In the case of the latter some friendships stretch back many years, and at times they seem to have belonged to a different person than the person I am today; other friendships are much more recent and these friendships have been one of the few blessings of having to live with dementia. Regarding these important parts of this book, my memory of what people say to me used to be very good, now it isn't so. I have relied upon written memories from friends provided over the past few months rather than testing my recall (and possibly our friendship!) by risking getting it wrong.

Moving on to the walking. As I do not drive and wish to keep fit, I walk a lot. I always have done.

We often commented on Keith's physical fitness. He walked for miles all over Dover to attend meetings and to return to school afterwards. He had boundless energy and laughed off our concern.

Lyn Dourthe, colleague from Barton Junior School 1995-2000

Also the title illustrates I hope that I try and back up with action the talking I do, and always have done both personally and professionally. Much of my writing starts as ideas in my mind when out walking either on my own or with a companion. If it is the former then the inspiration comes partly from the surroundings - the marshland near where I live or the beach at Whitstable nearby, and from inspiring music on my iPod; if it is with Rosemary or a friend then the ideas develop from our conversation about the events and thoughts I want to write about. *Walk the Walk, Talk the Talk* - seems so fitting.

Part of this book is a self-examination, and I once read that those who study others are wise, but those who study themselves are enlightened. I have lived for 60 years and I think I am still learning things about myself - some of these please me, others do not. Writing this book has seen me experiencing a wide range of emotions, from real joy and pride to real distress when my abilities didn't match my expectations of myself, and my fear that I might let my family and friends down. I hope that my honesty in this book does come through and that, by reading it, we become a little wiser and a little more enlightened together.

Not all of the words in this book are mine. So much of the richness of this book is down to the words of others - my friends - to whom I offer my sincere thanks.

Walking and Talking with my family

Dedicated to my family, the people I care most about: Rosemary, Gareth, Karon, James, Yvonne, Nick, Sabrina, Byron, Rhian, William and Jane.

Whether it is through moving around quite a bit as a youngster or whether it is an Oliver family trait, I am not, I'm sorry to say, someone who has retained friends from my time as a child. I do envy others who can say this is so, and who have been mates for many years since they were at school together, rather like celebrity friends Jimmy Doherty and Jamie Oliver (no relation I'm afraid, or at least I don't think he is!) Even as a child, whilst Mam and Dad's family were both quite large they were not always close, even though most lived within five or six miles of each other. Most now alas have either died or are distant geographically since I left Nottingham when I was 22 (although going to University at 18 was the real break.) I have to explain that my mother would only ever answer to 'Mam,' perhaps this was her northern background, although she was very much of a hybrid mix of Scots, Geordie, Yorkshire with some South African mixed in for good measure, but not a trace of southern England. Consequently, trying to find Mother's Day cards in the heart of southern England was always a challenge for me!

Now that you know this about me, you'll appreciate that there are many positives in the story of my cousin Jane and I reuniting after a gap of about 35 years. I regard Jane as the only living person I know (who I am still in contact with) who knew me when we were children together. She won't thank me for saying this but she was a bit like a big sister to me as she is a little older and wiser than me. It was with her, her mum (Auntie Maisie) and Jane's younger brother Andrew that I spent hours and hours as a child when my mother was at work. All school holidays at junior school were at their house. Fishing for tiddlers in Fairham brook with pink net for Jane and blue for us boys are treasured memories; bringing sticklebacks and minnows home in jam jars was an early introduction to death as they failed to survive more than a day or so. We were never taught what I have always taught children; to put them back where they were caught immediately afterwards.

Jane's family and mine would occasionally go on holiday together - my first trip to our beloved Cornwall was with my parents, Jane, Auntie Maisie and Andrew - and I was keen to take Rosemary there many years later to the Jamaica Inn on Bodmin Moor. It seems like a lifetime ago, and that smugglers were maybe still around then! Jane, being older, was generally tolerant of her younger cousin and this taught me a little of how to get on with an almost sibling relationship, which as an only child I would otherwise have missed out on. When at University I remember my friends being surprised that I was an only child and I think the many hours, days and weeks spent with Jane and her family are to thank for this.

Christmas was a time for the extended family. Uncles, aunts and cousins would come around, often on Boxing Day, for a big family party. I remember the artificial Christmas tree and Jane's mum always making a snow scene with chalk figures. I loved playing with balloons and I guess recently I thought about the deflating balloon being a metaphor for one's creativity, optimism and motivation when 'the fog' descends. The answer then is to burst this balloon and blow another up, bigger and brighter, which is what I would do as a kid.

It's a strange feeling when both of one's parents are no longer alive. In a way this feeling surprises me because as an only child we were in many ways emotionally close, but having left the family home to go to University at 18, and then to Cheshire to teach at 22, before moving even further from them to Kent when I was 25 we haven't been physically close for most of my adult life. That does not lessen the bond and the sense of loss when they pass away. Dad died, aged 83, in 2011, and Mam followed three years later in 2014 aged 82.

Neither knew I had dementia as we thought there was nothing to gain from telling them. Mam had lived with severe mental illness certainly since her early forties and possibly before this. When I went to Sheffield it hit her very badly. Within six or seven months she had her first spell in Mapperly Hospital in Nottingham, a place previously she had always cited in very unsavoury terms, almost as a threat. After spells in hospital, various medication treatments and electric shock treatment she would be discharged for a short while before slipping back again and needing re-admission.

Around the age of 50 she was finally diagnosed rather than 'having bad nerves' as suffering manic depression, later known rather more positively as bi-polar disorder. Her mental state would vary between quite stable and lucid to bed-ridden and totally disinterested. She told me that she had attempted suicide a few times between her late forties and early sixties, and would say that she was scared of living, and Dad was scared of dying. I think in her world this was accurate. She was sectioned for her own safety a number of times and whilst seldom aggressive towards others, and never towards me, this illness had a dreadful impact upon their marriage which came to an end around 1983.

They couldn't live together, nor as it transpired could they live apart, as there were long periods where they did spend time together even going on occasional holidays, for example fulfilling a mutual ambition to visit, on a package holiday, California and the Mid-West of the USA in 1989 whilst Rosemary, Karon, James and I were spending our year in Australia.

Mother was extremely bright. If she had reached 18 in a later generation she would certainly have gone to a very good university. She was proud to say she had 'matriculated' from her Grammar School with flying colours, and upon leaving school she had worked in the National Provincial Bank in Market Square, Nottingham, later to be part of National Westminster and then Nat West. It always puzzled me that she said she had to leave the bank when she got married and had me, and I thought this was incredibly unfair on her and other young women like her. How far we have come in sixty years, though many would rightly say there is far to go to achieve equality in the workplace between the sexes.

At around the time she married she reminds me very much in looks and personality of the actress Jessica Raines who first caught my notice starring in the drama *Call the Midwife* - possibly it is the fashions as well as the hair, figure etc of that era.

The rest of her working life was spent carrying out a range of often quite challenging and stimulating secretarial roles, the highlight being for her the ten years she worked as a secretary to the boss of a company checking up on people seeking loans. Her memory of names and people was exceptional, and I think maybe I inherited this from her.

I am quite surprised that over the past two years I have, on foggy days, really struggled emotionally to look at old photos of my mother with me or by herself - the latter as a young, very pretty and bright woman. I know she loved me and I loved her; we were very close. That's inevitable, I guess, with a mother and only-son relationship. When her health declined it made this much harder. I was hurt and confused, and my dad found the situation all round very frustrating and I suspect scary though he never confided this in me.

My father was a very different character, and I guess I am a classic blend of both parents and yet neither of them. He worked hard all his life in a range of jobs - early on as a bus driver, next taking jobs selling and delivering tea and then bacon to shops around Nottingham, before finding on-the-move sales a tough world and deciding to settle into a TV shop selling sets at a time when colour was just becoming popular and accessible.

After a year or two of this he changed direction completely by getting a job at Plessey Electronics factory in Nottingham and in his early 40s starting an electronics course at night class twice a week. He used to examine circuit boards, a semi-skilled role, and he saw skilled electronics engineers earning heaps more than him and doing a job he envied. His realisation that he didn't have the mental agility or skill for this did frustrate him, and he sought to reduce this by trying to steer me in that direction. I was a teenager at the time, and although I helped him with his Maths homework from college there was no way I was going to pursue this path either in a factory or dealing with physics. I had foolishly dropped art and geography at 14 to study physics and chemistry to O-Level and then failed them both - twice!

We had a mixed relationship. Both of us were strong personalities. We enjoyed going to watch football and spending time together - though he would never stand with me, plonking me near the front with the other kids whilst he stood further back with other blokes he knew. He liked a beer or two and so did I from about the age of 16, and we did drink in pubs together sometimes. Our sense of humour was very similar and I think I inherited my love of gardening from him.

Looks-wise he closely resembled Tommy Cooper - the hair, the height and the nose! He didn't like Tommy Cooper. Once we were on a train together going to see Forest play an FA Cup match against Crystal Palace at Selhurst Park. In our carriage there were two lads aged about 12. They sat looking at dad for some time before one of them decided he HAD to ask the question, "Ere, Mister, are you Tommy Cooper?' That was the first time I had heard this link, but Dad replied with a smile, 'No, but I wish I had his money,' and he told me after this wasn't the first time someone had mistaken him.

He inherited from his father a volatile temper and a hardness which I'm thankful not to share. He would sometimes fly off the handle and would often shout and be aggressive. He would only occasionally hit me, sometimes for little reason other than his frustration. He was also often very negative about my studies and my interest in sports other than football. I think he feared me becoming 'a bookworm' or getting 'above myself' - he and I were so different around trying to realise our ambitions in life.

Although I represented the school at rugby many times I think he came to just one game; he couldn't follow it and gave up, never to come again. I never discussed what I was doing with him because there was never any positive response. I think at one time I sought his praise and to know that maybe I made him proud, but it seldom came so I looked elsewhere for this assurance, firstly in my mother, then in myself and then in Rosemary and my family and friends. I know that in his way he did love me, but possibly because of his own upbringing, which was very hard, he found it extremely difficult to show this especially when I was living at home. I suppose our relationship could be summed up as 'quite good, but could have been better!'

Even our final day didn't quite go right. Rosemary and I were dashing up the A1 to be with him, having had a call from the hospital to say could we get there because Dad was unlikely to live much beyond a day or two. We got as far as Peterborough when I took a call to say that he had passed away. One of his favourite songs was Matt Munro or Andy Williams singing *Almost There*; on this occasion it was never more fitting.

I first got to know Rosemary, or Mrs Ottey as she was then, when I started my first teaching job in Nantwich in 1978. Her two children, Gareth and Karon, were pupils in Years 6 and 4 in the school where I was teaching. Sadly, her husband John had passed away in 1977 from bowel cancer, leaving her with two young children. I never taught either child, except for in Karon's case taking her class for PE whilst Mrs Drysdale (her teacher) taught my class music. In Gareth's case his enjoyment and ability in football brought him into my world via the school football team, and through this I got to know Rosemary as she used to kindly and reliably help out with transporting boys to away matches and then stayed to watch and cheer them all on. Over the course of the year we got to know each other a little.

Then, by chance, I rented a house in the same road as the school with Phil Amos, another teacher. It was near to where Rosemary and the children lived. Rosemary, also feeling adventurous, joined us on the school field trip to Ilam Hall National Trust Youth Hostel in the Peak District near beautiful Dove Dale. I had been twice with a Sheffield school as a student and was keen to co-lead the trip with Phil as a newly qualified teacher.

During 1980 with Gareth just starting secondary school and Karon moving into year 5 we became slight friends, and I remember very clearly when Rosemary asked me round to watch the FA Cup Final in May 1980 (which West Ham won 1-0). As the year progressed so did our friendship. In the September we talked about attending a night class. She had done a motor mechanics course a couple of years previously and was keen to learn another skill. I was torn between a photography course and a badminton one. After comparing ideas she wasn't keen on the photography option and opted for badminton so I followed suit. This helped firm up our friendship when the course began in September 1980 and the two of us, knowing the children were well looked after by our friend and neighbour, would go for a drink afterwards either at a pub in Nantwich (and there were plenty to choose from back then) or at her house.

By the end of October, we were feeling serious towards each other and I proposed to Rosemary early in November after giving myself the half term holiday back in Nottingham on my own to think it through. Thankfully, she said yes, and then we started to plan our wedding for the first day of Spring; 21st March 1981. I felt I needed to consider my teaching position in the same school as Karon, who would be my stepdaughter. I had already thought that two or three years in my first job was about right so had chatted to the Head about looking for a promotion and the chance to teach Year 6 rather than Year 4 or 5 which I had previously taught. He was understanding and keen to keep me, but when I explained about Rosemary and I he also saw the benefits (in his eyes) of me moving on, which I did at the Christmas break 1980.

The weather on our wedding day was awful. It rained very heavily so all the photos were taken inside the church, St Barnabas in Crewe, which we both attended at the time. The night of the wedding the weather deteriorated further to snow as we began our honeymoon with a night in the exotic location of Congleton before moving onto to four days in Ashbourne near to the significant Ilam Hall. I was only allowed two or three days leave at that time from my new job. Gareth and Karon stayed with close friends, Tony and Daphne, in Crewe. Thus began what has been over 35 years - and growing - of largely very happily married life, and if either of us was offered that back in 1981 we would have readily grasped it.

When I fell in love with Rosemary I also fell in love with her two children, Gareth and Karon. I remember saying to them in the lounge in Nantwich that I did love them as if they were my own and would continue to do so. I think and hope that this has been the case. I ALWAYS think of, and refer to my three children because I do not differentiate between them. Although James is our son from our marriage and has some of my genes and blood flowing through his body all three are treated the same. I have never tried to compete for their love with their dad, and I say I am never going to be able to replace your dad, but I hope they do see me as a father figure because that is a very important role which I have tried to fulfil in their lives since we formed our family ties 35 years ago.

I remember going for a drink in a pub with a friend who was considering a similar course of action - marrying a woman not very long widowed with two young children. My advice to him was to enjoy it but never to try and compete with an angel. My best thoughts now come to me when walking, back then it was often with a drink in my hand.

Although we did consider staying in Rosemary's bungalow in Nantwich, and we had a builder give us a quote for a dormer extension to the property should we need this for an addition to the family later, we decided to move south. Rosemary had long wanted to re-settle near her siblings in Kent and I still felt nomadic, I guess. She brought me to Canterbury in February 1981 and the weather was perfect. Rosemary said the prophetic words, 'If you like it in the winter you will love it in the summer!'

I adored the place and still do when the traffic behaves itself! I had only once been there before, back in 1968 on a scout camp from Nottingham when we camped near Downe House - home of Charles Darwin - and had a day in Canterbury ending with a trip to the cinema to see *Thoroughly Modern Millie* starring a young Twiggy. It also served to allow her family to meet me and me to meet them, and many of them became and continue to be very good friends and have supported us both extremely well over the years.

Having a new home of our own was a very positive move, and alongside this the two children changed their name to Oliver which again helped bring us together as a family. Rosemary and I both wanted me to adopt the children and I was upset when we were understandably advised that, as my income was quite poor as a young teacher with two children soon to be joined by a third one and Rosemary was not working, adoption was not a sound practical move. This we were advised was even clearer as both the children could well choose to go to University and, with Rosemary as the sole legal parent, the grant they would receive and any other assistance would be significantly higher. So the pragmatic approach won over although on the whole I did not feel it had any adverse effect on mine or their feelings. I was 25 at this time, and looked quite youthful! To present as I did as father to two children aged 13 and 11 caused some questions to be asked, to which I usually replied 'I've worn very well and look much younger than my years!' Once I knew these people and developed friendships then I could be more forthcoming.

I feel immensely proud to have three very different grown up children, each of whom has achieved a lot in their lives; each has developed into an adult that I treasure and enjoy spending time with. I have tried to encourage them and sit down with them in a non-judgemental way, and offer advice if it is sought and likely to be helpful. Rosemary and I have celebrated with them their successes and hopefully provided a safe, loving and secure upbringing, which I know they have applied admirably to raising their own children.

I am equally proud of the next generation of our family who have come along over the past twenty years - in this I mean my three grandchildren; Byron, Rhian and William. As your grandad the times we have had together and continue to have are amongst the most memorable and significant in my life, and that of your Nan/Grandma. We love you all dearly, and look forward to many more happy days in the sun, sharing news of your successes and ways in which you meet the challenges which life holds for you.

There's no place like home

I distinctly remember being most impressed by the fact that our current home has three toilets, and saying to Rosemary at the time that in forty years I had moved from a house with no toilet (at least inside the house) to one with three, and that this was an indication of the trajectory my life had taken.

For me a house needs to be a home. I am not a minimalist, nor do I live in a very cluttered environment. I like to be surrounded by items which are either useful or help maintain memories of people, events or places. Having dementia may well have made this more pronounced but it has always been a part of me; what is different now is that I am hesitant to throw things out, as I fear losing the memory it encourages if I do so. Rosemary and I often say how hard it will be for our adult children if and when they have the task of sorting out our house. We then follow this conversation by me buying another book or CD and Rosemary another item for the home or garden!

We have lived in our current home on the edge of Canterbury for over sixteen years; the longest I have ever lived in a house. It's ironic that when we had three children at home we lived in a three bedroomed property and two of the kids shared a room. That was the best we could afford at the time. Now there are just the two of us we rattle around in a four bedroomed property. On one hand that makes little sense but we love it here. I know where everything is and how most things work. We have a garden we both adore - not too big but full of colour and interest. We are close to the city amenities and shops but overlook rural splendour with a view of the river Stour meandering lazily past our garden and a farm which is home for donkeys, sheep, chickens, dogs and two very noisy guinea fowl - we rarely need an alarm clock.

How different this is from my first home which was in an area of Nottingham known as 'The Meadows' - that's the end of the rural connection as the meadows the area was named after ceased to be in the mid/late Nineteenth Century with the opening of the Clifton coal mine and the need for cheap terraced houses to home the miners, two of whom were my great grandfather and my grandfather.

I wish I could remember more about that first house. It was 26 Briar Street - near Hawthorn Terrace and Crocus Street, again teasing reminders of the former rural idyll on the edge of Nottingham. They say that having dementia heightens one's long term memory, that might be true but for me it is only for memories which were previously retained; rarely do I experience the delight of a new memory from long ago. I remember my tiny bedroom being at the end of my parents' room and the tiny sitting room which, between about 1942 and 1954, had been a shop run by my paternal grandmother who also lived in our house (or, rather, we lived in hers) for the first two or three years of my life until her death in 1958. The two up/two down house must have been crowded. We also shared it with Willie, my grandmother's cat, who was also busy catching the various rodents who dared venture into the place. I remember the cellar where coal and other junk was thrown and then stored, but seldom was I allowed - or indeed did I wish - to spend time down there. We had a yard with a toilet in it and I remember the customary mangle for squeezing washing (and fingers.) Neighbours kept chickens, but we didn't. I guess some of my toys would have cluttered the little space we had.

My father had also been born in this same house in 1927, and when my parents married this became their home until 1962 when I was six. I suspect most people see their early days in a slightly overly positive way, but whenever one reads anything about 'the good old days' in The Meadows, or more popularly named 'Medders' one can see the tears well up behind those rose coloured specs. Life was hard for people there, but it is fair to say that the sense of community was very strong. Everyone knew everyone and their business, and what they didn't know I guess they made up! People did care and because my dad and gran had kept the shop everyone was their friend, and in turn mine.

I remember it being something of a wrench to leave behind these friends, especially Richard and Theresa who were the children of a Polish family nearby and 'DooDoo,' our next door neighbour - Mrs Dewsbury - who, when my gran died, became a surrogate gran to me. The last time I saw her was in March 1972, a short while before her home and ours fell victim to the bulldozer two years later, and she moved to the warmth and comfort (I hope) of a care home. I remember the day, as it was a Saturday and I had been into town to Selectadisc in Arkwright Street - a dark, slightly sinister feeling record shop, full of the local cognoscenti and with a rather strange smell in the air... I had bought the newly released Paul Simon solo album. I had awaited its release since becoming a fan in the wake of Bridge Over Troubled Water. The first solo album after the acrimonious split with Art Garfunkel is the one with his face slightly masked by an overlarge parka which prompted me to spend my first few weeks' wages buying myself a parka and trying to replicate the look. As he was 5ft 3ins and I was 6ft 4ins this didn't work well.

The terraced, Nineteenth Century 26 Briar Street was swapped for 4 Cerne Close on the large Clifton council estate in May 1962, and my black and white world turned to one of colour when we moved to Clifton, one of the country's largest council estates with a population of around 30,000 at its peak in the 1960s. The Meadows was on the northern bank of the River Trent and Clifton on the southern bank. Little did I ever see myself as a southerner, or imagine that life would take me much further south later beyond this natural divide between the country's north and south.

My primary school years were extremely happy both at school and outside of it with family and lots of friends. The estate was built in the early/ mid 1950s to house slum clearance from the city, and we made this move just before we were forced to. Each house had a garden and an inside toilet and bathroom - luxury! Before the estate my father would tell me how this had all been open fields and woodland with the small village of Clifton and the even tinier one of Glapton at its edge. The estate had shops, pubs, churches and still retained some open space and woodland. The proposed swimming pool and leisure centre finally arrived when I was away as a student in Sheffield and the planned cinema never did materialise; instead an entertainment centre was built - this was more of a working man's club; a glorified pub really, and very common in the north in the 1960s and 1970s. I worked there for a summer as a student and recently spoke about this with an actor friend of mine, Mark Arden. Mark was originally a stand-up comedian mentioned in Stephen Fry's *Chronicles* memoir and who went on to star in *London's Burning*. Mark had twins at my school in Canterbury and he too, I discovered, had worked behind the bar in this same venue as a student a few years after me.

I played for hours either in the garden with my toy plastic soldiers or games of football on the patches of green using the NO BALL GAMES signs as goal posts! The thing was these were vast communal games and most tenants had kids and most of those kids were playing in the game so it wasn't an issue, unless the ball went over the privet hedge of who we considered to be a grumpier soul whose kids had left the nest years before. I guess we would be those 'grumpy souls' now in that situation with noisy kids outside!

As an only child, but with lots of friends, I was equally comfortable with my own company or with other people. I was one of the brightest children in my class of 52 other children at Milford Junior School. Two girls passed the 11+ exam and no boys. I was lucky in that all the boys on the estate went to an enormous single-sex comprehensive whilst the girls were sent to either the grammar school, a bilateral one or a secondary modern. The boys' school was then streamed and I was assessed academically to be in the top of the bilateral forms. Each term we were re-assessed and half way through my second year (Year 8 in modern terminology) I was moved into one of the three Grammar streams where I managed to stay, and access O-Levels, which you were only able to do in these three streams. I didn't really thrive or enjoy my secondary school but did enjoy living near my mates on the estate, which I guess kept me sane during what, for most, are turbulent teenage years. This, though, was made a bit harder by my parents' attitude that 'the grass is always greener on the other side of the fence' or in our case the other side of the estate. In the twelve years I lived on the estate before leaving for college in Sheffield I lived with my parents in four houses, the longest being seven years.

Spending three years in Marshall Hall (albeit in different rooms) as a student was a strange but reassuring experience for me, and moving into the Victorian house for the fourth year was easy. Much easier as it happened than my next move.

Completing my studies meant I needed a teaching job. I desperately wanted to stay in Sheffield - I loved the city, the people, its proximity to my beloved Peak District and the fact that some of my mates were getting jobs locally. I tried and failed; they were not taking on many primary teachers and most jobs were in the secondary sector which I was not keen on. I drew a line across the middle of the country and applied for jobs within the central band. I had interviews in Telford New Town, and in Lincolnshire before getting my first job in a town I had never been to or even heard of before applying: Nantwich in Cheshire.

Nantwich is a picturesque, small market town with a large number of either original or mock Tudor buildings in its centre or outskirts. My time in Nantwich was relatively short - three years - two and half as a bachelor (first lodging with a family of strangers and then with the next door neighbour of the school caretaker who, with his wife, became good friends of mine) and then eight months or so living with Rosemary before I was able to help realise her long time ambition to move back home to Kent.

Considering our house in Fordwich was a place where we had so many happy, contented and positive memories it didn't get off to the best of starts. Initially it was considered on the rebound from a bungalow we'd fallen in love with, tucked away in Bekesbourne and which we had got close to securing

41

before the vendor had second thoughts about fleeing Kent for Cornwall and decided to stay put. We only knew Fordwich because we would travel down to Kent from our Cheshire home on a Friday evening armed with house details which various estate agents had mailed to us during the previous week, and we would sit in the May sunshine on the patio of the Fordwich Arms overlooking the river and contemplate where we might seek to view. Number 2 The Willows at Fordwich was one such property.

The house was semi-detached, like the one we lived in up north, and about the same age, built in the early 1960s. It had slightly bigger accommodation as it had a dormer upstairs and a considerably larger garden - in all the plot was about a third of an acre. The house had been designed and built by the original owner with the existing next door neighbour twenty years previously. They had done a lot to the house, and then left about ten years later, after which four other owners had come and gone in rapid succession each couple doing nothing to improve the property, indeed many had seemed to make their stamp of negligence or incompetence shine through.

The house had three bedrooms; one downstairs and two upstairs, one of which was Rosemary's and mine, and the other after 1982 was shared by Karon and James with a curtain separating them. Gareth had the downstairs room. Over the course of our 14 years there we completely transformed the property by way of decor and in 1992 had a lovely large Victorian-style Conservatory built after the removal of an old lean-to fixture grandly termed as a conservatory.

Access to the house was by public footpath as it sits on The Stour Valley Way; a beautiful long distance footpath stretching from Ashford to Sandwich and through our front garden. Also in the front garden was a substantial Bramley apple tree which bore buckets of fruit every year, more than we could use, so friends and family benefitted. I remember in May 1991 when Forest lost the FA Cup final to Tottenham 1-2, I went out into the garden and burst the red and white balloons I'd festooned in the tree. Did I get sympathy from Rosemary and James? Not a bit!

The garden was very large with lawns, a large vegetable plot, soft fruit bushes, well-stocked flower borders, a wooden greenhouse in which each year I nurtured seedlings and, once ready to plant out, replaced them with tomato plants grown in soil wrapped by offcuts of lino made into collars, which were the cheapest option.

We all have many happy memories of the time we had there as a family, and of our involvement in the village community. I say village but actually Fordwich is a town; the smallest in Britain with a population of just over 200, and the smallest active Town Hall with a Town Council and Mayor who meet in there. In the Middle Ages it was a thriving port on the River Stour which was navigable to this point. The Caen stone used to build Canterbury Cathedral was brought there from Normandy and unloaded before finishing its journey to the city along the dusty road by cart.

James was born there and for a couple of years could claim to be the youngest resident born in the smallest town in Britain. We really enjoyed most of our days there and threw ourselves into village life. I was, for some years, Secretary of the Friends of Fordwich - a charity raising money for the ancient church in the town. I was also a church sidesman. Rosemary was active in some women's groups and always helped at a stall at fund raising events. The only down-sides were with the traffic and the walk to the house on wet, muddy, dark winter days and nights.

We infrequently return to see our favourite home. Going back anywhere can be a good or a difficult thing. When we do, we go with a purpose, and that is usually to follow the track upon which our house was situated, and then wander through gates and over stiles to enjoy the sights and smells of the woods with the annual blue carpet of bluebells.

The five years from 1995-2000 were spent in the very friendly village of Shepherdswell situated midway between Dover and Canterbury. Our time there coincided with me working in Dover as Headteacher at Barton Junior School. Of all our houses *Crafnant* was the prettiest - a three bedroom detached with attractive eyebrow windows out the front.

With me getting a job as head teacher at Blean Primary School in 2000, Rosemary still working as a dental nurse in the city and James looking to work in Canterbury and attend the city's college of further education, it made sense to move back to the city, and that is where this chapter began.

The Sheffield student years (1974-78)

This chapter is dedicated to those who travelled with me as students, and to those who have followed your own course at university since. I hope it was as good for you as it was for me!

Having decided in the sixth form that I would like to leave home and go to College, the next question was to ask myself where to go, what to study and how to get into higher education. No one in my very large extended family - the Olivers - had stayed on for A-Levels at that time or even considered university. John, a cousin on my mother's side and two months younger than me did go to a college in the north east the same year as me, but dropped out for a number of health related issues. Expectations upon me from school and family were low academically. In my year at school I think maybe 5% went to college or university. I am convinced that there was such a waste of talent and ability in that Council estate comprehensive of 1,600 boys and I was not surprised when eventually after a series of poor OFSTED inspections a few years ago it closed its doors for the final time. My own expectations were different then, and I think this has helped forge the person who I am now and that hopefully I have tried to pass this on to others - my own children and those I have taught. I used to say, 'Aim for the stars and you might reach the moon.'

Doing only two A-Levels narrowed the choice somewhat, and then these were not likely to materialise into good grades. In those days there were different options available, and one of the most plausible for me was to go to Teacher Training College or a College of Education as they had quite recently become. I liked the look of Sheffield and Stephen Williams ('Will'), one of my best friends at school, had got a place there. I applied and was rejected without an interview. My second choice was Birmingham who did invite me for an interview which I attended and must have done okay at, because they offered me a place on their course to study History which in those days was a passion of mine, and still is to a large extent, and Education with a view to teaching either in a primary or a secondary school. This was in the Autumn and then I settled into my final couple of terms A-Level study with a goal in mind.

I was, however, uneasy about Birmingham. Something didn't seem quite right with the set up or the course, or me. So in the June as soon as I had finished my A-Level exams I rejected the place before my results were known and saw an advert in the paper for a job at Nat West in their Trust and investments department in Nottingham. My parents, who didn't want me to leave home, were thrilled and delighted and actively encouraged me to apply. My mother had worked for the bank when she left school until being married and having me brought her job to an abrupt close - no maternity-leave back in 1955.

I got the job and it was in the bank's offices near Maid Marion Way in Nottingham, (coincidentally, very close to where I recently learned the regional Alzheimer's Society offices are located.) The team of three I was attached to were all very professional, experienced and patient people who took me as an 18 year-old under their wing. We managed people's investment portfolios when they were alive and then supported spouses when one of the marriage partnership died. Dealing with the abstract data and spreadsheets was straightforward, and speaking with clients was fine until I went on my first visit to see a recently bereaved lady. I shall never forget it, and it was a defining moment for me. The lady was very upset and the experienced colleague I was with was well used to this sort of a meeting and he helped her (and me) through it. I was left though with 100% knowledge that despite the highly successful initial appraisal I'd had the week before, I felt that after seven weeks working in this role, it wasn't for me, and that I needed to return to my original plan which was to go to college/university and train to be a teacher. But where?

I had rejected Birmingham as I was unhappy about the prospect of going there. My other leading choice back on the UCCA form was Sheffield. My A-Level results were okay. I sat two and got them both: C in History and E in Economics. Not good in 2016 but in 1974 they were good enough - the exams were tougher then (only joking, honestly!) I rang them and got an interview on the 18th September which seemed to go quite well as they offered me a place there and then to study Education, History and Urban Studies - a mix of History, Geography, Sociology and Science. Urban Studies later morphed into Environmental Studies when I did my honours year at the University of Sheffield. I started at Sheffield on the Collegiate Crescent site on 24 Sept 1974, and on that day so many doors started to open up for me. The first person I remember talking to that day became a pal there and then, and has stayed a mate ever since...

I initially met Keith in 1974 when, as a second-year student at Sheffield City College, it seemed a good idea to welcome the incoming Freshers to Marshall Hall. Ok, this ploy was designed to meet fresh-faced, female students, so imagine the disappointment when in walked 6' 4' of prime male beef! Introductions over, then Keith uttered the magic words, 'I'm a Forest fan!' The beginning of a lifelong friendship was ensured – our shared profession, teaching, being relegated to second place.

Little did we know our support of Brian Clough's Nottingham Forest would take us together on memorable trips to European Cup Finals in Munich and Madrid - as well as less salubrious places, such as Gillingham and Southend! *Adrian Taylor ('Tats') - my friend from 1974 onwards*

It might help the reader to explain that I, like Tats, gained my place to Sheffield City College of Education. This notion of a higher education establishment seeking solely to train teachers was coming to an end, having been established earlier in the century and expanded in the post war years. Too many 18 year-olds were seeking this route and there were not enough jobs out there to justify this. The country was seeking to steer bright youngsters into other careers through higher education.

Dr Peake, our Principal, wanted to align the college with the red brick Sheffield University and become part of this institution. The city council however, did not want this as they had their eyes on the college site with more student living accommodation for the expanding Polytechnic. The city's Labour dominated council had greater control than the more independent University. As is often the case, during my third year in 1977 a messy compromise was achieved. I was party to this as I was invited to sit on the student council, partly to give a better balance against those from the Trotskyite hard left who I, and many other moderate voices, had little time for.

New students entering came in as Poly students and the College was no more, being renamed and joined by Totley College as Sheffield City Polytechnic (later renamed Sheffield Hallam University) and those students in my year completed their 4th year as joint members not only of the Poly but also of Sheffield University. It was at the University that we had the use of the academic and cultural facilities plus our exams and degree whilst still living in a building owned by and shared by the Poly. Politics is seldom far from education.

I worked hard and I played hard in my four years as a student.

Workwise, I was diligent, always attended lectures and got course-work in on time albeit with occasional very late nights fuelled by Neil Young and Tetley's Bitter! The two qualifications I gained were the Certificate in Education (Cert Ed) which was a three-year course and the requirement to teach in the days before teaching became a graduate profession. Cert Ed grades were Distinction, Commended, Pass and Fail. My grades in the three subjects I studied (Urban Studies, History and Education) were Distinction, Commended and Commended, which were good enough to proceed to the fourth year resulting in a Bachelor of Education (Honours) from Sheffield University. The joint subjects for my degree - although in Education - were History and Environmental Studies and I really enjoyed this final year, the only slight disappointment I recall was that I was told I was just a couple of marks away from a 2:1 but settled for the 2:2 which most of my mates also achieved.

I also gained a Football Association teaching certificate which in my first ten years of teaching proved as useful in securing jobs as the more academic awards. Seeing young graduates in Canterbury celebrating their degree ceremonies and having attended two as a parent, my mind drifts back to mine in July 1978 at the City Hall Theatre in Sheffield. All I remember is that the don doing the long speech was named Bean and he began with puns about being a 'has Been' or 'old Bean,' this alongside feeling sore hands from constant clapping are my sole memories of this event and there was no photographer there - or not one we could afford to record the event. My father bought me a pewter beer mug as a reward which I both appreciated and used (frequently!)

My life in Sheffield began in the same hall of residence as Keith but on a different floor. However, a shared love of Nottingham Forest meant we soon got to know each other, and by the second year I had moved to be on the same floor. Indeed, I made the mistake of moving into the room next door to Keith. Mistake? Many of us shared a love of music too, preferably played loudly but not always satisfying each other's tastes. Keith's music idol was Neil Young, not renowned for upbeat, lively tunes and with a generally dirgeful voice. Keith loved to sing along, loudly and pretty much out of tune and wearing headphones! We suffered not only Neil Young's songs but Keith's singing!

The immense joy we shared in enjoying Forest's glory years of league title and cup finals will live with me forever but a pre-season friendly in Montpelier provides one of the great moments. As Keith, Tats and I were camping nearby, we went and were the only Reds fans there. Not only did we see our heroes but Clough and Taylor were happy to make the occasion special by chatting to us for a while.

Dave Kerry, my friend from student days

All my friends were very similar to me in outlook and tastes. We would go out boozing most nights and my £10 a week grant stretched to this, with beer (15p a pint), burger/fish and chips, records, and that was about it.

I lived in Marshall Hall for three years and then shared a lovely Victorian house in Collegiate Crescent with a number of friends and students who I didn't know before we were housemates. Despite being an only child I loved all this sharing and communal living and could have done it all my life given the opportunity. Apart from my singing and guitar playing I reckon I was a good housemate.

I first met Keith at the start of the new academic year in 1977 at Sheffield City Polytechnic, where he was studying for his Honours Degree in Education. He was entering his fourth and final year, as I was embarking on my second. I had been allocated a room in a rather grand Victorian house, which had been converted into student accommodation on the Teacher Training site, I was a 19-year-old girl, and did not know any of the other students in the house. Keith occupied a room two doors away and a group of us soon became good friends, socialising and walking down to one of the nearby halls of residence for our meals together.

Keith first struck me as a friendly, very reliable and dependable person, who was conscientious towards his studies, but always set aside time for relaxation and following his favourite team, Nottingham Forest. As I got to know him further, my instincts proved correct and I rather envied him for his very balanced and clear view on life, recognising the goals he wanted to achieve. Keith had a wonderful sense of humour and as a group, we shared a great deal of laughter and developed a fantastic camaraderie.

Keith was a popular student and was always very supportive towards his friends. I remember his door always being open for a chat, good advice and a cuppa; one particular time after a long and frustrating train journey back to Sheffield after visiting my parents. My studies involved organising an open evening with my fellow students to promote awareness of the course. Without hesitation Keith and a couple of our mutual friends showed me support and encouragement by attending this event and giving me very valuable constructive feedback.

After finishing college and entering the big wide world, we kept in touch for a short while and then unfortunately lost contact for a few years. The next time we met was approximately 15 years ago at a college reunion, which my husband and I attended. I was not in the least surprised to learn that Keith was a head teacher at a Primary School in Kent, knowing that his consistent nurturing leadership, knowledge and presence would be appreciated by both staff, pupils and parents.

Some years later I was very saddened to learn that Keith had been diagnosed with dementia and greatly admire his pragmatic approach to the situation, combining his experiences, professional skills and eloquence to convey this through a variety of media in a quest to educate and enlighten others in order to improve care and treatment for fellow sufferers and their families.

My personal first-hand experience of dementia started approximately 12 years ago, when my elderly mother was diagnosed with a form of vascular dementia. I understand the huge impact this has on someone's life and their family members and recognise the sadness, frustrations and struggles that are faced. Although awareness, treatments and services for this condition have greatly improved over recent years, we still have a long way to go in order to achieve consistency and clarity nationwide. I am my mother's eyes and ears and her window to the outside world and have witnessed both ends of the spectrum when it comes to the various approaches towards her condition.

Thank you Keith for having the courage to highlight and bring to public attention the struggles and concerns of someone personally suffering the onset of dementia: respect.

Patricia J Dale (nee Shaw), my friend from student days

We took part in torrents of water fights in Marshall Hall, and often the staircase was like Niagara Falls, resulting in the lift being swamped and rendered out of use. I am amazed that Marshall Hall survived intact until only recently when the bulldozers achieved what we thankfully didn't and demolition was its end rather than being washed away into the rivers Sheaf and Don. Buckets over open top toilets, rice pudding baths, rooms re-assembled outside when the occupant was out. Madness but great fun; and one time you were the culprit, the next the victim.

It's hard to believe that it's over 40 years ago that we first met at Sheffield City College, but pleasing to know that at least one first-class teacher was to emerge from it all! For myself, I can say that it was a real pleasure to get to know you and others, and I had a really good time there. Plus, the qualification gained enabled me to have a long and enjoyable career in youth work (informal education, don't you know!)

I'm sure you can remember the infamous water fights between fifth and second floors in Marshall Hall, the Friday night discos, discussions about who were the best progressive rock bands at the time, watching that fabulous Forest football team conquering Europe, and endless football-related discussions!

Alzheimer's and dementia feature more and more in the news and general conversation these days, especially amongst us Baby Boomers, and I feel that there is a lot of confusion about what can be done to combat the condition - various diets, lifestyle choices, etc. so I think that it's invaluable that someone such as yourself is able to give a very personal view of how to live with it through your talks and now this publication. Great stuff, Keith.

Dave Holland, one of my student mates.

Talking of antics, playing for the College Rugby XV involved high jinks both on and off the field. I played for two years as a second row forward, a position I felt less suited to than the lock number 8 position I'd played for four years at school. Men's rugby was different in one major way to school rugby; the competition with the opposition didn't end at the final whistle but continued in the pub or bar. The teams drank like fish. At one trip to the army barracks at Harrogate we lost the rugby but won the drinking contests. That included the mini bus driver and prop forward, who couldn't manage to change gear on the return journey to Sheffield, leaving it to the front seat passenger. When we got to his home he fell over the pots outside the front door, only to realise it was the wrong door - he had tried to get into the wrong house!

Our professional careers intertwined as we both became head teachers in Kent and I was delighted when my daughter attended Keith's primary school in Canterbury. Being close to the school, it made me smile when I revealed to staff members that in contrast to the studious, mild-mannered leader of their school, I could remember the budding Martin Johnson let loose on the rugby pitch – think of the T- Rex in Jurassic Park and you'll picture the scene! Ha ha, happy days!

Adrian Taylor 'Tats'

My mother, who heard only tiny snippets from me, would be convinced every health issue I have encountered since the age of 22 had two words written all over them - rugby and booze. She might have been right but I, like most young blokes in that scene, thought I was bullet proof... I will use that label again later.

I have to say that I haven't been anywhere near drunk or even merry through drink for over 35 years - since my stag night - and that was spent with... my ex-student mates!

I remember once in our group using a Ouija Board and we got really spooked - the glass zoomed off the table and smashed on the floor, and at 2 am we left the hall of residence and searched the nearby Victorian graveyard in the dark with pathetic torches to find the grave of the person we had connected with. Without success, I must add! Never again have I been tempted to do anything like this.

Many of you will have read *Welcome to our World* and the piece I wrote on pages 131-134 about some of my other adventures as a student.

One lifelong lesson I learnt during my second year at Sheffield was around the risks attached to ego, pride, festering feelings and falling out with friends which can cause such distress - not just to the protagonists - but to friends who fear getting drawn in on one side or the other.

Dave Foster and I were good friends. Alike in the sense of having strong personalities but different also in many ways. We were, as I said earlier, part of a close-knit group of six friends who hung out a lot, who lived on the same corridor in the hall of residence and who camped in rain-sodden Wales and the nearer Peak District which made the falling out even harder for us all. Like so many arguments it was over something and nothing - he said something which upset me, I said something even more upsetting back, he upped the ante with something even more offensive and with lots of swearing - I have always very rarely sworn, even though living in Australia with friends who swore readily has added a few words to my vocabulary. Well, the outcome was that we didn't speak to each other for almost a year. Tricky within a close community such as where we lived and enjoyed ourselves, yes - and studied! Neither of us would give in. Neither of us would take responsibility for making friends again, and our mates just didn't know how to be peacemakers.

Our friendship did get back on track and in April 1977 Dave, Terry, Anton and myself went camping in North Wales. Dave's parents had moved to Abergele when he was a teenager from Manchester so this expedition began with a lunch at his parents' home. From there we lugged our camping gear up to the station and stumbled onto the train into Snowdonia to have a few days in the picturesque countryside. Our destination was a place called Blaneau Festiniog. Just a name on the map - should be lovely, we thought.

Well it was a bright sunny April Saturday tea-time when the train drew out of the tunnel approaching Blaneau station.

'Dave, where the **** are we going to pitch the tent in this place?' was Terry's opener. There wasn't a patch of grass to be seen. Everywhere was piles of slate. Not very promising, I thought. My usual response to challenge at this time was to suggest, 'Let's go to the pub, and come up with a plan, 'cos there's no way we can stay here.'

As we walked down the main street there was NO ONE about, everywhere was closed and the only living thing we saw was a solitary, morose looking straggly sheep shuffling down the centre of the main, deserted road, obviously heading home to get the rugby results!

The pub was closed until 7:00 and then would be totally 'dry' on the Sunday as all that part of Wales was back in the 1970s.

Terry's next offering was, 'This is ****!'

He was right.

Terry did make the suggestion that we should return to the station and get the next train out of there and find somewhere else. *Anywhere else* I think is what was actually said.

We ended up on a small campsite next to a farm near Maesteg which was actually quite pretty. It did also have on the site a laundrette. Useful for our clothes. Forget that, we were 20-year-old students living the hippy dream! No, it was useful because the disastrous trip got worse when the Welsh weather turned inclement. It rained and it rained. Our tent, after two days, was absolutely drenched and so were we. In the end we stuffed the tent into the tumble drier in the laundrette and I remember sitting there watching it tumbling through the circular window. I looked at Terry. He looked at me before we both fell about laughing as we were both thinking, stuff the tent, I should climb in there to dry off!

Dave was a good mate and I hope I was for him too. I remember well his wedding at Holton-le-Clay in Lincolnshire as coincidentally, a few months previously, I had an interview at the village school but didn't get the job. The only time I managed to encourage Rosemary to visit Sheffield was back in late 1980 and that was to see Dave in hospital where he had been admitted with a back problem. Dave and I attended each other's weddings. He and his wife were our guests and witnesses when I was christened in Crewe aged 25 back in 1981. When I returned to Sheffield for two reunions, one in the 1990s and one around 2001, it was with Dave that I spent most of my time. The last contact I had with Dave was a couple of years ago when we exchanged friendly emails after he had picked up my film on YouTube about living with dementia, and he wrote some kind and sincere words.

Whilst I had a large and close circle of friends as a student in Sheffield, Terry, who also features in this story, was probably my best mate for those four years. He was from Birmingham and it was when visiting him in 1976 that I made my only visit to the city and we had a great week of culture; Stratford and Lichfield being places we visited, and lots of pubs. I was Terry's best man at his wedding to Liz, and he was mine at our wedding. There are few people I have met in my life whom I would trust and confide in and Terry was one of them. For four years he was the closest to a sibling I've ever known.

He began teaching Sociology and History in a comprehensive school in Hereford, and I lived in Nantwich, so it was quite easy to visit each other and we did, numerous times. It's a shame that we haven't seen each other for over 30 years now and our sole contact has been via Christmas cards.

Those of you who know Sheffield might be interested to know of my old haunts. I guess most times outside of campus were spent either in local pubs such as The Pomona, off Eccleshall Road which sold Home Ales which, like me, had travelled up from Nottingham; The Broomhall Tavern and Seven Seas nearby, both of which were popular with students; The West Street Run was a challenge to students' livers in that it was a well-known pub crawl. Money not spent in pubs probably went into helping create the Branson empire as he had an early record shop in The Moor, unsurprisingly called *Virgin Records*. Beyond that, I used to love either sunbathing in the Botanical Gardens during the particularly hot June and July of 1976 or better still walking The Round Walk out from Hunters Bar through the parks, past Shepherd's Wheel on to the beautiful moors which ringed Sheffield and provided the city with its lungs.

My Sheffield years were amongst the happiest of my life, but there were challenges both academically and emotionally, one or two I've written about here. I didn't seem able to sustain any long term relationships with female students. All my girlfriends during the four years (and I guess there were three or four) couldn't be described as serious for more than two months, although all of them started out as friends for a longer period before we went out together and in all but one case remained friends afterwards.

Each week I, along with friends, would attend a disco or two either at our college, the main University or in the city on a cheap student night. Usually I felt uncomfortable in these settings and used to say they felt like a cattle market and some of the worst behaviours I witnessed at that time were at discos. Not my scene at all. However, one exception was my 21st birthday event which Olwyn Roy (a fellow student) and I booked for Genevieve's in the city. We took over the night club issuing free tickets to around 150 student friends, and this many years before Facebook had even been thought of! I think it was a good do, although this is based upon what people told me afterwards as I fear drink robbed me of many brain cells that night.

When not out drinking or listening to music whilst writing essays we often discussed and developed our shared interest in politics and books, often into the early hours. I did read a lot then, and tried to read broadly, helped by friends such as Dave Kerry who steered me towards English editions of French favourites of his such as *The Outsider* (*L'Etranger*) by Albert Camus and *Journal of a Thief* by Jean Genet.

The impact on my mother of me going to Sheffield has stayed with me ever since in one way or another but I cannot, and will not regret it. College and University were for me part of the education journey which has given me enormous pleasure and potential to do things with my life that neither I nor anyone who knew me as 'that snotty-nosed council house kid' could even have dreamt of.

The reasons I tell these stories here are because they are part of me, and they illustrate how one can play hard and work hard and come out at the end with a good degree, good memories of student days, a good job at the end of it and the life changing experience that living away from home with like-minded good friends can bring. So often these days I see the additional pressure that students live under and I think how lucky I was.

Once a teacher, always a teacher

This piece began very differently as an original much shorter idea written in 2013. Following suggestions from April Doyle during a Life Writing course, I read Dear Fatty *by Dawn French, and this is my attempt to follow that thread. This letter is dedicated to a person who encouraged me to write and continue to teach, and who, like the dear friends who have contributed to this chapter have inspired me so much by your faith and support.*

For so many reasons this is my favourite piece I wrote for Welcome to our World *and that is why I chose to read it at the Waterstones book launch in Canterbury on 6th November 2014. I hope that you like it, and please forgive my indulgence in using it again here.*

Dear former pupil,

As I sit at my desk pondering this letter to you, autumn is swiftly approaching, and is often regarded as a time for reflection as the vivid red, gold and orange foliage transforms the greens of summer to a hot flush before the winter chills set in. Whilst I do enjoy what this season provides, it is tinged with a little sadness as the realisation sinks in that summer has slipped away like the setting sun and that one feels about to be gripped with a melancholic iron glove.

As a teacher and a head for over thirty years, early September also saw the end of the long summer break, and a return to life at school. Whilst I loved my time working with young people like you, I was always unsettled and anxious around the last days of the holiday, and remained so until the first day's register was marked, or the opening assembly of the year was completed. Then with your smiling faces in front of me I was comfortable casting off the mooring from the holiday and floating into the new term focusing on you, the most important people in my care.

Rewards from my career far outweigh what I contributed, and I don't mean financially. Whilst my salary latterly was far more than I could have imagined as a teenager leaving the Nottingham council estate, and I'm sure there were higher paid jobs out there than teaching, I always saw teaching as a vocation. With your help to keep that as my focus I never wavered from that throughout my career. I am reminded of the wise words of Abraham Lincoln when writing to his child's teacher 150 years ago. These were shared with me by the parent of a pupil some years ago whose view of the teacher he wanted for his child matched my attempts.

'Steer him away from envy and teach him the secret of quiet laughter.

'Let him learn early that bullies are the easiest to lick.

'Teach him the wonder of books, but also give him time to ponder the eternal mystery of birds in the sky, bees in the sun, and flowers on the green hillside.

'Teach him it is more honourable to fail than to cheat; to have faith in his own ideas, even if everyone tells him they are wrong and to be gentle with the gentle people and tough with the tough.

'Give him the strength not to follow the crowd, to listen to all men but to filter all he hears and to take only the good which comes through.

'Teach him to laugh when he is sad and that there is no shame in tears. Teach him to scoff at cynics and to sell his brain to the highest bidder, but to never put a price on his heart or soul.'

I do wish that the OFSTED Gestapo would read and digest these great words of wisdom - I did and tried to follow them, I hope that this came over to you when I was with you, if not then please accept my sincere apologies, I did try.

As a teacher and head one can make a real difference to the lives of young people, and I derive a great sense of pride and satisfaction every time the paths of a former pupil and myself cross. For you may be surprised but in my mind you remain as a child, you have never aged or grown up in my memory. Childhood is a real treasure and these memories sit well alongside this.

There are so many of you I could write about, and thinking back to that first class who I remember so vividly, despite the fact that it is now 36 years ago and many of you are parents yourself (some of you might even be grandparents!)

Soon after being diagnosed, my wife and I attended two meetings of people with a similar diagnosis. The meeting was designed to bring together those below the age of 65 who had recently been through the local Memory Clinic. The doctor setting up had an opening slide entitled 'Living with Dementia' by Dr. Richard Brown. I said to Rosemary as quietly as I could, 'I taught a Richard Brown about 25 years ago in Canterbury. The last time I saw him he was eleven and moving on to Grammar School, I reckon he must be early to mid-30s, about the age of this guy.'

The presenter overheard, and to my delight he announced, 'Yes, Mr. Oliver, you DID teach me for two years and I remember with great fondness being in your class, including your great impression of Gollum when reading *The Hobbit* to us!'

Well, I was amazed. We chatted at length during the interval and I mentioned to Richard that I had a project he had written about Australia back in 1988. It was excellent, and I had 'borrowed' it to help inspire other subsequent children with writing their projects. At the next session I was able to ceremoniously return the project to rapturous applause from the group. Now the roles are reversed; I had cared for Richard as his teacher, now as my consultant he cares for me. Thank you, Richard.

Soon after this, through a mutual friend in Australia, I made contact with Amanda, who I had taught in Adelaide back in 1989. Amanda was by now a mum and a teacher herself, and indeed had taught in the UK and had tried, unsuccessfully at the time, to contact me. In October 2012, I had a meeting in London to train as a member of the Alzheimer's Society Research Network. Rosemary was going to attend this training with me and coincidentally Amanda, her husband and two young children were going to be in London that day. We had a lovely time together strolling along the south bank near the London Eye before heading into a restaurant where the food was good and the conversation was great as we shared memories of the year we spent at Norwood Primary School in Adelaide.

I am delighted that so many of you have returned into my life recently, often in the most surprising of circumstances. In 'An Amazing Day' I have written about Amy who contacted BBC radio during the broadcast of my interview with the Prime Minister. Subsequently I am delighted that we have become friends and, as I write this, we are planning to meet for the first time in over twenty years; oh how time moves so quickly. An even longer gap was the case with Angela, who Rosemary and I recently met by chance at a party of a mutual friend. I hadn't seen Angela for over thirty years, and whilst we were enjoying the party we were getting ready to leave when Angela came up to introduce herself. Over an hour later we finally said our goodbyes!

Often former pupils will just stop and say hello in the street, and sometimes this leads to me asking. 'What are you doing with yourself these days?' One day in Canterbury, a young woman who was entertaining a growing crowd busking with her musical pals saw me, stopped her performance and came and took me to meet her friends introducing me as her head teacher and saying lovely things about her time at Blean. If you read this Milly, you made that day for me and as I told you at the time, your music was brilliant.

Each September I am asked to deliver a talk to Occupational Therapy students at Canterbury Christ Church University and at one of these talks a student came forward and introduced himself as Ben; I had taught him almost twenty years previously. It was great to catch up and share what had led him to being on this course and the work which he hoped to do once he had graduated.

Another opening line I hear from some of you is, 'Are you Mr. Oliver? You used to teach me!' As I previously mentioned although my looks have changed since the time in question, the adult in front of me has changed much more. Sometimes this opening question will come from someone coming to do some work at my house such as Wayne who works for British Gas and now services our gas boiler, or Thomas who was a lively nipper when I think of him as a ten-year-old in my football team at Barton, and who has grown into a burly six footer working with an electrical company.

One-off contacts are nice, but to me I really love the feeling I get when someone like you transforms in my mind from the primary school child to the adult who I am proud to say I taught and helped grow into the person who I'm delighted to re-connect with, and to not only talk about you the child, but as the adult you have become.

Once a teacher, always a teacher. I guess that label fits me to a tee. Since retiring I do miss the children from school, and to address this for the past three years I have been made extremely welcome at Wincheap Primary School, near to where I live in Canterbury. I have loved hearing the children read, and have been boosted by the knowledge that I can still engage with young people and support both their learning and their developing confidence. I am a bit like a grandparent: I see them relatively briefly, make a fuss of them, enjoy their company and chats and then disappear until next time, usually the following week. I am told by the school, and my experience suggests, that I bring much to our time together, but rest assured I take FAR more away with me when I walk out of the school each time.

So far this letter has been reflective and has looked back over the past; to close I would like to look to the present and the future. Maybe there is a link here to my efforts in the Dementia Envoy role. The work I did with you as your teacher was so important, and my current role is now important in a different but parallel way. I am committed to continuing to utilise any teaching skills I retain to raise awareness around living well with dementia and to challenge stereotypes and stigma. There are still talks to plan, audiences to speak to, and messages to convey, and as long as I am well enough and have the support I've been blessed with to date, I will continue to try to teach.

Thank you and bless you.

Your teacher and friend,

Keith Oliver

Having written and 'sent' this letter via this book, I would like now to share with you the words of some dear friends, some of whom are former pupils that I taught between 1981 - 1995, and some of whom are ex-colleagues who worked with me in schools between 1995 - 2010. It will come as no surprise to all that much as I hold dear my former colleagues I am giving first voice to the pupils, beginning with you Angela, as I have to say you were the earliest of these friends in my career!

My memories of attending Littlebourne Primary School are really happy ones and key to where I am today.

Mr Oliver, as I knew him then, was my teacher in Class 3, I was about eight or nine I believe. First impressions of this extremely giraffe-like man (due to his height) were that of a dedicated, kind but firm, interesting and motivating teacher. Something that stood out was how Mr Oliver would share with us his own experiences, which made his teaching real and exciting. Mrs Oliver also made regular appearances facilitating craft activities, such as Macramé plant pot holders, (incidentally, I still have mine.) One of the qualities I remember of our teacher was his ability to include everyone in his class, even if it meant giving a child with spina bifida a piggy back to the local recreation ground to watch the

Queen Mother come through the village in her car, as there wasn't time for the child to walk there. The school had been notified of this last minute and Mr Oliver wanted us all to have the opportunity to see the Queen Mother and wave.

Several years ago, during a staff inset day, we had a guest speaker who said that if there was a teacher or adult who had helped you on your way, try to say thank you if you can. I thought about primary school and the help I'd had there and also the encouragement from both primary and secondary school teaching staff. Saying thank you was not going to be easy, as I didn't know how to contact anybody.

Moving on to 2014 and during the 70th birthday party of a mutual dear friend, Tessa Read, I happened to look across the hall to see Mr Oliver. Many years had passed, I wasn't sure if it was him or not, and I kept looking over. Eventually, I went across and spoke to Keith (as I now know him). To my delight both he and his wife, Rosemary, remembered me. The rest of the afternoon was spent reminiscing and sharing precious memories of my primary days in Keith's class, over 30 years earlier. Amazingly, I was able to thank Keith for being such an inspiration all those years ago as my teacher. Now he continues to inspire me and others through all the work that he does to raise awareness.

I believe that we have no choice in the hand that we are given, but we do have a choice as to what we do with that hand: that is what Keith is doing and I am so proud to be his friend and to recognise the impact he's had on me.

Angela Chandler (nee Giles), former pupil at Littlebourne Primary School, taught by Keith, 1981-82

Keith was my class teacher when I was nine years old. He had something of a reputation: known for his booming voice, which he deployed rarely but to great effect. He was an exceptional teacher; much liked, but even more respected.

My child's memory recalls the small details: the way he would always slightly pull his trousers at the knees before sitting himself down; his array of ink stamps used to validate our best pieces of work; his system of in and out trays on either side of his desk to process our work. Keith (or Mr Oliver as he was to me) was in equal parts dynamic and demanding. He taught the eldest pupils and was recognised by parents as a driving force within the school. It is that same energy that I still see within him now in the range of projects he leads and connections he makes.

Over twenty years later, I find myself driving my one-year-old daughter home from her swimming group. She's fallen asleep, and for once, I'm able to turn off the nursery rhymes and put on the radio. It's Radio 4: I've been tuning in on my journeys to work recently, trying to re-discover some cognitive capacity after a year's maternity leave. The *You and Yours* programme is on, and it's about dementia. I turn up the volume: my husband's grandmother had dementia in her final years, and we had all been a part of her journey. She had been very much the 'classic case' – small incidents of forgetfulness, then longer periods of confusion, and the odd near-catastrophe (she was once discovered cooking cucumber on the gas hob with smoke billowing). She was a proud woman, and kept her difficulties as well hidden as possible. As grandchildren, we never really saw it until the very end; she would make such efforts to maintain the conversations when we visited, and we would only learn afterwards how exhausted it made her.

Her formal care felt like the stuff of last resort. The battle to prove she was 'bad enough.' The home visits that barely addressed the most basic needs because there simply wasn't enough time. The multitude of assessments to try and get more support as her needs grew. The eventual admission to a dementia care home. It all felt so reductive: so focused on what she could no longer do, what risks needed managing, how to alleviate the 'burden.' There was little attention paid to supporting her to live well and to get the most from her remaining life. It was instead a baseline of risk management while she ebbed away.

I am listening to the radio presenter introduce the next guest. It's Keith Oliver, whom he says was diagnosed with Early Onset Alzheimer's in his fifties while Headteacher at Blean Primary School. 'It's Mr Oliver!' I say aloud to nobody (my daughter is by now snoring.) Is it really him? His voice comes over the radio, and instantly I am nine years old again. It hasn't changed, this voice lodged so deeply in my childhood consciousness; and here it is again now - on national radio! The programme is drawing to a close. I pull up on the driveway and hurry my daughter into the house, hoping she'll amuse herself for a few minutes so that I can contact the show. I have a huge need to say 'I knew him when..!' I reach for the iPad and tap out a brief email in the closing moments of the show – and to my delight it is read out on air just minutes later!

The next day I receive a voicemail from the producer of the *You and Yours* programme: Keith wants to get in touch! I am excited, and also a little nervous. All over again I am his pupil – and yet when we meet a few weeks later, he becomes also my friend.

As the months go by and I get to know Keith really for the first time, I am stunned by how different his world is to the experiences of our Grandma. His dynamism is still evident – if anything, augmented – in the number of projects he leads, the talks he delivers, the connections he makes with everyone from local support groups to national charities, university researchers to broadcasters. One real high point was hearing him speak on the radio again, this time in conversation with former Prime Minister David Cameron! I feel pride at having had this special prior knowledge of Keith and the history we share.

Despite his growing national profile, Keith remains self-effacing and honest about the challenges he faces. He is ever focused on the next task, the next opportunity, to share with others the possibility – and reality – of 'living well' as he so rightly puts it.

Last November I attended the launch of Welcome to our World, a life writing project which weaves together stories and memories from Keith and a local group of writers experiencing dementia. Telling our story, it seems, is one of the most powerful experiences we can share, enabling us to define ourselves to others and make connections with them. It's not only about our past, the person we were, but crucially about reflecting upon the person we have become and are becoming: the thread of being that endures within us all. It is this connection that, to me, is at the heart of 'living well.'

I am one of the many people who have connected with Keith through hearing his story. For me, though, it is also a re-connection to my own past. It has taught me that our lives can touch and re-touch at different points along the way, sometimes in the strangest of circumstances; that the passage of years can see relationships can grow in new directions; and that though we may change, something within us remains always the same.

Amy Merritt (nee Morrish), ex pupil at Swalecliffe Primary School, Whitstable, taught by Keith 1994 - 95

Often when delivering talks I will refer to Dr Richard Brown, my consultant psychiatrist. I shared Richard's care when he was a child for two years back in the late 1980s and now he shares the responsibility for my care. I was amazed to meet up with Richard again back in 2011 after a gap of 23 years. He, like almost all of my ex-pupils, remained of primary school age in my image of him. What did not surprise me at all was that he had gone on to be a doctor, and an extremely good, caring professional who I am thrilled and privileged to have as my consultant. Here's Richard's fascinating and unique part in the story...

The school aquarium mirrored the playground outside. Danios darted about in silver shoals like children playing football. Angelfish glided about in twos and threes. Still and solitary catfish with their whiskered faces drifted at the fringes. Keith involved us in planning and stocking the tank. I was captivated when he produced a beautiful encyclopedia with panels of vivid photos of aquarium plants and fish. It was a way of using nature to teach children something about taking responsibility for the lives of others. Uniquely fortunate to have been in his class twice, I was aged ten when we assumed shared responsibility on a rota for feeding and tending to them.

One day I examined the floating thermometer and its thin red line of alcohol had separated. To jolt it back to a single column I dropped it into the water. I loved the buoyant parabola it made is it bounced back from the water, but then I fatefully misjudged. It plunged and shattered on the gravel. Red fluid seeped out, blending with the water. I was mortified and feared for the fish. But I was surprised and relieved both by the calm and forgiving way that Keith endorsed the idea of releasing the other children on the rota from class to change the water and clean the tank, and more so still by the supportive way they rallied round to remedy my shameful mistake.

It was a rich education at Pilgrims' Way. The school sat between the Spring Lane and Barton Road estates and the more affluent streets off New Dover Road. Keith had then, as he does now, enormous presence both in his physical height, his resonant voice with his distinctive Nottingham accent (which can always be detected in any adjacent room) and his ability to communicate; but also for me with the way he populated my imagination with nature trips, astronomy, geology, his own enthusiasms such as Australia, our projects and craft work, and the stories he read to us. Things that you always carry with you.

Years later, now qualified as doctor, I returned from the Maudsley Hospital in London to Canterbury as a higher trainee in psychiatry. The Living Together with Dementia course was well established in the local department, providing education, space for reflection and support for couples newly affected by a diagnosis of dementia. I was asked to provide the opening talk explaining dementia, its causes and treatment.

The attendance list included the names Keith and Rosemary Oliver.

I had learned of Keith's diagnosis only a short while before, and had considered writing to him, but here was my chance to catch up with him in person. Nevertheless, the prospect heightened even more my sense of the audience I was to speak to. This was no undergraduate lecture in clinical medicine. Stark facts about anatomy, classification and pathology seemed diminished in the face of human realities, stories and experiences of my patients and their spouses.

Wanting to be sensitive but candid to my audience I agonised over the tone and content in a way I had never had to before.

I found an exquisite platinum print of a dandelion head to serve as a familiar object that mimicked the shape, fragility and intricacy of a brain cell. I spoke about the Nun Study of Aging and Alzheimer's disease, whose findings said something of how physical changes in the brain do not always parallel the reality and disability of a person with dementia, and how traits in early, mid and later life have continuity and predict something of our future and risks with Alzheimer's disease.

When I finished I was not sure of my success: an okay first effort maybe.

The subsequent sessions, when people spoke with dignity and authenticity of their sources of strength and sadness and their connecting stories, were a real education. The shared dialogues between multiple patients, not just the one to one of the consulting room, opened up so much. As I was taught at medical school - the patient is the ultimate text book.

It was Keith who approached me before I had chance to seek him out. I had no clear expectations that he would remember me as one of countless former pupils, but he recalled not just me, but all of 'Class 10,' our personalities and our parents. He was familiar with the Nun study and spoke of his own reading and ideas. I reminded him of reading us the Hobbit at the end of the school day, of my love of Tolkien's maps, Keith's own rendition of sly old Gollum. We spoke of his links with and love of Australia and my class 10 project on the topic that remarkably he had always kept in his office as a head teacher. He produced it the following week - a message from my past with my labours, spelling mistakes and his written comments throughout the pages.

Three years later I took the consultant post back home in Canterbury and now, as Keith's consultant, our conversations continue. A theme that comes up is the shift demanded of a person affected by dementia to relinquish their former levels of autonomy, self-reliance and mastery, and instead try to find a new interdependence with others. Not easy to negotiate, but illustrated by mine and Keith's interconnected and interdependent lives.

I am reminded of the dialogue between the models of person-centred care and relationship centred care for people with dementia. I do not know what level of distinction Tom Kitwood would have perceived, but in the way that it is articulated by many people now, person-centred care has evolved to emphasise much about autonomy and independence and has at times inevitably taken on something of consumerism and western individualism. However, Kitwood wrote of personhood as 'standing and status bestowed on one human being by another,' doubtless occurring in our relationships and connectedness with others. Relationship-centred care recognises something more about the importance of positive relationships between people with disabilities including dementia, their families, their caring organisations and their communities.

As I look to my own future, which may very well include a time living with dementia, what will give me greater confidence in the face of it is a connectedness with others and a sense that I have unqualified regard from all those to whom I remain connected.

Richard Brown, former pupil at Pilgrims' Way Primary School and Consultant Psychiatrist KMPT

Before handing over to ex-colleagues, I think it's important to note my long term commitment to life-long learning and to my recognition that schools need to be a place to learn as opposed to work - this is the same for staff as well as children. I learnt as much from the pupils I taught such as Amanda, Amy, Angela and Richard.

Once a teacher, always a teacher has been suggested by some friends as an alternative title for this book. Whilst I appreciate the sentiment that is expressed with this and can see the rationale, I also feel it only covers a part (although a significant part) of my life and personality.

One of the few regrets I have around the period when I was diagnosed both at the time and looking back was having to stand down from the Masters course I was a third of the way through at Canterbury Christ Church University. For some years I had considered embarking on a Masters in Education course, and with the backing of school governors when the opportunity arose in 2009 – 10, I successfully applied. The course was perfect for me as it was based in Canterbury and had education leadership as its focus: my day job! The two pieces of course work I submitted each received merits with marks of 63% and 78% and the lectures, although in an evening after school, were engaging and stimulating.

However, it was during a number of the lectures that I felt my powers of concentration, recall and ability to express myself were changing. I'd look at other members of the group and think he/ she must be X years younger than me, and they are able to engage as I used to: I must be getting old!

I do admire people like my dear friend, Kate Swaffer, who managed to complete university courses despite having dementia, but my engagement with universities is now solely through me trying to utilise what teaching skills I retain when delivering an occasional talk or lecture to these bright and eager minds.

When trying to inspire children I would say to them, 'Aim for the stars and you might reach the moon!' What I meant by this was to aim as high as possible, stretch yourself but be prepared to accept something close to your fullest dream. We are all lifelong learners who learn partly from our mistakes as well as our successes. From this we are then better able to move forward without carrying the burden of regret with us in our briefcase or satchel!

Any leader or head worth their salt is only really effective with a supportive, loyal and able deputy and I have been blessed to have a number of exceptional deputies, the first of whom was Jacky Neale:

It's Barton Junior School, September 1995, the first day of the new school year and excitement - or rather a feeling of apprehension - is in the air. We have a new head teacher, and although we have met Keith several times, no one has ever worked with him or really knows what to expect.

We need not have worried. Keith settled quickly and necessary changes were gradual and readily accepted. He even listened to our opinions! He became popular with the children, although they were concerned because he was so tall. 'When he stands up, Miss, he just keeps on going!' They also likened him to Roald Dahl's BFG as he strode along the corridors, his trench coat flowing out behind him.

I enjoyed working with Keith, and have many fond memories of our five years together - best of all - Flatford Mill. Keith introduced the annual Year 6 residential visit to John Constable country. It was magic and children and staff alike will remember and treasure those visits forever.

I am sure that Keith and Rosemary are concerned as to what the future holds, as indeed we all are as old age approaches. I do have some experience of care in later life and it does vary enormously from brilliant to indifferent. Most importantly it is not the building or even the facilities that matter but it is the staff. As in a school, the staff's understanding, patience and kindness are what makes a safe, warm and stimulating environment.

Jacky Neale, ex-deputy head, Barton Junior School

I am sure Jacky would agree that is exactly what we strove for at Barton, and I think on the whole we did achieve this. Also at Barton, I 'inherited' Lyn Dourthe, an exceptional SENCO who I invested one of the best two hours of my career with when I first arrived, to meet with her in order to listen, and respond to her previous frustrations and future aspirations for the children fortunate to be in her care.

Lyn like a number of ex-colleagues, has continued to be a most valued and trusted friend:

Change is always worrying.

When we, his colleagues at Barton School, knew that Keith had been appointed as our new head teacher, we were all apprehensive that this young man would come in as a new broom and sweep away all that we were used to doing. However, our worries were unfounded as it soon became obvious that he would take a step by step approach and work in conjunction with us on a much needed modernisation of the way in which the school operated.

My job in the Special Needs Department was in fact made easier by the continuous support which I received from Keith.

Keith calmed our fears as he prepared the school for the first OFSTED, and with his leadership we received a good report.

Keith was a hard working head teacher and very thorough in every aspect of his work. Written reports arrived on our desk within minutes of the end of meetings.

When he moved on, his legacy was a much improved school.

Lyn Dourthe (ex-SENCO (Special Educational Needs Coordinator) Barton Junior School)

Moving from Barton to Blean was a big leap. The school was the largest and arguably the school held in highest regard in Canterbury. How do you improve this? I knew that improving the leadership team was an early essential and two key members of this new team were Jenny and Hilary. Here are their contributions:

I met Keith while teaching at Blean Primary School situated just outside Canterbury. I moved down to the area in 1997 from Lancaster with my husband and our three sons and also, as my father had recently died, my mother. We eventually found a house in Blean village for all of us. I retired from teaching five years ago now, but have many fond memories of my career and especially of having had the privilege to work with Keith.

I considered myself to be very lucky to get an appointment at Blean School in 1998. I was a 'returning teacher' and initially was appointed as a class teacher, but progressed to eventually become a deputy head of the school. I well remember opening the door of the school to welcome Keith when he arrived in April 2000; it was exciting to greet this new head teacher who took up the post after what had been a somewhat 'rocky' period for the school. Keith turned out to be an excellent head teacher, leading Blean School through several successful OFSTED inspections. He worked extremely hard and was liked and much respected by staff, governors, parents and pupils.

Keith was always keen to investigate new ideas in education and once lent me a book on 'The Creative School.' I found it inspirational and wanted to adopt some of the ideas discussed in the book. However, I am not sure that Keith was initially enthralled by one of these ideas which involved setting fire to cardboard models of houses to re-enact the Great Fire of London with a class six year olds! He no doubt questioned the wisdom of having lent me the book! Nevertheless, after ensuring all fire and health and safety precautions would be taken, he let us have a go and the results were very exciting and inspired some very good writing from the children.

Another retired colleague has reminded me of the time Keith came into the staff room having just done a dinner duty (he always took his fair share of these!) He rather put everyone off their sandwiches when he described having just had his lunch sitting next to a child who unfortunately had contracted hair nits and had been fascinated to chase these round his plate as they dropped from his head! Oh the many and varied joys of primary school teaching!

After many years of being a successful head at Blean, Keith was persuaded by Kent Education Department to take a sabbatical from the school to become an advisory head teacher for two years, working in a supportive capacity with other schools in the area. By this time, I had joined with other senior colleagues to become a member of the senior leadership team. It was an interesting and challenging time of my career – and we certainly realised then, if we hadn't already, what a demanding and great job Keith had been doing at Blean. Although all went well, we missed him.

After two years, Keith returned to the school. As members of the senior leadership team we worked closely with Keith, and I have to say that it was not long before I felt that he was not quite the same man as the one who had left us. Sadly, everything was made clear when returning from hospital he called us all into his office and shared the information that his health was being investigated. Later he confirmed that he had been diagnosed with Early Onset Alzheimer's Disease. This diagnosis was particularly poignant for me, as I had quite recently lost my mother after caring for her with Alzheimer's; during this time, Keith had been very supportive. After his diagnosis Keith then had to retire on ill-health grounds.

For many people this could have been the end to a story. But it is typical of Keith that in fact he turned his diagnosis, devastating though it must have been for himself and his lovely wife Rosemary, into the start of yet another interesting chapter in his life. Since being diagnosed, Keith has worked tirelessly to raise awareness of dementia both in the area of Canterbury and nationally – even appearing on national television! He has demonstrated that having a positive and enquiring attitude can have a profound effect on lessening the impact this disease has on one's life. As in so many other aspects of his career, Keith has set a brilliant example.

Jennifer Samuel, ex-deputy head, Blean Primary school, Canterbury

I had been appointed by Keith's predecessor (in January 1999) so had worked at Blean Primary School for about a year before his appointment as head teacher.

A new leader usually means change after a settling in period and therefore there is some trepidation from an existing team.

I need not have worried - Keith led by example. He always had the needs of the children and the school at the heart of his leadership and recognised that the teaching team - both teachers and teaching assistants - were integral to the success of the school. My role under Keith was Special Educational Needs Coordinator.

Keith was interested and involved in the education of all of the children and was always very supportive of those who had additional educational needs. This was demonstrated when, for one staff development day, the whole of the staff attended the SEN Exhibition in London, attending various seminars and having the opportunity to look at resources and latest developments in this field. It was followed by the opportunity, for those staff who were interested, to visit a London Theatre show in the evening - much appreciated and great team building.

Keith was also keen to look at maximising the impact of Teaching Assistants on the education of the children and had planned to do further study on this via Christ Church University. Unfortunately, he was unable to do this when he had to retire from his post earlier than anticipated.

Some other memories also spring to mind...

For example, when the teachers did their own version of 'Strictly,' he played an important role as one of the judges and enjoyed getting into character. The children loved it (and still do) when the teachers performed and 'sent themselves up' at the end of the year. Similarly, he would join in the staff pantomimes.

Being a keen football and Nottingham Forest fan, during the World Cup, Keith allowed a more flexible timetable and arranged for those children and staff who were interested to watch the England matches in the school hall.

Another tradition introduced by Keith were the residential visits to Flatford Mill in Suffolk; memories which the children and staff will always hold dear.

On a personal and professional level, I feel privileged to have worked alongside Keith for many years at Blean Primary School. He is a man of great integrity and it is not surprising that he has channeled the energy and enthusiasm he brought to teaching to raising awareness of and championing living well with dementia.

Hilary Burnage, SENCO, Blean Primary School, Canterbury

The priceless gift of education: Asia 2003

Under the headline, *Head's Vietnam trip to see sponsored boy*, the article in *The Kentish Gazette* dated 15th May 2003 began: *'A child in Vietnam who owes his education to the support of Blean Primary School was able to thank the head teacher who went out to visit him.'*

My wife and I visited Vietnam during the two week Easter holiday and were prompted to do so by my wish to see the ten-year-old boy, whose name was Liem, to take some gifts from our school community to him and his school, and to get a sense of this far-off country and the charity called Christina Nobel Children's Foundation, named after its inspiring founder. We had supported him for two years in order to help Liem and other street children have a better start in life. The project started with a conversation I had with Chrissie Barr, a parent at Blean who, with her family, had also supported the Christina Noble Children's Foundation, I think maybe through their local church, St Mary Bredin, in Canterbury.

The Foundation was founded in 1989 to help support impoverished children in Vietnam and Mongolia, and I was very keen that our school commitment should be long term; we were funding Liem for the long haul not just as a short term token. We started the commitment at eight, when he started school, and ended our support when he was fourteen and no longer in education. Our financial commitment was just over £200 per year, but we always raised and sent a bit more and asked for it to be given to Liem and his mother. We did this by creating fun and enjoyable events in the school calendar such as a cake sale, an aerobathon and a non-uniform day. We also gave Chrissie some 'goodies' to take to Vietnam on her occasional visits either on her own or with one of her daughters, Lily or Alys.

Liem lived with his mother in a tiny hamlet on the outskirts of Ho Chi Minh City (formerly Saigon) His mother was blind, and there was no known father nor siblings or pets. Next to their wooden house with a tin roof and sink outside, was a coconut tree which gave them tiny status within the village and a source of food, heat from the leaves and nut shells which they burnt and shelter from the blistering sun. Liem's ambition was to be a doctor and then he would find a cure to restore his mother's blindness. Alas, neither ambition was to be realised.

As a school community we took Liem to our hearts and I felt it important to try and make him as much part of our school family as was possible. We received six monthly reports on his progress with an occasional photo. These were always added to a 'Liem' noticeboard which greeted visitors to the school in the entrance foyer.

Parents were informed about the trip to Vietnam and the purpose of it. Their children often mentioned Liem at home. They were then invited to send in toiletries, stationery and anything else which would be of use to either Liem or others in his school. We were overwhelmed by the response, and Marks and Spencer's in Canterbury generously donated a Beckham T-shirt - at that time the only English word he was confident using was 'Beckham,' which perfectly illustrated the footballer's place in the minds of children around the world at that time. I contacted Thai Airlines who we were flying with, and they readily tripled our baggage allowance for free when told what we were taking and its purpose. Then all we had to do was manage to carry it!

Joy and Peter Wood had arrived first and they greeted us in the entrance to the centre. The meeting took place in the air-conditioned offices of the Foundation and the four of us were cordially met by two of their staff and an interpreter, as Liem spoke little or no English and his mother none at all. Liem and his mum had been brought to the meeting on the back of a staff member's motorbike - the most popular form of transport - and it was amazing what we saw being carried on them in and around the city including large families, household furniture and livestock.

After introductions, we gave Liem the gifts we carried with us including a lovely watch which Marlene Washington, one of the deputy heads at Blean, had bought for him. This, along with the Beckham T-shirt and baseball cap, was hastily put on and then worn with great pride. We gave him some toiletries which his mother appreciated, and some stationery along with the boxes of goodies for the other children in the school or centre. Liem, although very shy and almost overwhelmed by the occasion, was very keen to express his thanks, and he did this by way of a Vietnamese folk song he tunefully sang for us, and the presentation of three amazing sets of miniature chairs and tables made from old beer cans. They were beautifully constructed and mine featured prominently in a cabinet outside my office back in school for a number of years after this visit and attracted great interest.

I had always wanted to visit Vietnam since our daughter had back-packed around the country a few years earlier. My image of the country was so negatively formed and entrenched around black and white or gory war images from the horrendous conflict which I grew up with most nights on the TV news and then compounded by Hollywood movies in the aftermath of the war. I was sure from Karon's experience that these childhood memories of mine needed challenging and changing. I managed to encourage Rosemary and we planned to have some more relaxed tourist time afterwards in Phuket and Thailand, again both of which had been on our daughter's earlier itinerary.

It was late evening when we arrived in Ho Chi Minh City and the sultry air hit us as we stepped out of the airport terminal, that along with the cacophony of sound from what seemed like dozens of lines of traffic jostling and bickering for position. The smells and lights also stretched one's senses as they all seemed to blend in together.

We were met by Katy Wood on a motor bike. She was a teacher in Ho Chi Minh whose mother, Joy, worked with me at Blean and who, with her father, Peter, was also in the city at that time and keen to meet Liem with

Rosemary and I the next day and to spend some time with us in the city. Our hotel was the Majestic Hotel, and was known as one of the 'hotspots' in the city back in the late '60s and early '70s, when American hacks such as Michael Herr met with the military to tease stories for their interested readers back home. Michael Herr went on to write the book *Dispatches*, which influenced me when I was in my early twenties and keen to learn about the conflict in this far off land. One can also imagine Graham Greene staying or drinking there when writing his classic novel in the mid-1950s *The Quiet American*, a book later to be made into a movie starring Michael Caine.

These are some of the memories of the same event from Joy Wood:

I enjoyed working at Blean during Keith's reign as head teacher. Under his leadership the school flourished and it was a happy place to work.

During 2002/3, our youngest daughter went to work in Saigon, Vietnam. At that time a parent at the school, Chrissie Barr, had become involved with a charity which worked with street children in Saigon. She travelled out there taking with her things the children had collected - clothes, toys, toiletries, etc. Keith was very interested in the good work undertaken by the Christina Noble Children's Foundation, and he suggested that the school sponsor a child. The child was Liem, a boy who lived near Saigon with his blind mother. The sponsorship paid for his education and his family received a small income so that Liem did not have to work on the streets. They only received this income if he attended school. We organized activities at school to fund the sponsorship.

This was a wonderful thing to do and the children at Blean learned so much about the lives of children growing up in a challenging environment. A relationship grew between the children at the school and Liem.

During the Easter break in 2003, my husband Peter and I decided to visit our daughter in Saigon. During her time out there she became interested in the work of the charity and helped there as a volunteer. Keith and Rosemary also wanted to visit Saigon to meet Liem and his mother.

He had a gift as described here by Keith for us to take back to Blean. The visit was a very touching and humbling experience which we shared with the children at school on our return.

During the next few days we were able to meet up and enjoyed spending time with them in this exciting and very different city, going for a swim in their hotel pool and enjoying the local cuisine. It was indeed an adventure for all of us. I have very happy memories of this trip. Seeing our daughter, meeting Liem and enjoying Keith and Rosemary's company. Wonderful memories and happy days. *Joy Wood, former colleague and current friend*

Our four days in Ho Chi Minh were extremely full-on, alongside seeing Liem at the Christina Nobel Children's Foundation we wanted to see more of the country - to sail on the Mekong river, to visit a beautiful Daoist temple, to explore the Cu Chi tunnels which I had read so much about previously, and hopefully to visit Liem's home and/or school. We succeeded in all of this apart from the home and school which I felt was a real pity both at the time and subsequently. There were two reasons for this - one explained to us and one not.

The reason given was that we had met him and his mother at the centre in the city and that needed to suffice and within the state communist system the school and home needed to be out of bounds to visitors from overseas. I respectfully accepted this and still do. However, I did also learn afterwards that had I bribed the taxi driver charged with escorting us about during our stay he may have added this to our schedule by way of a detour on one of our out-of-city excursions in his crystal clean, white nine-seater modern, air-conditioned vehicle which seemed to be available to just Rosemary and me. Oh well, I did what I thought was right and stuck by this.

One excursion in our minibus was to the Cu Chi Tunnels, which were created outside Saigon (Ho Chi Minh City) by the North Vietnamese and Viet Cong in the mid/late 1960s as an underground labyrinth containing hospitals, military and commissary supplies along with routes under US military bases. The Americans despite all their know-how and military hardware struggled to detect and then eradicate them.

Few images carry greater power than that of the innocent eight-year-old child running naked along the road having suffered horrendous injuries from a US napalm attack on her village. We were travelling along that straight track with paddy fields still along the margins of the single lane highway just as it was back in June 1972. My thoughts went to that photo of Phan Thi Kim Phuc and I wondered what had happened to her since that awful moment in time at Trang Bang. When I got home I googled her and discovered that she had been taken to live in Canada where she was given a better chance in life through education which she had grasped in both hands, marrying and having two children alongside achieving a doctorate and a role within UNESCO. Amazing what education and love can bring from hate and hostility. That has been my mantra for as long as I can remember, and here is another classic illustration to support this.

My recalled impressions of the Cu Chi Tunnels are firstly how ingenious the Viet Cong were to try and establish a level fighting duel with the Americans by way of death traps which contained lethal, faeces-coated, sharp wooden spikes in a hidden pit with trip wires concealed by vegetation.

The Chinese presence was clear in the range of weapons proudly displayed alongside improvised weapons made from redefined scrap metal in the accompanying museum.

The actual tunnels were so small. Although not great with heights, I am not at all claustrophobic and was happy crawling through the tunnels, despite the fact that at 6ft 4ins I would have towered over the builders and occupiers of the tunnels and with the added encumbrance of a rucksack which I omitted to remove, I did often get stuck!

If there was a propaganda element, then it was discrete and subtle - nowhere did we see anti-American statements.

Both Rosemary and I had our eyes opened on this excursion and it enabled us to see the Vietnamese people as peaceable and friendly, rather than the demonised images we had been given forty or fifty years ago.

The boat trip along the Mekong on a junk was an amazing experience. Again there were very few tourists about and we had the boat almost to ourselves. Part of the reason for this was that at this time (March/ April 2003) Asia was enduring an epidemic of the SARS virus and this had severely affected the tourist industry in the region. Consequently, everyone was keen to give us first class service, including, as I mentioned, our private driver and on this trip a guide almost to ourselves. Our young female guide who greeted us aboard with a drink of fresh coconut milk in its shell was a very bright young graduate from the city's university who thankfully spoke fluent English (albeit with an Americanised accent.)

Amongst the sights we saw and experienced that day were a jungle village where the food offered by the family with was a fish mounted on a stand as if it was still alive and swimming, and snake in a jar of vinegar!

A fascinating hour was spent in a riverside hamlet where people were making a local thin pancake and other foods both for themselves and for sale. Everything was fresh and very cheaply priced. I remember trying dragon fruit at this place for the first time - a white fleshy fruit with black bits is how I remember it. We also took in the views of families living in junks and throwing out their household waste into the murky depths of the river.

The Cao Daoist temple built between 1933 and 1955 in Tay Ninh was another excursion out of the dust and bustle of Ho Chi Minh City and was about a two-hour drive north. It was lavishly decorated inside and out in pink, red, yellow, beige and turquoise/ blue, and impressively constructed, looking almost - without being disrespectful - as an amalgamation of Disney and cathedral. I remember the image of an eye which was a significant symbol, and dragon columns.

My emotional side was intrigued by the seven stone cobras, which were prominently displayed and whose significance was to represent the seven main human emotions. Cao Daoism is an amalgamation of Buddhism, Daoism, Confucianism and Christianity with a little Islam for even greater diversity and has almost three million followers in Vietnam. Although there were other tourists visiting everyone was most respectful, and shoes and spoken words were left at the entrance thus allowing us to better experience the calmness of the setting.

After the meeting at the Christina Noble Children's Foundation, the three excursions and a day walking around the streets of Ho Chi Minh City trying to avoid the beggars, some of whom had tiny babies who looked very distressed or doped, we retreated to the sanctuary of our hotel swimming pool with Joy and Peter - we were an easily identified target as westerners. This was the only time we met up with Joy and Peter other than to see Liem and his mum, as they soon departed for a trip further up the Mekong to Phnom Penh. The time to leave Vietnam had arrived. We flew out with mixed emotions; the last five days had been truly memorable, but we did need time to relax now and that is why I chose to book us a few days in a quiet location on the tropical island of Phuket.

Phuket, before the horrendous Tsunami of a few years ago and a greater influx of tourists, had some gorgeous places, and Cape Panwa, where we stayed, was one of them. The resort was like paradise and I remember sitting on the secluded, quiet beach under a palm tree thinking, this is as good at it gets. Although there was no sign of Leonardo Di Caprio, who I know likes a good Thai beach, we did see two heads from primary schools in Thanet about 50 metres away, another example of a small world. We also shared the beach one day with the crown princess of Thailand and a military entourage including a frigate which anchored in the bay. The Thai staff were amazingly polite and nothing was too much trouble for them.

Each day the resort ran classes or demonstrations, amongst which we accessed ice sculpturing, I attended two Thai-speaking classes and picked up some useful tourist vocabulary, which I was able to put to use later at Bangkok House, our favourite Thai restaurant in Canterbury. Rosemary attended a flower arranging course based on the use of orchids - the traditional Thai flower: one adorned our pillow every morning after the maid had serviced the room.

After this beautiful break we headed off to the hustle and bustle again, this time in Bangkok for a few days. I wasn't keen on Bangkok beyond the regal majesty of the Grand Palace, although my feelings may be coloured by the fact that I developed a dodgy tummy there which took a while to settle, and which we think led to a series of further infections over the course of subsequent years. Whether it was picked up in Bangkok or had remained dormant for a few days after the snake, fish and fruit eating in Vietnam I do not know.

We were keen to get out of the city and we took a mini bus to Kanchanaburi in order to visit the bridge over the River Kwai, and then a ride on the death railway built by allied soldiers held captive by the Japanese during the Second World War. This was amazing. We first saw the bridge from a speed boat which whizzed us along the river at great speed before disembarking us at the station for the steam train into the jungle. I could not help thinking of the thousands of emaciated young men, beaten, sick and yet defiant as they worked until death on this track which we now experienced as tourists.

Whilst the train was far from comfortable the views were stunning, and the feat of engineering was inspiring as the train wound its way towards the Burmese frontier, stopping several miles short as, at the time, crossing the border was prohibited.

That pretty much brings to an end the travelogue element of my story; we returned to school lighter with luggage having left so much of it at the centre in Ho Chi Minh City and, whilst we bought lots of souvenirs, they didn't make up for this.

What we did return with was what travel is all about: experience, memories and a better insight into the way of life in other countries around the world. That is something special.

Living and working in Australia

This chapter is dedicated to our Aussie mates - Alan, Glenys, Hellen, Julie, Paul, Sue, Pete, Bev, John, Amanda and her family, Kevern, Wendy, Ashlea, Casey, Jan, Wayne, and the many other dear friends we have met and loved over the years who, despite the tyranny of distance, are 'bloody bonza mates.'

For those readers seeking an account of our travel around Australia I need to point you towards our earlier book, *Welcome to our World* pages 167-174, where you will be able to read of our adventures Down Under as something of a travelogue along with advice to those who seek to travel with the concerns and challenges which dementia presents.

What I hope to do here is to explore with you, not the places within this wonderful country which over the past 27 years have come to mean so much to Rosemary and myself, but more the impression and impact it has had upon us.

These days it is much easier to hop on a plane and visit far flung places which previous generations could only dream of seeing. Having said that, to actually spend a considerable amount of time, in our case initially a year, living and working in a far off land is something quite different.

In 1987 I had suggested to Rosemary, and then shared with Karon and Gareth, the idea of arranging a job and house-swap through the League for the Exchange of Commonwealth Teachers based in London. Our favourite destination was quickly identified as Australia, and then we began to do some research.

It emerged that the part of the country which most appealed to us by way of climate, location and lifestyle was Adelaide - the largest city in South Australia, the driest state in the driest country in the world. Sounds good! It was on the coast and quite central to other parts of a country.

We brought our five-year-old, James, into the loop and he seemed to take it all in his stride, even saying much to our mirth, 'Are we in Australia?' when we attended an Australian tourism event at the cricket ground in Canterbury! Little did he know that the journey was a bit longer than the ten-minute drive from our home to Kent's St Lawrence ground.

At that time, Gareth was mid-way through college in Reading, Karon was completing her A-Levels and looking to go to University and James, who'd just turned six, was at the local primary school. Karon was happy to delay University for a year and accompany us for what was a gap year, and Gareth originally planned to complete his degree and then join us three quarters of the way through the year. For a number of reasons he was not able to actually do this - he completed college and went straight into work with an insurance company. James was probably too young to comprehend the significance of the venture, and he would be comfortably enrolled into Year 1 at the same school in Adelaide where I was to teach. Now, almost 28 years later, and given the opportunity to reflect and write about his experience here is the first of two pieces from James:

As a six-year-old, there wasn't much I remember about the build up to the adventure that was 1989. Dad had arranged to take part in a teacher exchange and we were going to live in a far-off land called Australia for a year. This was a place I'd only heard of, seen on a globe at school, or learned about through the sagas of Ramsey Street, Erinsborough. All I knew for sure was that it was really far away! Even further than Nottingham!

This would also be the first time I'd experienced flying. Being afraid of heights, I was somewhat apprehensive, but found it to be incredible. The world looked like a scenery model and at night, entire cities looked like small constellations joined together with a row of street lamps. When we stepped off the plane, it was like opening an oven door. A far cry from the foggy and drab British December we had left behind.

Having met the relevant people at the airport and been taken to our new home, we soon settled into our new (albeit temporary) way of life in 'The Hills.' Having been told by Mum and Dad beforehand, I was well aware of the silent assassins that were some of the local wildlife. Remembering to bang out our shoes and gumboots (wellies) before inserting a foot, checking for redbacks under the toilet seat before, well, using it, and not to stray from the clearly cut paths when walking through the bush that surrounded our home. All of which soon become nothing more than habit. The house itself was a split level bungalow with its own swimming pool and access to a residents' tennis court. It didn't have much of a garden, but to be honest, when you're six, these facilities more than made up for it!

Now, don't worry, this isn't going to be a diary-esque account of the entire year through the eyes of a child, but an insight into what was a truly life-inspiring year. Much of it was fairly unremarkable to be honest. You know: school, homework, family time during the evenings and weekends. The things I would normally do here in the UK, only with better weather and only having to walk halfway up the driveway to use a swimming pool. However, part of the year when Dad and I didn't have to be in school (we went to the same one) we took advantage of exploring this somewhat mythical land.

One of these trips sticks quite dominantly in my memory above the others. The Ayers Rock Trip was something extraordinary. Visiting the opal mining town of Coober Pedy, we stayed in an underground hotel carved into the rock from where the precious stones themselves were mined. I don't remember much about the hotel itself, but the whole concept of an underground town was something I'd never experienced before.

After being coach-driven for days along main roads that were no more than sandy tracks, we camped at a site near to Ayers Rock (now known by its

Aboriginal name, 'Uluru') At that time, there was the opportunity to climb Uluru itself, following a predetermined route. As I mentioned earlier, my head for heights was much worse as a child than it is now, but after some encouraging words from Mum and Dad, we started the ascent together. Unfortunately I was unable to complete the climb and returned down the Rock with a couple of friendly strangers. Looking back now I'm glad my parents were able to continue and successfully complete the climb. I would feel so guilty if I was the reason they would miss out on a lifetime opportunity to achieve this, and I'm so proud of them for making it up there.

A few years after our trip, they stopped allowing the public to climb the Rock. Although being too young to appreciate the scenery and landscape (to me, that was boring adult stuff), I remember being fascinated by the fact that it was so different to anything I'd seen before. To me, it was practically the surface of Mars! Something of a strong contrast to the North Downs!

When the time came to pack up and leave the land down under, I remember for Mum, Dad and many of our new friends, it was an emotional time. Like saying goodbye to a holiday romance, but after a year-long relationship. This is something I can only really appreciate now as a 33-year-old man, but at the time I was a six-year-old boy and the goodbyes were merely another part of the continued adventure.

I think that our year in Oz is something that, although being a great experience at the time, I only truly appreciate looking back on it as an adult. As I sit here and write this piece, I think about my Dad being the same age, bar a few months, as I am now. I think about how it must've felt carting our family halfway around the world to do something like this. Living in a country none of us had ever been to before. To embrace the lifestyle without really knowing for sure if it would work out. Even knowing it would only last a year, it's still a huge responsibility! But you know what, I'm so glad he did, even if I wasn't old enough to truly appreciate it at the time.

I think it taught me that sometimes in life you have to take risks to make incredible things happen. Hopefully something I have either learned from him or inherited. To some, 1989 was just another year. To me however, it was a pivotal year in shaping the man I've become today.

James Oliver

The exchange took 14 months to apply for, get accepted onto and then to match us up with a suitable teacher and their family. Rosemary and I attended an interview in London, where we first met fellow exchangee, Hellen, and her husband Maurice, both of whom went onto become dear friends on the same programme as us.

I first met Keith and his wife, Rosemary, in 1988 as we were both preparing for a teaching exchange year in Adelaide, South Australia (SA). We got to know each other through various activities and events throughout the year, in particular the 'Red Centre Tour' during the July holiday, which presented a number of challenges as well as a wonderful experience of the Australian Outback. Subsequently, my husband and I emigrated to Adelaide but our friendship with Keith and Rosemary continued to flourish during their annual visits to SA and our trips to England, as well as email correspondence.

During those years, when Keith was a primary school principal and I continued working as a teacher and specialist support person for children with vision impairment, we had regular discussions and compared notes about education policies, practices and curriculum development in our relative environments.

Our journey with dementia began together too. Keith's diagnosis occurred at about the same time as my husband's. Although our situations were very different in terms of age and role, we have been able to continue informed and supportive discussions about the various aspects of dementia and dementia care.

It was a steep learning curve for all of us and both our families were fortunate to find dedicated, caring professionals who have tremendous vision and drive to promote and achieve the best possible care and lifestyle for people with dementia.

In parallel, on opposite sides of the globe, we both took up the challenge, joining with our specialist doctors and support workers in fighting the good fight as champions of the cause through public speaking, participation in research projects and fundraising for the improvement of facilities for people with dementia.

Keith and Rosemary have, until recently, continued their annual visits to South Australia. This has allowed us to attend a number of Dementia Care and Dignity in Care functions together, deepening our understanding and broadening our networks.

I have tremendous respect and admiration for Keith, and for Rosemary as his wife and primary carer and supporter. I believe they have approached what could have been a very negative, life- changing diagnosis with vigorous, positive energy and determination to make a difference for others. Of course, we have had huge challenges to overcome and the journey has not been easy, but I am sure Keith would agree that no worthwhile achievement is ever easy. With the support of his professional team, he continues his life purpose as a passionate educator, only now from a different perspective, setting a fine example for all around him both near and far, known and unknown.

There is still a long way to go in terms of public education and government support, but tremendous progress has been made, both in the UK and Australia, in understanding dementia and particularly in recognising the support needs of people with younger onset dementia.

Hellen Riley, friend.

Friends such as Hellen are to be cherished, and the way she has dealt with severe challenges since we have known her so stoically inspires not just Rosemary and I, but many others who are also proud to call her their friend.

It always inspires me that friendships can be sustained despite the tyranny of distance - we have a board hanging in our garden which clearly states 'Adelaide 16,687kms - it's a bloody long way' - IT IS! Whilst I cannot vouch for the absolute accuracy of the distance quoted on the board from our garden to our beloved second home, I don't think it would be far out. The journey is a long one, and despite being fortunate enough to have made it 17 times over the years it does not get any shorter or easier to manage, in fact travelling economy probably gets a bit harder the older one gets.

We are also lucky that Aussie mates have made the trip to spend time with us in the 'mother country' which has been a real pleasure in allowing us to share some of the treasures on our doorstep, or as they would say 'in our backyard.'

Friendship is one theme of this book, and some of our best friends are Aussies we have met and come to love over the years. This started on day one when we first touched down in Adelaide on a blisteringly hot New Year's Day in 1989. We were met by Kevern Doolette, the school head at Norwood, where I was to be teaching for the year.

Kevern was the funniest, friendliest person and head teacher I have ever met and became a very dear friend, as did his dear wife Wendy and two lovely girls Ashlea and Casey. All came to stay with us a few years after the exchange and we stayed with them on return trips and Casey spent a bit of time with us when she was taking a gap year to travel with a friend.

We all sadly lose family and friends but Kevern's untimely and premature death in his mid/late 60s hit me, and many others, hard. I have missed him and his friendship, never more than when Wendy came to stay with us accompanied by her sister, and when I was doing the advisor job, as I know he would have been interested and proud that I had followed a route he had also done as a secondment some years previously. We would have had so much to talk about and share.

Kevern taught me more positive things about leading a school than any other head I have worked for or met, one aspect of which was the benefits to one's school of networking - he was an early master of this and if a manual could have been written, he would have written it and then many others would have learnt from him, as I did. He put people first - the children, his staff and the parents and the Authority, important though they were, had to fit in and queue up in fourth place - but he did this with a smile and a good reason, never nastily or aggressively.

Two other Aussies who have inspired me, both as teachers and as friends, are Bev Endersbee (who has written elsewhere in this book) and Julie Reece; although I never worked with Julie, we have spent probably more time in her lovely company than any other Antipodean mate. Although retired from the secondary school classroom Julie continues to use her immense talent as a teacher to inspire a generation of Australians into the benefits of travel and the link with their past and heritage primarily through projects linked to World War One.

It did not surprise us at all that when we were once glancing through the national newspaper *The Australian* when on holiday over there we saw a full page article about the Australian Teacher of the Year - it was our mate, Julie Reece.

In 1989, my husband Paul and I met an English couple, Keith and Rosemary Oliver, and their young son James, when they came to Adelaide in South Australia for an exchange year of teaching at Norwood Primary School.

My sister, Sue Royal, was the deputy principal at the school - hence our connection to the Oliver family. Over that year we all became very close friends and shared many weekends away to some of our favourite locations in our state:

a school camp to Burra; houseboat weekends on the River Murray where many varieties of South Australian wines were enjoyed; dinner parties with a wide range of friends and many other wonderful times together. Laughter, food and wine, and crazy carry-on all created a treasure chest of fond memories that will last us all a lifetime.

Over the years the friendship developed from afar as we all dealt with the tyranny of distance between the UK and Australia. More recently in the past decade as I have been involved in bringing school groups to the UK and Europe for World War One commemorative tours, Keith would always make himself available to share with these young Aussies the many layers of Canterbury's fascinating history. Keith would meet us on the town walls wearing his 'Crows' scarf and Akubra hat, and then take us all through the amazing narratives of this Roman/ Saxon/ Norman settlement. Keith engaged our kids and adults and gave his time and himself so generously. I will always treasure those walks with our tour groups.

Like many people, my knowledge and understanding of dementia has been limited to those few older people in my life who have developed this debilitating disease. I learnt of the struggles my close friend, Jan, experienced as she dealt with the progression of the condition with her beloved mother, Mary. However, this story was one I always saw in the context of old age: horrible, frightening - but only something that ever happened to old people.

So when we received the crushing news that our dear Pommy mate, Keithipops, had been diagnosed with Alzheimer's five years ago, it just didn't compute! It could not be possible... Keith was younger than me... he had a brilliant mind and was an incredible educator. And to make this seem even more confusing and hard to accept was the fact that when we saw Keith after his diagnosis on some of our visits to the UK, and when he and Rosemary came back to SA on holidays, Keith seemed just like he always did to us... it just didn't make sense.

However, it is real... it is there and every day Keith and Rosemary have to face whatever that demon throws up at them. Keith has been very open with us and has trusted us as friends with sharing some of his crucial fears and in the last five years we have gradually gained a tiny insight into the struggles and challenges that dementia creates. In saying that however, the daily truth of this condition is only one that the key players really know and fully understand.

Like Keith, I was a teacher for over 36 years and now, in my retirement from the profession, have been able to reflect on the nature of many things.

As difficult as it is to accept the situation Keith has found himself in, there is something very special that Keith has given to us and I guess to many others who have come into his life in the last five years.

Keith has continued to be a teacher: maybe not in the way he saw for himself originally, but in a way that I believe has changed lives. He has crystallised the very essence of what we should all focus on: TIME. We float through our lives often assuming we will be here forever, that our plans, hopes and dreams WILL happen because we want them to. Often we waste time, energy, and emotion, on things that happen to us that are in actual fact trivial and silly.

Keith's courage and determination to maximise the time he has, has been inspirational and has impacted on a number of decisions I have made very recently. These decisions have involved risk and indeterminate outcomes and in the back reaches of my thinking I often used Keith as my mentor: the enemy of time raises its head and I think that with some of the risky paths I have chosen they are set in the context of having a go NOW, giving it a try NOW; not assuming the future will allow me to chase my dreams - and to that new perspective I can thank Keith my courageous and gutsy friend who I will always count dear in my heart. The nasty demon of dementia is present, we know that - BUT today it is still a loser as our mate is a winner, still inspiring others and still teaching.

I salute you my Pommy mate. CARPE DIEM.

Julie Reece, friend and teacher

We were keen to assimilate the four of us into the local community where we lived in the hills overlooking Adelaide and the school community in which I was to work in the eastern suburb of Norwood. Our house was really very ordinary; single storey, mix of wood and brick with a steep drive to the property and separate garage, or shed, as the Aussies call them. The garden sloped quite steeply - these were the Adelaide Hills after all - and had a small patch of grass which needed mowing, a few flowers and lots and lots of gum trees - mostly stringy barks, which constantly shed their bark and gum nuts.

This was a real fire risk area, and in the early 1980s two Ash Wednesdays had burnt out various properties killing a number of people relatively locally. After this Garry, our exchangee, had installed an above ground outdoor swimming pool into the plot with a pump attached to a sprinkler system which would saturate the house and garden immediately adjacent to the house. One of my weekly jobs was to test the pump and sprinklers, and if there was a fire to utilise them. Fortunately, like all fire drills I've been involved in over the years, the real thing never happened. What did happen though, is that for the hottest months of January, February and March many school days ended with a dip, a swim and a cool drink by or in our pool. I think this took my keenness to teach swimming (despite being quite a poor swimmer as a youngster) to a different level, and over the past six years or so, I've developed a passion for swimming, especially in the sea.

Not only did we exchange houses and jobs, we swapped cats for the year. When packing to leave for the airport in December 1988, our cat Joshua sensed something was amiss and plonked his sizeable frame on the half packed case. It was to be an exchange year for him as well as he wound our Aussie exchangees around his little paw and got away with things we wouldn't allow! They had two cats - Honey, a large, dominant male ginger and Sparky a much more timid, thin jet black female.

One story we always tell surrounds the fear we had of the cats straying at night and getting bitten; you may have heard that Australia has the world's most venomous snakes, and some lived in our garden, although we never saw one there. One night, Honey was there, as always, waiting for his supper, and he would have eaten Sparky's, too, given the chance. Sparky was nowhere to be seen. We rang the neighbours: no joy. We searched and called for her, again not a sign; this was unusual and concerning. We asked Honey, who was a vocal cat and he appeared to respond with 'I haven't a clue.' We asked him a number of times and he seemed to be losing patience with us. He wanted just to eat and lay down for the night and our anxiety was disturbing him. Eventually she did appear, strolling in, curled tail raised as if nothing was amiss. Honey went straight over to her, gave her a mouthful of cat abuse and such a swipe with his right forepaw. It was a real picture!

Of course the seasons are the opposite in Australia to the UK. 'Christmas where the gum trees grow - there is no frost and there is no snow' is the start of a popular Aussie song. The climate in Adelaide is very hot and dry in the summer/ autumn (Dec - May) and then mild and wet in the winter (June - Aug) and very mixed in their spring (Sept - Nov). Regular temperatures of 35-42 degrees Celsius would often occur, and that is hot, especially in a house or school neither of which had air conditioning at that time. School did close early; 2.30pm on days of over 34 degrees, but some kids weren't collected so they stayed and played indoors or did homework. From 12.30-1.30pm they were outdoors playing cricket, tennis or if they had sense sheltering under a tree. This surprised me. Almost all of the kids wisely wore a hat as part of their school uniform. One pupil from my class at Norwood was Amanda Drury who I am thrilled to still keep in touch with despite a gap of 20 years - here is her story to share:

I first met Keith Oliver when I was ten years old. I was a quirky, bubbly Year 5 Australian student, growing up in the '80s, full of energy, questions, and a love of learning. He was a bubbly, equally quirky, around 30-year-old, Year 5 teacher from England, come over teach a bunch of Aussie kids on a year-long adventure.

The year was 1989, and school was back; it was early February and HOT! The mercury was hitting over 40 degrees that week (that's about 104 F), and I don't think Mr Oliver quite realised what he was in for. In those days there was no air conditioning, at least not at our school, fans were a commodity too! So it was over 40 degrees outside but about 50 degrees inside, and school was going to go till at least 2.30 in the afternoon. I am sure Mr Oliver was thinking, 'What have I got myself in to?'

As the school bell rang we all rushed inside to meet the tall, handsome man with the funny accent, who would now be our teacher. He was tall, but not all that tall by Australian standards (in fact I think he was about the same height as my father, though I hear back in the UK he was known as the BFG.) He was wearing a long sleeved shirt, long trousers and a tie (not exactly the best attire for an Australian summer) and he had a thick brown beard and a funny sense of humour.

Despite the heat (which he took in his stride at first), he started our day full of energy, eager to tell us all about his home country and his town of Canterbury in Kent, South East England. He described it beautifully as a little country city with a beautiful cathedral at its centre and weather much cooler than ours all year around. We were all enthralled by his description of this far-off land we had never heard of, and he didn't lose our attention for one minute. He then directed us to a table where he had set out several items from Canterbury for us to look at, from key rings to coins, little dolls to post cards, brochures to photos, there was quite a selection. We all got to take one thing home, and so his bond with his Aussie students had started.

Judgement was passed, as it always is on the first day of the school year, and we thought this teacher was pretty neat! We were going to have a great year!

The heat didn't bother me in those days, it still doesn't, so I was pretty full of energy all day. However, by the time the soaring heat had reached its peak and lunch break was upon us, Mr Oliver had pretty much lost all of his energy. Being English, and having never experienced more than around 32 degrees Celsius, he came in after lunch looking pretty exhausted. His class by that stage was full of very wet ten-year-olds (it was a daily ritual during summer to have water fights during our hour long lunch play, and sometimes the grounds man put on the sprinklers for us too). He was equally as wet as us, but for very different reasons! His beard was dripping, his long shirt sleeves were rolled up, and he was wet through. He presented the last hour of the day in a quiet manner, I'm sure, counting down the minutes till the school bell, and the ability to get home and rest.

He lasted a couple of weeks before the heat proved just too much for him, and some of us were concerned we had scared him away! He was off sick for a couple of days. I was asking every day if he was ok; I liked him, and his English ways, and I did not want him to leave! The other teachers at the school assured me he would be back, he was just unwell with heatstroke, something that can happen when you are not used to the climate.

I eagerly awaited his return, then one day there he was. He sauntered into the class, a very different looking man to the one we first met. There was no beard anymore, and he wore very sensible shorts and a short sleeved shirt, collar undone, no tie: now, that was more like it. Mr Oliver had finally become acclimatized to our Aussie summer, but perhaps not our Aussie ways quite yet. As always though, he took everything in his stride, a rather long stride, which gave him an air of authority, but also friendship, care and respect.

We had the opportunity to write to Mr Oliver's students back in England. Each of us got a pen pal from Canterbury, and I kept mine for about two years afterwards until we both started high-school, and time for letter writing was not so available. I wonder what she is up to now, and how many of my class mates kept in contact with theirs?

Aside from the everyday humdrum of classroom life, Mr Oliver was also determined to experience all he could of Australian school life. He got involved in our Sports Day, in full sports colours, had an active part in our school fete - The Night of Nights - watched our swimming carnival, and came along to school events and camps for The Festival Choir. This was to work on a performance of the music from the movie *Ghostbusters* - a big hit in the late 1980s. He played a big part in our school community, and left a lasting impression for years to come.

In fact, his impression was so lasting that I decided then and there, I wanted to be a teacher, just like him. He was one of a few teachers that influenced that decision, including my teacher I had the year previous to him, but he was a big part of it. It was a fleeting wish along with wanting to be an actress, singer, and all kinds of things children want to aspire to, but it was one that stayed with me.

Fast forward, some twelve years later, and I was a new graduate teacher, out of university, ready to follow in Keith Oliver's footsteps, to be a primary school teacher; but not just any primary school teacher, a teacher with adventure at the core! I was eager, and bold, and a little too confident. I wasn't going to wait another nanosecond, I wanted the experience he had, I wanted to teach overseas! And where else would I go? Well, to England, of course! I managed to secure myself a position in a school in Plumstead, South East London, and Mr Oliver was never far from my mind, as I followed in his footsteps.

Unlike Keith though, I had a Year 2 class for my first twelve months, one full of bright bubbly kids, eager to hear about Australia! I have many funny stories I could tell of my journey in England, like the time we were doing Gym Class. Over there the kids have their PE lesson inside, and in this school the Junior Primary kids did not have a PE kit, they were expected to strip off to underwear and singlets for their PE lessons. It was a strange thing for me to get used to, something we would never do in Australia, but then we have our PE lessons outside, and our school uniforms are more fitting to PE than the English ones.

So I took my class to the gym for their first PE lesson and asked the kids to take off their pants (pants in Australia are trousers you see, but in Britain they are something very different which I wasn't aware of!) Pretty quickly I had a room full of almost naked 6 and 7 year olds, and I had to quickly direct them to put their pants back on!

My first experiences in England were much like Keith Oliver's in Australia and I took a bit of time to get used to the climate too. This time it was the cold.

So I now had some understanding of what it must have been like for Mr Oliver, on his first day at our school in Adelaide, Australia, having to get used to a new climate, and new culture, while learning how to teach a new bunch of Aussie kids with Aussie accents, and Aussie words like *textas* (marker pens), *thongs* (that's flip flops to you Brits, not what you think they are), and of course *pants* (trousers, never knickers). It made me think of him, my experience in England, and I wanted to find him. Only, I hadn't kept in contact with him, and did not know where he lived. I hadn't forgotten though that he was from Canterbury.

I visited Canterbury my first school holidays, and stayed two days there. It was as beautiful as Mr Oliver had described. A city surrounded by rolling green hills, a river running through the middle, with punts you could travel in, and a beautiful cathedral at its centre. Keith certainly had done it justice with his description!

In those days the internet was fairly new and there were no Smart Phones as we have now, so I used an old fashioned telephone book to try and find him. I must admit that when I saw the number of Olivers in the book I decided it may be a little harder to find him than I thought. I tried ringing a few, but no luck there, most did not answer. I also was not aware of his first name then either, I only remembered him as 'Mr Oliver,' and I was not even sure if, after 13 years, he would still be teaching in Canterbury.

Then I thought, how about the schools in the town, but there were a few (can't remember how many now but at least two I think, and it was school holidays of course so they were closed). In the end I guess I did not try hard enough. I was taken so much with the beautiful city of Canterbury, and only had two days in which to look at it, I decided not to worry about it and enjoyed my stay there instead, wondering where he might be and what he might be doing. Was he still a teacher? Did he still live there at all? Where was he now?

I came back to Australia in 2004 and started a family of my own. My life was moving on, and I did not think about Mr Oliver much anymore. Then one day, out of the blue, and by coincidence, only a few months before my family were planning to visit the UK, Mr Oliver contacted me! Another teacher I had kept in contact with had given him my email address. He was trying to make contact with as many people he could from his past as he had developed early onset dementia. My gosh, I was so sad to hear that my quirky old Year 5 teacher had had such a thing happen to him! He wasn't that old either, how could this happen to such a young person? I could not believe that it had happened.

I got to meet him once again, in 2011, just 21 years since I had last seen him. He hadn't changed a bit; a little greyer around the edges, and maybe a wrinkle here and there, but still as fun and quirky as ever. It was great to see him again, and be able to introduce him to my young children who were five and two years old by then. Both my children are much like me, quirky, energetic and chatty, so he appreciated meeting them. He showed us some photos from the days in 1989, as we enjoyed a nice meal on the banks of the River Thames.

It did not surprise me to find out that Keith Oliver had taken his dementia by the horns and given it a good shake. He was not going to let it beat him! He was doing all he could to preserve his memory, in every way he could, and being so smart, quirky, creative and clever, he also found great ways to be able to live with the disease with relative comfort. He wasn't going to let it stop him enjoying life to the best he could. I am so proud of him, and wouldn't expect anything less from that great man I met all those years ago!

It's been quite the journey for us but the thing I remember most about Mr Oliver, and the teacher he was, was his great care for his students, and the fun he brought in to each and every day. He is a teacher who will stay in my memory for life.

Amanda Drury, ex-pupil Norwood Primary School, Adelaide, now a teacher in that city.

It never ceases to impress and amaze me what ex-pupils remember and say to me, and as I describe in the chapter 'Once a teacher...' their words mean so much to me. I am immensely proud to have been a teacher and to have been BLESSED and privileged to have played a small part in helping shape the lives of the people I have taught.

Most Australians love most sports, with cricket, swimming and Aussie Rules Football being prime examples of the South Australian appetite for competition, and in the case of the first two a chance to take on the Poms also adds an extra sense of purpose. When teaching there I taught sport to my class and also took the school's cricket and softball teams. In the case of cricket, I had some idea of what I was doing - but softball was a new game to me and the kids really taught me; my role was to encourage and organise and I left the finer points of the game to them. In both sports Norwood did quite well winning some and losing some.

Aussie Rules is a passion for many of our mates and having seen a few games I sense why this is - it is brutal, fast and high scoring, beyond that I didn't really understand what was happening. I played it a bit in PE with the kids at Barton in Dover and they quite enjoyed my Pommy version of a different game.

With Adelaide on the coast having a lovely clean (though shark occupied) gulf running along its western boundary, most Aussies are keen swimmers, none more so than our dear friend Alan Brokenshire. It is with Alan and Glenys that Rosemary and I have spent the most time as guests since we have been in Adelaide over the past 20 years, staying with them in their annex known as The Shearers' Quarters. They are dear friends, and it is only health issues that have got in the way of them contributing to this book, but they are very much here in spirit - hence their mention in the dedication. Alan and Glenys share so many of our interests - we are so alike and yet physically a world separates us - we love gardens, swimming and walking, we love talking and listening, we love nature, we share a sense of social justice, we enjoy writing and reading, and doing the Saturday morning quiz together on local radio in Adelaide, and we love a good sushi washed down with a drop (or two) of Aussie Moscato - South Australian, of course!

Another sport which features in the Australian sporting calendar is their round of the Grand Prix season. Back in 1989 this was held on the streets of Adelaide, and came in early November when drivers were competing for points which might determine the year's champion. Nowadays it is held at the start of the season in Melbourne. In 1989, as our school was close to the circuit, we had a day's holiday on the Friday, partly because of the noise of the racing cars in that part of the city, and partly to allow staff, children and parents the chance to attend the preliminaries to the big event. Little did I know then the impact this would have upon James, my then seven-year-old son...

Whilst I am now 33, I'd like to tell you about a day when I had not long turned seven. As a family we were living in Adelaide, Australia, as Dad was taking part in a year-long teacher exchange. Among many fantastic adventures over the course of this year, none were to play such an influential role and fuel a passion which would shape my adult life as much as this. It was a hot and sunny Friday November morning and as the Channel 9 TV adverts said, 'The Formula One circus is in town!'

Before the Australian grand prix moved to Albert Park (Melbourne), the streets of Adelaide hosted the race. As a result, many of the local schools would remain closed for the Friday and teachers and students alike would go to watch the action. It was only a practice and first qualifying session, but the excitement I felt as a seven-year-old was incredible. The noise, the speed, the smells; I was instantly hooked.

Early November saw my first experience of what would become a significant passion throughout my childhood and continuing through adulthood. Dad and I went to see the Formula One Friday practice which, at the time, was held around the streets of Adelaide. The experience was incredible. The memories of seeing the likes of my all-time sporting hero Ayrton Senna, as well as Alain Prost and Nigel Mansell et al in action from trackside is something that I will hold eternally dear. This experience, thanks to Dad, would spark a lifelong passion and ultimately (although much later in life than I would've liked) shape a career path that can both be traced back to that sunny day at the side of the road on the other side of the world.

James Oliver

Now this chapter may be closing in our lives. This has been the first year since 2003 that we haven't been back to Adelaide. We thought long and hard about whether we should go again since it is - as the sign says in our garden - 'a bloody long way.' We want to move on from this chapter in our lives with only happy memories of the friends, the places and everything else associated with this amazing place Down Under, and we are fearful that it might be pushing our luck and capabilities to embark on one more trip. Having said that, never say never...

Nottingham Forest

Seldom have I heard truer words than these expressed by John McGovern on the cover of *I Believe in Miracles* retelling the amazing story of 1977-81 of 'our' magnificent football team Nottingham Forest:

'We were like one of those comets you see flying across the night sky. We burned brightly, but it was all too brief. But, boy, did we burn brightly for a while.'

McGovern was the quiet, unassuming club captain during those halcyon days, and as Mary Hopkin sang back in the late 1960s, and the Forest's Trent End chorused *Those were the days my friend, We thought they'd never end...*

My passion for the beloved 'Slippery Reds' began as soon as the opening strains of *Robin Hood, Robin Hood, riding through the glen,* were first heard by me, not on the TV like most other seven-year-olds at the time, but on the tannoy as the boys in Garibaldi red (rather than Lincoln green) ran out on to the hallowed City Ground turf back in May 1963 to face the formidable Tottenham Hotspur, who were probably at the time the best team in the country.

I remember nothing of the game other than the crush of the crowd and the 1-1 scoreline, a big improvement on the 9-2 defeat Forest had suffered at Tottenham earlier in the season, largely due to Jimmy Greaves, our nemesis. As a keen football follower my father had wanted to take me to a match for some time but my Mam had dissuaded him due to her total lack of interest and the thought of her 'Keithy' being squashed in the crowds. I'm so pleased that he didn't take me down the road to his initial favourite team, Notts County, as the thought of being a Magpie rather than a Red is enough to bring on nightmares! Notts County had fallen from the dizzy heights my father had witnessed from the terraces when watching his heroes - Tommy

Lawton and Jackie Sewell - and now they languished in the old 4th division whilst Forest were a mid-table top division outfit.

Football in the 1960s was very different then to now. Children tended to support their local team, often taken along by their parent. Big money which came with TV companies wasn't available and transfer fees and players' wages were much smaller. Consequently, I would suggest loyalties both from fans and players was much greater. Something which has stuck with many of us both football-wise and in life generally.

Our team in those days were not the Man Utd or Tottenham Hotspur success story, but they were *our* team and although run of the mill, we loyally turned up at each match to cheer them on come rain or shine. Apart from one season when they amazingly finished second in the top division and qualified for Europe alongside a trip to the semi-final of the FA Cup there was really little else to celebrate. Until a certain gentleman named Brian Clough arrived to walk on the Trent!

As John McGovern so correctly said, the period 1977-81 was really 'Roy of the Rovers' stuff and could be seen almost as fiction had we not experienced it. For a provincial team who had no recent pedigree and were languishing in the second tier to first gain promotion by the skin of their teeth, then conquer the English league and go on to do the same in Europe not just once but twice is truly remarkable - a miracle!

For me what is also important is that I shared this with friends and that it happened at a time in our lives when this was easier to do - we were in our early 20s with no real ties and a bit of money in our pockets. My trips from Sheffield and then Cheshire to both Nottingham and wider destinations such as Munich, Madrid, Montpelier and Manchester are still clear in my memory. Even when on holiday in the south of France, Tats, Dave Kerry and I discovered our beloved Reds were playing a pre-season friendly along the coast from our campsite in Agde so of course we had to go to see them.

The game (we did win 1-0 thanks to Tat's beloved 'Robbo') was almost as good as the two hours we spent collecting autographs and speaking to local kids before the match and then in the company of our heroes, Clough and his assistant, Peter Taylor after the game. Tats and Dave spoke more with Clough, and I spoke more with Taylor who had been a childhood friend of my dad's back in the Meadows.

For such famous, big names they were courteous and very friendly and talked to us about football, past times and holiday resorts in the south of France which were quiet and likely to give them an escape from the media spotlight.

Cloughie later sent Rosemary and me a card when we got married although this was prompted not so much by this meeting as by a prompt from Terry my best man.

Much of the enjoyment from supporting a team is celebrating together with friends when they win, drowning one's sorrows together when they lose, and chewing over the previous 90 minutes seeking to suggest ways in which the result could have been different if only.... I was recently reminded of an exception to this by my old mate, Tats. He clearly recalls an incident when we were leaving the City Ground, walking up the incline as always with Tats and Dave Kerry towards Trent Bridge to head for... the pub. We had just drawn the first leg of the European Cup semi-final 3-3 with Cologne, the German champions, and as the headline in the morning's paper would state many felt 'sunk by the Jap sub.' This being because a late equaliser had been scored by Cologne's Japanese substitute which made the second leg a much trickier prospect. Was I in doubt? No way! Chatting with some German fans leaving the ground my prediction for the second leg was a clear 1-0 to Forest. What was the eventual result? 1-0 to Forest, and we duly booked our seats on the special train from Nottingham to the Marianplatz and the Olympic stadium in Munich, where amazingly, the team from the smallest city in Europe to have previously, or since, won Europe's premier football competition played their match.

The following year, 1980, it was business as usual, and as European veterans this time it was off to the final in Madrid - by bus this time. Coincidentally, our opponents on this occasion were again German as Hamburg awaited us in the final.

I have watched the game many times on TV and it was a tense affair - even more tense than the overnight stop en route in San Sebastian which at that time was quite an unfriendly place for non-Basque separatists to dwell. Also I have to say the end of the final in Madrid was the only time that I have ever been tear gassed. Tears of joy were replaced with gas-induced tears. Forest fans might have a rowdy element like most teams but they have never been noted for some of the awful violence that some teams' fans are renowned for. However, the reputation of the English led the Spanish police to rush to the gas at the end of the game to empty the stadium and cause the good hearted celebrations to be adjourned to the local bars.

Like all bright comets, they do move on and fade, and that is what happened with the not so Tricky Reds. My last visit to the City Ground was with Gareth in October 1980 when I took him to see a match against his team - Man Utd. The result was a 2-1 win for United, and although I did see Forest a number of times in, as Tats states, less salubrious locations such as Charlton, Southend and Gillingham, it was never the same. One brief moment of glory was my last trip to the old Wembley on 29th March 1992 when I saw Forest beat Southampton 3-2 in front of 68,000 people in the Zenith Data Cup - hardly Europe's most prestigious competition.

Those were the days my friend, we thought they'd never end - but at least I can say 'I was there!'

Politics

In what has been defined as an incredible year for British politics, I was taken by Richard Madeley's comment about me and a potential political career – as were others who have had a preview of this book. The first time in my life that this was proposed was during my student career (You can read about it on page 132 in *Welcome to our World*)

Rosemary and I recently took William, our eight-year-old grandson, to Runnymede and whilst there I couldn't help but reflect upon how little politics has changed in 700 years and how inspiring certain events in history can be if one is prepared to think and reflect upon them. Here we were at the place where English democracy was born and from that much of the justice system in the free world. The moving designs on the Magna Carta seats, the Kennedy memorial, the RAF memorial and the steps of individuality all contribute to make the site a special one - maybe all politicians should go there and take something positive from the experience.

I have always been a moderate with regards to politics and have found those who try to advocate and promote extreme or strong views to be difficult company. As a student I was on the student council with the University having been invited, proposed and then supported to represent the quiet majority with reasoned points of view.

As a twenty-one-year-old I learnt the importance of using the right words at the right time to the right audience in the right place, and then to refine and repeat this until the opposition are prepared to listen. My intention would not be always to convince, and rarely to convince them that I was right and they were wrong, but solely to try and extend their thinking and encourage them to see things differently. I wish more politicians would use this philosophy, one which has stood good teachers in good stead for as long as the profession has existed.

When I was seconded to Kent County Council as a primary school adviser for two years from 2008-10 I saw politics in all its guises, and this is one reason I wished not to make the role permanent and to return to my school at the end of the secondment. Negotiation is a required political skill and I am not sure I am any good at it. There is a lot of game playing and falsehood which I know I am no good at. My strategy has always been about trust and relationship. Knowing myself and what I think is right and then trying to implement that for the good of others - surely politics should be about this rather than power and influence under the guise of 'doing good.' There is a parallel here taking my experience in education into that as a Dementia Envoy and Ambassador in working with the NHS and the voluntary sector.

Since having these two roles I have met a number of politicians both from the County Council and from Parliament. Some have impressed me and others have not. One I met at the House of Commons really upset me at first as he said the usual about me not conforming to the stereotypical image of someone with dementia - he meant old and infirm both physically and mentally. He did though listen intently to me and was noble enough to say how useful our conversation had been and how it had helped him and had changed his perception considerably for the better.

Another MP, despite being well briefed before attending a meeting I was co-chairing had no clue at all about dementia, had not bothered to read the communications sent to him and likened 'dementia sufferers' to 'arthritis sufferers' such as himself. I very seldom get angry, but I did with him and let him - and others present - know it!

The Prime Minister's 'Challenge on Dementia,' introduced by the then PM, David Cameron, has done a great deal I feel to raise the profile of dementia both in the media and beyond. It is now at the stage where this needs to be built upon and resourced in order to deliver the positive changes that we all crave around care and cure.

Surprisingly dementia did not figure strongly in the last Parliamentary election in 2015, although I did attend a pre-election health hustings organised by the National Dementia Action Alliance on the subject in London with Chris Norris, and our supporters Jess Amos and her fellow placement student Ellie Anslow.

On the podium were Jeremy Hunt, Secretary of State for Health alongside a Labour Peer and the LibDem spokesman on health. I put the question to them about the importance of effective care plans from the point of diagnosis, and the need to link far more closely health and social care. The response from the politicians (including the Secretary of State) were encouraging and, since this time, significant advances have been planned on both areas. To enable everyone present to have a better recall of the questions and responses Jess and Ellie's diligent notes from the meeting were taken by the DAA and circulated to the great and the good present on the day which gave me a sense of pride in these two conscientious young people.

Back in the days of a Labour Government they tried to establish a children's ministry by merging education with aspects of health, social services, housing, the police and other smaller agencies. The idea was to place the child at the centre. A great ideal and one which as an experienced head teacher, I initially supported. It encouraged not only schools who previously had been in competition to work together, but also different agencies, with our shared aim being the young people in our care.

After endless meetings, some of which I attempted to chair smoothly as the adviser, the metaphorical chair was taken from under us because there was the realisation that it was utopian and unachievable partly because everyone had their own interests, hesitancy to share resources and information and their own agenda and language and either could not, or would not seek to find a way to understand others around the table.

What then happened was that members retired to their bunkers, battened down the hatches and got on with their own job in their own isolated way. This is always more likely to happen when resources are stretched and people feel underfunded.

Sound familiar? If this was happening in the period just before the 2008 crash and soon after, before austerity struck home, one can see that now it is even more of an issue. If only those in positions of being able to bring about positive change could see that working together is actually far more efficient and rewarding, not only for the professionals but for those they purport to serve.

I guess politics and being political is at the centre of this and this is one reason why a career in politics was never for me, and as for a chance to speak on *Question Time* – well, time will tell!

Writing inspired by facilitation and support from Liz Jennings

This piece was inspired by a challenge set for the group by Liz during session three of our Life Writing course in June 2014, and was entitled 'Sensory Writing.' Each member of the group visited four tables, at each of which there was a student to help us engage with memories inspired by the smell, the touch, the sight or the taste of the items on the table. Here's what I came up with:

The smell of coffee

That distinctive, rich and tempting aroma of coffee immediately tempts me to take time out of what I'm doing and sit down in the morning sunshine on our patio, admiring the view over the river which meanders alongside our boundary and the flood plain which extends beyond. With instant coffee I feel the smell often carries the biggest appeal as the flavour can disappoint, something which rarely occurs when the dark brown brew is poured freshly plunged from a cafetiere.

I drink mine white with one sugar, Rosemary prefers hers black, and so the strongest aroma drifts across from her cup. Ritual is part and parcel of the experience, so the cups nearly always come accompanied by a biscuit or half a scone each - the half being an attempt to reduce calories and, consequently, guilt and weight.

I guess part of this starts in childhood, when my experience of coffee would have been from a bottle with a label clearly adorned with a military looking man in a turban which had leanings towards the Raj and was marked 'Camp Coffee with Chicory.' Everyone seemed to drink that in our street, and no one explained to me what the chicory meant. If they'd have said it was another name for the required biscuit, then I would have believed them.

Anyway, coffee break is over, the sun has disappeared behind a cloud and whilst still every bit as enticing the view must be replaced by the list of jobs which lurk on my to-do list and I'm left with what we began with, the smell of the coffee.

The touch of a shell

Bluff Beach is a real gem secreted away half way down the west coast of the Yorke Peninsula in South Australia. I would be amazed if you had heard of it, indeed most South Australians will not have done.

The reason that we know it is that our dear friends, Bev and John Endersbee, have a beach home there overlooking the magnificent bay where the sand looks every bit like freshly fallen snow.

Like all good memories, this brings back a combination of the sights and the people associated with the place, and in this case both are, as Tina Turner would say, 'simply the best.' Speaking of simply the best, that so accurately describes our friendship with Bev and John who are the real reason we visit Bluff beach - it is to share this wonderful place with these wonderful friends.

The beach is washed daily by an incoming gentle tide of crystal clear lapis lazuli sea which, without fail, leaves behind a myriad of shells. The shells range from the large abalone with a shiny inner side which catches the light and seems to emit all the colours of the rainbow, to a dull, chalky exterior; through a range of sea snail shapes to the tiny barely visible ones which are no less colourful despite their size. Every beach walk taken there has resulted in more shells to add to our collection.

These cherished, colourful reminders from Bluff Beach welcome visitors, and are one of the first things they see when they come into our home in Canterbury, as well as being a treasured reminder of Australia.

Now, since knowing Bev, I have always bowed to her having the final word...

My hubby and I have been privileged to know Keith and his awesome, supportive wife, Rosemary, for many years, both academically and through the bond of friendship. We've had hilarious occasions and many shared moments, including sharing and comparing the curriculum between Oz and the UK. This goes on to this day with Keith answering numerous questions that my hubby constantly fires at him. As time has gone on, Keith still answers with insight and good humour, especially when they share a three-hour trip in the car to the Bluff on the Yorke Peninsula in South Australia

We adore having them come and stay with us at our holiday home, sharing reminisces, swimming, and marvelling at the organised way Keith has streamlined his life as he positively comes to grips with his Alzheimer's, doing this with, of course, the terrific support of Rosemary.

We are impressed and inspired by Keith who continues to live his life using small props to aid his memory such as his diary/notebook in his top pocket: a great idea. We also loved his description of how he can have three different types of days (fog/cloud/sun) which puts things in perspective for us. A lovely way to describe his days. In our time with Keith he has always continued to be positive and cheerful and we love both of them dearly.

We were shocked and saddened when we discovered Keith as a young vibrant leader at his school had to relinquish something he loved dearly due to his onset. We felt very privileged to be included in his circle of friends that he felt could trust in to share his predicament. We follow daily through his Facebook page and are in awe of what he is doing – giving so generously of his time to help others and advance the knowledge base of Alzheimer's. We love listening to his talks and learning so much, as previously we had no real knowledge about Alzheimer's.

Bev Endersbee, friend and ex-colleague from Norwood Primary School, Adelaide.

A Cabinet of Curiosities

These two pieces were written at a course designed for people with dementia and carers being run in 2016 by Nicky Thompson, Canterbury City Council's Community Development Officer. The first piece was based upon some exhibits we had seen at the city's museum and we had ten minutes in which to write, here are my efforts...

A Cabinet of Curiosities
An eclectic collection of objects prompting memories
Some funny, some sad; some sensible, some mad

Some help us to separate less
From what is at our core; some help more

A glimpse into one's past, to help better understand the present
Faded times long since past; shadows stretched and cast

An image and an object are worth a hundred phrases
Promises and loyalties unbroken; words left unspoken

An array of photos of those who fit into our past story
Bright, smiling faces; from distant, faraway places

One can capture the spirit of a life fulfilled
To stop the recede; A challenge indeed!

The second piece was inspired by an exercise looking at what can make us happy and enable us to live well outside of medication. Why not try this written exercise yourself?

A Prescription for Happiness

From the prescription pad of Dr Alzheimer:

- Cuddles with my wife to start and end each day and at least four kisses taken and given in between
- Sit outside in the garden as often as possible with my wife and a cuppa
- Listen to a favourite piece of music daily
- Read for thirty minutes every night before sleep
- Talk positively to someone I know - or a stranger - at least once every other day
- Put the TV off at 9pm each evening and play a game with my wife and do the 'I' crossword with her

This prescription does work!

Envoy and Ambassador

This chapter is specifically dedicated to Reinhard, Jocelyne, Lewis, Alex, Lisa, Jane, Ian and Elizabeth who, when it would have been easier to create extra distance, didn't; they have walked the extra mile to help me despite the additional challenges which maybe this presented to them. Thank you to you all, and to quote Jocelyne, 'This one is for you.'

I often reflect on the five months taken to complete my diagnosis. This was an exhausting and difficult time, which was made far easier by the care, compassion and straightforward nature in which my assessment was conducted by Dr Elizabeth Field and her colleagues. This enabled me to come to terms with the diagnosis much more readily after this – I will always be grateful.

It seems like a lifetime ago that Reinhard Guss first visited me at my home, some weeks after an article in the East Kent edition of the Kentish Gazette dated 17th February 2011. The newspaper had contacted my school following information received that the headteacher had shockingly been diagnosed with Alzheimer's in his 50s and had had to retire early.

I had known Gerry Warren the journalist for many years, and had worked with him on numerous stories over the years relating to my work and schools. I trusted Gerry and invited him to meet me at my home. We talked for over an hour about life as a teacher and how I was now. I am sure he was perplexed by what he saw and heard - we are about the same age I suspect, and I got a sense of Gerry's empathy and placing himself in my shoes.

Gerry did a magnificent job with his article. I was proud to have my name and photograph attached to the piece which filled a full page under the headline *The Day I was told I had Alzheimer's*. The article was very positive, and gave an accurate picture, and I learnt then that the person who writes the article doesn't usually write the headline - this was to perplex me again in the future.

I was told afterwards that the article was the first of its type in the area and had made a very positive impact upon so many others affected by dementia and the professionals in the area, one of whom was Reinhard. Age UK Canterbury prominently displayed the article on the board strategically placed in their entrance foyer, and when the extremely supportive Dementia Lead there, Judy Ayris, visited us to help us with a variety of forms etc. She already had a head start on who I was which was helpful.

The Memory Clinic told me that many other patients had commented upon it favourably during their appointments, one lady being inspired to book a holiday, something she had not done since her diagnosis.

The article gave me confidence to come out, and to speak out, as having dementia had tempted me at first to withdraw into myself.

The only negative was when I saw ex-parents from the schools where I taught: they had pretty much written me off and said they were terribly sorry in what was meant in a kind way, but which left me feeling upset.

Gerry went on to write two more stories about me - one when I returned to Blean Primary School for my retirement assembly and leaving party with staff, and again when *Welcome to our World* was launched in November 2014. Gerry taught me a lot which I have used more recently when speaking with the press such as The Guardian, The Reader's Digest and the BBC.

So, that is how I got to first know Reinhard. I soon discovered that he had known of me rather longer, as his wife and my assistant headteacher at Blean are sisters!

The initial contact was formally made through Dr Elizabeth Field, a colleague of Reinhard's at KMPT, who had led my assessment leading to diagnosis at the Memory Clinic.

He and I would meet roughly once a month from our first meeting on the 23rd March 2011 and we would discuss my health, Germany (his home country), family, our shared passion for gardening and, gradually, a confident and trusting professional friendship emerged.

At first I didn't know where this would go or what, if any, plans Reinhard had in mind for me! He knew I wanted to do something to fill some of my days which could be construed as useful, and I learned that he was looking for a service user ally to work on some projects within our area by telling professionals what living with dementia for this person was really like. Also Reinhard was the Trust's Lead on Young Onset and as a man of 55, I qualified for this label and could be a useful resource to him.

We got on well together and one of the first joint projects was for me to go and speak to the county's Mental Health Trust Board at their June 2011 meeting in Maidstone. As I don't drive Reinhard took me and to say I was nervous is an understatement: talk about throwing someone in at the deep end! Reinhard was I am sure anxious but he concealed this well and was extremely encouraging and supportive. I met Justine his boss and she made me feel welcome and as at ease as it was possible to feel. Then it was into the Dragon's Den! I was asked to speak for ten minutes, and I had prepared a talk to fill this time. My theme was my diagnosis and how well the team had supported me through this process, and how, now, I felt as though I had fallen off the cliff edge and was floundering in a rough sea.

The board were attentive and I remember one person - the first, but not the last time someone has said this, saying that I didn't look or sound like I had dementia. My response was that he should have met me before I had dementia when I was really firing on all cylinders! That was the only comment he made to me. The Chairman and Justine left the meeting following me into an anteroom with Reinhard and they were both very appreciative of my contribution.

Little did I realise then the journey and the pathway which was about to stretch out in front of me. Our monthly meetings continued over the summer and early autumn when we were joined by an enthusiastic young University of Kent psychology student on placement with KMPT from Yorkshire, and at that point two became three. I'll let Ian introduce himself:

I first met Keith on my undergraduate placement within an older people's team. I was fortunate enough to collaborate with Keith and Reinhard Guss, a consultant clinical psychologist, conducting research into what was helpful and unhelpful in facilitating service user involvement. However, this often didn't feel like work, as it was conducted somewhat informally over tea and biscuits!

Having heard many of his talks over the years, I was always struck by how genuine Keith's account of living with dementia was, and how he tried to take positive steps each day to ensure he was living well.

I have only worked with people living with dementia for the past five years, but I have seen a definite shift in the attitudes of service providers - they have learnt the importance of the voice of the person with dementia. I certainly hope that this trend continues in the future.

Ian Asquith, Trainee Clinical Psychologist, University of Sheffield

Ian Asquith brought much more than youth and enthusiasm to the team. Ian is extremely caring and diligent in all that he undertakes. He was looking to me to help teach him about dementia and life in general and we found that he taught me as much as he learnt about these two areas, and his knowledge of IT was a real bonus.

Ian wanted to conduct a piece of research about how one person could adjust and live well in the first year after diagnosis. Between the three of us we constructed a proforma, which I completed after taking part in an activity which was either dementia related or not. I still have all the completed examples including attending dementia events with Ian and Reinhard, clubs I attended and holidays I went on with Rosemary - either just the two of us or in a larger group.

One key element of this was to examine the impacts - both positive and negative – that the activities had on me, and then what perhaps I could learn from this. Finally, what would be the potential lessons Ian could take and share with others through his written research.

Ian was extremely patient with me, re-explaining theory and practice as it struggled to go into my brain, and then he always responded with a smile to my lack of patience in return when I lacked understanding of his other commitments beyond solely supporting me. The project was written up by Ian and me for a faculty newsletter of the British Psychology Society.

I was not at all surprised to hear later that Ian had achieved a first class honours degree the following year in applied psychology.

In March 2012 Reinhard, Ian and I were delighted to be accepted to present a poster at the Alzheimer's Disease International (ADI) conference at the Excel Centre in London. Again a bit like the Trust board meeting - throw him in and see if he can swim in the deep water! I had been to conferences as a teacher, head teacher and adviser and helped behind the scenes but I had never in 35 years spoken at one! Here we had the biggest dementia event in the world and we were a small part of it.

One tale I have from our time working together was our attendance at an international conference, where the late Sir Terry Pratchett was speaking to other delegates; rather than interrupt and ask for a picture, Keith requested that I take a picture of him stood behind Terry, which naturally I obliged!

Ian Asquith

Our poster attracted a lot of interest. Ian is now well on his way to the next part of his mission which is to achieve a doctorate at Sheffield University - my old stomping ground. I'm sure he is a far more conscientious student than I was when I was a wayward under-graduate there. I am very proud of my tiny part in supporting Ian along the way and I know he will be a great success when he qualifies as a psychologist.

Soon after the ADI, Reinhard managed to convince me that it would be helpful to carry a role into conferences and pieces of work I was increasingly being asked to take on connected to service user involvement in Kent, and tentatively (at least initially) moving into London. We discussed this and his opening suggestion was 'Dementia Champion.' Whilst I understood his thinking (with Ambassador taken by the Alzheimer's Society and Advocate already in existence with legal implications.) I wasn't happy with the champion label as I felt it implied I was the best at the task, or something beyond my capabilities. So we went into a meeting with KMPT with a job description written by me in ten minutes and then spent the next thirty minutes throwing in and out role titles before settling on 'KMPT Dementia Service User Activist.' The next day I was thinking about this label when talking to Nick Branch, my son-in-law, who is an associate professor at Reading University, and whose views I trust and respect totally.

Well when Nick had stopped laughing he looked at me and said, 'You can't use that, Keith; the doctors, government officers and professionals will think you have just come off the barricades and ask where you've put your balaclava!'

'I see that, Nick, and I was uneasy about it - but we spent time discussing this.' I showed the role description and talked through the other suggestions and how they were not suitable, before asking him, 'What do you suggest?'

Nick thought for a moment and then offered what was to become a significant suggestion, 'I think the ideal role title would be Dementia Envoy.'

Wow, Nick had cracked it, I thought. I got straight onto Reinhard and Janet Lloyd and Ian who had supported me at the meeting to offer them this idea. Their response was a unanimously positive 'Great idea!'

Reinhard worked on it and came up with the full title on 16th April 2012 of 'KMPT Dementia Service User Envoy,' and that is what I remain today. I am flattered that David Cameron as Prime Minister borrowed the label when appointing Denis Gilling as the first World Dementia Envoy.

Two years ago, when we wrote *Welcome to our World*, the authors were invited to write about their thoughts on being a member of the Forget Me Nots group. Lisa Bogue drew out some quotes from the book's authors which she used in training sessions with the Alzheimer's Society to illustrate how a positive project, through constructive challenge and support, can help participants live well with dementia.

'Meeting by meeting I gradually learnt a considerable amount in order to play a more meaningful role in the group.' *A Charles (page 48)*

'I have found being a part of this group to be very stimulating - it is good to exchange thoughts and views with my peers on numerous subjects surrounding dementia and coping mechanisms.' *Chris N (page 96)*

'This group has given me a purpose. So now I am a member of this wonderful group with so many wonderful people. Everyone's experience of dementia is different. Who would have thought it! Here is me with a diagnosis of dementia and I'm involved in all these things. This group has opened a whole new life for me.' *Chris R (pages 104 & 123)*

'I have found the Forget Me Nots have been very good. It has been great to see people doing lots of good things, interesting and worthwhile projects, despite our dementia.' *Rose (page 194)*

Since then everyone's dementia has progressed to varying degrees on varying days. New members have joined and a few have chosen to retire from the group. The group still meets monthly, though we have now moved to a larger room within the same community centre to accommodate growing numbers and to give us a little more room to stretch out and break up into smaller groups at times for more focused discussion. It is also fair to say that the group continues to occupy a place nationally where our voices are sought and listened to and can on occasions make a difference.

All this is very positive, but there have been greater challenges. Issues around current and future direction within the group - some seeking a greater social element, others wishing to retain the business element - have caused some stress to people. Some are wanting greater political activism and confrontation, while others seek a more diplomatic course of action. As in all groups, sometimes strong feelings arise which can be difficult and it requires great patience, understanding and perseverance from all attending.

I stood down as co-chair in March 2015 after occupying the role for three years since the group's formation. I had mixed feelings about this and spent six weeks on holiday in Australia prior to announcing this giving some thought to the decision. I talked it through with Rosemary and I decided that, for my health's sake and for the future of the group, I was no longer able to co-lead meetings effectively. I struggled with the enormous email traffic and threads that seem to arrive in my in-tray connected to the group, and felt that support, which was still available wasn't, through anyone's fault, sufficient to help me deal with these concerns.

I was also very lucky because Chris Norris who had joined the group in April 2014 was well able to take up the baton and run with it, building upon what had been established and taking the group forward as the new co-chair alongside Reinhard and Elizabeth. All this meant that I was able to move to the back benches smoothly and comfortably knowing that the right decision for all had been made. Since March 2015 I have actively continued in a supporting role as a Trust Envoy and have seen the group evolve and achieve more successes and try to address the challenges from within and without.

Despite these challenges I return to the key reasons the group exists: to provide a network of people with a diagnosis who are willing and eager to come together to do something to help move the cause of involving people with dementia further forward, and in this vein I would like to use the words of Chris Ryan, a fellow Forget Me Not, and then Rachael Litherland, a professional who has worked with both me as an individual and with the group on projects. First, let's hear from Chris:

I first met Keith at Forget Me Nots. I had got my diagnosis for frontotemperal dementia about two months before. While being part of the post diagnostic group we were told of places we could go to with other people with a diagnosis of dementia.

We went to a couple but they were not for me. I needed more stimulation, not just a coffee and a chat, so I spoke with Reinhard, my consultant. He said a new group had been formed in Canterbury and they were called the Forget Me Nots and they were looking for more members, and he thought this group was what I was looking for.

At my first meeting I sat next to Reinhard and after about an hour I said to him, 'Who are all the doctors here? It doesn't seem to me that anyone else has dementia.' He said. 'Just me and Elizabeth are professionals - everyone else has a dementia.'

I couldn't believe this as they were all having a proper meeting, with minutes and a chairman - who turned out to be Keith. He was so professional answering questions, giving advice and the amount of paperwork in front of him was amazing. He has been a driving force behind the group and has taken us to a new level. We sit on interview panels for the NHS, we talk at conferences. We also wrote a book that went worldwide. These things I would never have done if it was not for Keith and the group.

I'm very hopeful that we can go onto greater things involving government policy for people with dementia. We want to see change, to make things easier and better for us all. Keith is very inspiring to us all and proves life doesn't stop at a diagnosis of dementia.

Chris Ryan, Forget Me Not member

And now, here are Rachael's thoughts:

I first spoke to Keith on the telephone four years ago. We were discussing the involvement of people with dementia and the importance of supporting a wide range of people to speak out about the things that are important to them. For me, this is still the essence of Keith - an inspirational and considered individual activist, but also someone who values the importance of collectivism, collaboration, and recognises the strengths in working together.

I have seen the Forget Me Nots group in East Kent flourish over the past few years, co-chaired ably by Keith and subsequently Chris Norris. This group has been an instrumental member of DEEP - a national involvement network of people with dementia managed by Innovations in Dementia, and Keith has been involved personally in a number of our campaigns, most specifically around the importance of appropriate language when discussing dementia – 'Dementia Words Matter.' As a person that has frequently featured in national media campaigns, Keith is an important advocate of descriptions that empower people with dementia.

But dementia is only one side of his life - and he is a great example to me, and to other people with dementia, about the need to put energies into other parts of one's life - walking on the beach, helping school children with their reading, going to the theatre or the cinema, writing (and inspiring others to do so). The last I heard from Keith he was going to try to persuade Rosemary to attend a Billy Bragg gig with him! It is a pleasure to know Keith through work, but to also call him a friend.

Rachael Litherland, Innovations in Dementia/DEEP

Co-chairing became too hard for me due to my dementia around January 2015, and I did resign and hand over to Chris Norris in March 2015. I think I should have placed a time frame on the role when setting it up initially as I did worry about giving it up but then realised this was for the best for me and the group.

When the Envoy role was established I insisted that it would be reviewed annually by myself and this was supported by Reinhard and Janet which meant three things: firstly, both they and I could draw a close to the role more easily than if it was permanent, also that I felt it meant that theirs and students' support was more secure and that the commitment from all parties was kept fresh. This has proved to be the case, and at the May 2015 review I asked Chris to take a share in the role. I was very pleased that he agreed.

Having taken part in a couple of Cognitive Stimulation Treatment courses, I was looking to become involved more in helping greater understanding around the subject of dementia. I was put in touch with Keith Oliver who was the KMPT Dementia Service User Envoy and co-chair of the East Kent Forget Me Nots.

They were doing a life writing project and, with Keith's help, I was instantly involved in working alongside seven other people with dementia. The end result of the project was that a book was published called *Welcome to our World* which has sold locally, nationally and internationally in large numbers.

Over the past two years, I have worked alongside Keith giving numerous talks at conferences, seminars and all manner of groups connected to the NHS and outside organisations. We are constantly changing people's perceptions around dementia and endeavouring to remove the stigma that society and health care professionals wrongly have about dementia.

Dementia is the greatest health challenge facing society now and into the future and must be addressed. Without doubt, the time has come for action to improve the lives of those affected with dementia. Organisations and the NHS now need to not just talk the talk but take action to walk the walk. Keith does and, through his leadership and inspiration, many others now do.

Chris Norris, KMPT Dementia Service User Envoy

Wrestling alongside the Forget Me Nots and students to address the many challenges dementia brings has inspired me both professionally and personally, as I see people engaging with improving the world a step at a time.

Life can be tough when you're living with dementia, and yet the Forget Me Nots, and many other people I meet with a diagnosis, get on with not only getting the most out of their own lives, but also improving the lives of others.

Now when I meet people recently diagnosed with dementia, I have in my head Keith and the other Forget Me Nots, and I know – because they show me again and again – that there can be hope for a life well lived post-diagnosis.

Dr Elizabeth Field, Clinical Psychologist, KMPT

Whilst I try extremely hard to fulfill the Envoy role, increasingly I am called upon to serve on boards and at events outside of Kent, usually in London but also increasingly beyond. I am happy to work with any organisation or charity who I see as helping the cause of involving people with dementia in helping to create better services and raise public awareness to help others either living with dementia or professionals supporting us. I think the selection of my talks included in this book should bear witness to this hope. Since early 2015 I have also been extremely honoured to represent the Alzheimer's Society as an Ambassador.

My first encounters with the Society were far from positive. When first diagnosed in 2010, I went to the Society through their website and phone line, expecting that this national society would have a presence in East Kent. This hope was unfounded at the time. There were some good things available in West- and Mid-Kent, but nothing nearer than Ashford.

I did attend a support group in Ashford for three or four monthly meetings but most of the members were in their eighties. Staff and members were friendly but it was a long established group and I didn't feel really settled there. Also the head office steered me towards 'Talking Point' which my diary reminds me I did in April 2011, but never went back again! The online blog was being used as a pressure valve release for carers and former carers who were facing severe challenges of various sorts in their lives, often linked to carrying out their caring role with a loved one: this was not the sort of thing a newly diagnosed person should be sign-posted towards. I have spoken to many others since, thinking it might have only been my experience but this is clearly common to many.

Whilst the Society are currently looking to maintain its present use which is important to those using it, they are also looking to refine aspects so it may better meet the needs of younger people with dementia, or anyone recently diagnosed looking for inspiration and uplift.

In the early days, the online factsheets were a great support and a source of good, no-nonsense, succinct information. They are regularly added to and revised and continue to be excellent. Also I got to know some of the

Society's wonderful staff and Jeremy Hughes, the extremely able and totally committed CEO of the Society.

I make no apology for frequently saying to Jeremy that the best thing about our nation's Alzheimer's Society are the people who work for it and for the way they care for the people who use its services. The first of these outstanding professionals that I met and respected was Gaynor Smith who heard my negative views of the Society from first encounters and then did something about it. Her efforts around service user involvement set the bar very high and as she has moved to other causes those following her have benefitted from these foundations.

Others who have inspired and supported me over the past three or four years include Lisa Bogue, Jane Cotton, Sarah Tilsed (though with the DAA), Katie Bennett, Tim Beanland, Matt Murray, Janet Baylis and Adrian Bradley, all of whom I am delighted to say I class as 'professional friends' who have kindly contributed to this book.

I know well from my role as a head teacher and School's Improvement Adviser that staff training is crucial to enable organisations to meet the needs of those who use the service and deliver it.

One aspect of my involvement with the Alzheimer's Society which gives me the greatest sense of achievement is sharing the delivery with Lisa Bogue of a training package a team of us have worked on over the last three years. We have trained almost 200 Society staff members on how best to involve people with dementia in the society's work. Initially this was designed to train staff as service user champions, who would then cascade the training to colleagues. This worked quite well, but it was when we slightly modified the day and broadened the audience to all staff - both experienced and new recruits - that the training had a major positive impact. I do hope and trust that this training or a modification of it will continue to feature within the new structure, despite any staff changes which might occur.

Lisa's move from the Alzheimer's Society to Cancer Research is a real loss to the society and a real gain to her new employers. This is not just my view but one shared by many who know her which is why I wanted Lisa to write a contribution towards the introduction to this book. One person who knows this better than most is dear professional friend and ally Matt Murray, who I first met and worked with in his role within the Alzheimer's Society Research Network, and more latterly after he took over on an interim basis the role previously held by Gaynor Smith.

After delving deep into the archives of my emails, I've worked out that I have had the pleasure of working with Keith since 2011 when he first joined the Society's Research Network. Upon receiving his first batch of research proposals he said he was raring to go. I responded with my trademark enthusiasm and our collaborations have been very much in that spirit ever since.

One of Keith's unique qualities is his ability to constructively challenge the status quo without upsetting anyone in the process. An example of this has been his suggestions of how to make the Research Network role more dementia-friendly so that others can follow in his footsteps.

Keith is a real pioneer, and this was demonstrated in him being one of the first people with dementia (if not *the* first!) to win an Alzheimer's Society People Award in 2015 in the 'Realising Potential' category. It wasn't his dementia that won him the award though, it was his achievements, too many to list in such a short piece.

Over these five years I feel that I've learnt more about dementia from Keith than from anyone else.

First and foremost, from Keith I have learnt that he's not just a person with dementia. He's an educator, a devoted family man, a nurturer, an expert by experience, a reader, a leader, an innovator, a trusted colleague, a friend, a music lover, a man of great determination and most importantly, a cricket fan! I'm still learning from Keith.

Matt Murray, Engagement & Participation Manager, Alzheimer's Society

Gaynor writes:

I was beginning some work on a new plan for engagement and participation at the Society and Keith was keen to offer his personal and his professional experience as a teacher. Together we developed training on engagement and participation for the Society's employees and volunteers.

We co-presented the training and refined it on the basis of feedback from participants. Since then, a large number of people with dementia have worked with colleagues to refine and deliver the training across England, Wales and Northern Ireland.

Gaynor Smith

The Alzheimer's Society is, at the time of writing, undergoing a major review, and this is right to do. There is much it should be proud of and this can be built upon, and there are areas which do need attention in order that even more people affected by dementia today and tomorrow are able to access quality services and support as near to where they live as possible.

As I write this, we now have in Canterbury a very able, enthusiastic dementia support worker, Kate Comfort, who has established a Service User Review Panel (SURP) which is proving very positive for those involved, and hopefully providing value to the Society.

I first met Keith when I was asked to escort him to the Alzheimer's Society Head Office at Devon House where he was due to co-deliver Service User Involvement training. I was welcomed at the station by a tall, confident chap, sporting a fantastically bright outfit and beaming smile which immediately paved the way to us forming a great relationship - ever since that day I put special effort in to match/compete with Keith's bold attire - he usually wins!

When we arrived at Devon House, I was left feeling somewhat redundant as it was Keith who seemed to escort me, not the other way round. Keith organises and plans his life meticulously and it is often a struggle to get our diaries to align as he is such a busy man. Even though I felt pretty unnecessary, I think Keith was reassured by my presence and it enabled me to meet the man I had heard so many positive things about and have continued to learn from and be inspired by.

I am always amazed by his drive and enthusiasm and his ability to navigate his life around dementia. Instead of being constrained and trapped by his dementia, as I see daily with many other clients, he has used his diagnosis as a chance to force real change, informing, educating and influencing opinion on a multitude of levels, from the ground to government level.

Since our first meeting, we meet each other occasionally for a catch up. This has involved visiting the fantastic film club he set up with Liz Jennings, which brought together a wide range of people living with dementia and their families to select, watch and then discuss a number of films. This was a huge success and, again, I was amazed by Keith's dedication to involving people with dementia in alternative ways. This, alongside Keith and the attendance of five other people living with dementia at the Service User Review Panel (SURP) that I facilitate has further proved the need to ensure that people with dementia are at the heart of brainstorming ideas, decision making and managing everything and anything dementia-related; after all, who knows dementia better than those living with it on a daily basis?

He truly is an ambassador and inspiration for people living with dementia, and I believe he has given hope to a lot of people newly diagnosed, and/or those struggling with the challenges of dementia.

Kate Comfort, Dementia Support Worker (Canterbury area) Alzheimer's Society

Finally in this chapter I want to pick up Matt's point about the award which the Alzheimer's Society so generously gave me in 2015, and which is proudly displayed in my lounge as I write.

I accepted this award mainly on behalf of the *Welcome to our World* project and the team involved. When I arrived at St James' Palace I had no expectations beyond enjoying the occasion with Rosemary. I was delighted but also worried when met by Hilary and Wendy - could they be nominated for the same award as me?

I see the potential benefits of recognising worthy people and celebrating their efforts which can motivate others. I am also comfortable serving as a judge on panels for awards. But I do not feel worthy of receiving awards, and I do not seek them.

In 2013, I was awarded the Kent and Medway NHS Partnership Trust Volunteer of the Year award and was in a different place, both physically and emotionally, then. I no longer feel comfortable with the competitive element of individual awards - how can one committed volunteer who gives 100% be judged against an equally committed other? I was relieved when told Hilary and Wendy were there as guests as we had been the previous year.

Honorary awards are very different to me as there is no competition there. Last year I was nominated for the Kent 'Most Inspiring Person' in dementia. I was unsure whether to accept the nomination, talked it through with Rosemary and then agreed but said that I did not want to be part of the process.

I was delighted that I came second by one vote to a far more deserving and enthusiastic winner and my first action upon hearing this was to email her my heartiest congratulations. One person with dementia who helped judge wrote me an email about why she had not voted for me, which I found very upsetting and which made Rosemary very upset too. Again, I don't remember exactly what people say or write, but always remember exactly how they make me feel.

Also at a meeting, I expressed my relief that the deadline for the National Dementia Awards had passed and that, despite an intention to nominate me this would now not be possible. I was genuinely happy that this was the case. This then sets the scene for the 2016 Kent awards and the following piece from a dear 'professional friend' Tess Read:

I completely understand that you do not want to be nominated, BUT you are inspirational. Let's face it, what an amazing ambassador you have been in every sense of the word.

Please, Keith, could you just possibly rethink about not wishing to be nominated? Not only have you spoken so openly in public, but you formed an extremely strong backbone for the dementia group in Whitstable. You are an exceptional, real, loving person, who in my opinion needs to be put in the pages of history. Also to be acknowledged as a person who, despite difficulties, always delivers that which he had promised in any capacity.

I will understand again if you say no, but I honestly, really, hope you will maybe, change your mind.

After talking this through with Rosemary, I did agree to Tess nominating me and here is the resulting nomination which Tess kindly agreed to me sharing here.

While running EKIDS I have met many very different people, none of whom have been so totally open and honest about their diagnosis, so utterly helpful in explaining their very private thoughts as Keith. Not an easy thing to do at the best of times, but to be able to give out so generously to everyone else while, I feel, he must have had agonising thoughts and experiences, is to me the essence of giving.

His inspiration as a headmaster has given him the strength to go on teaching. Not only to those who attend our group of Early Onset Dementia, but also to those who help. No one knows everything about dementia, and we are all still learning, and no doubt, Keith will go on teaching. Teaching not only how it feels to be in the position he is in, but actually helping us and the professionals in how to respond to those with dementia, how to reach out and connect, and also to listen to those in a similar position but who are not as charismatic to be able to put it across clearly to anyone of any level. Keith listens to everyone. He responds to everyone. He was not at all keen when asked if he would be put forward for this nomination. This is consistent with the man who is an honest and very private man, who has opened up for the sake of his amazing cause. Teaching the world of dementia, reaching out to everyone and helping them to become aware.

Tessa Read, founder and chair of East Kent Independent Dementia Support (EKIDS)

I really do appreciate Tessa's words and the sentiments she expresses so eloquently, but I still do not feel I deserve this.

Similarly, this book is a TEAM effort and recognition of the work we have all put into it would mean an awful lot to me. It is a bit like the teacher or head again - I was always keen to lead and be the person at the front but only when representing others, not solely myself. All those professional friends alongside Matt, Kate and Tess who have contributed to this book are exceptional, talented and committed people. In a time of austerity and challenge to be so is no easy task, and the only way success will be achieved is by recruiting and retaining quality staff who are well trained and supported, and by full, honest and transparent involvement of people with a diagnosis, present and former carers and enthusiastic volunteers. I am excited and honoured to be able to play a small part in this now and in the future, in part by walking the walk and talking the talk.

Working together

I coined the phrase 'professional friend' some time ago to best describe the relationship which I am fortunate enough to have with a number of people who work hard to support people like me who are affected by dementia. It reflects my previous existence as a head teacher where I think a number of people would have seen me in this role, and aligns closely to the Kitwood flower which I often quote and which is very much part of my way of thinking.

Dementia certainly has brought us together but it is our humanity and interest in each other as people which takes this to places which we can celebrate and share through these individual stories.

All of these friends are also allies - we talk together, we walk together. Sometimes they load the bullets which someone like me is better placed to fire, on other occasions the reverse is the case. It does work: 'united we stand, divided we fall,' is as true in this context as it is in many others.

Many of those who have contributed here first walked into my world through the national Dementia Action Alliance (DAA) which is based in London, and which I have been an affiliate of for four years. My involvement has grown as my knowledge, understanding and confidence within the organisation has grown. For the first year, I attended quarterly meetings; I sat and quietly listened trying to understand and remember something of the content of what were often very interesting presentations; I tried to build a network of contacts as I had done in my former education roles. I said very little publicly leaving it to others better able and placed than I.

This changed, I guess, at the annual meeting at Westminster Hall in November 2013 when I was asked, with the support of student Alex Bone, to present with Nada a summary of the DEEP documents. It went well and encouraged me greatly. I suspect it awakened some to my presence. Since then I have spoken at a number of the national group meetings and for the last year have sat on its board. One reason my confidence has grown within the group has been the admirable support of Sarah Tilsed, a key person within the DAA:

Having worked for the Dementia Action Alliance for five years, I have met so many wonderful people whom I am pleased to now call my friends. Keith and I have known each other for a few of these years through the DAA, and it's been an absolute pleasure to know and work with him.

I love how he always looks immaculately stylish, especially in his fantastic green attire. Being a personal shopper has always been something that I have wanted to do, and I can safely say that Keith needs no assistance in choosing outfits!

Admittedly, I didn't know much about dementia before I started this role, but I think that even if I didn't work in this sector I would have a much better understanding of it as stories about it are everywhere. This is partly a result of 2012's Prime Minister's Challenge On Dementia, which has done so much to raise awareness of it, and made people want to take action to help improve the lives of people affected by dementia.

We still have a long way to go to remove the stigma in its entirety and find a cure; however, I think there are such brilliant initiatives and inspiring work being carried out.

Sarah Tilsed, Engagement Officer, Dementia Action Alliance

I have always totally supported what the DAA is setting out to achieve; that is to bring together as many agencies and people associated with dementia to work together in collaboration to make this country a better place to live with dementia, and a better place to work for those who treat and support us. I see big players and little players working together; the bigger organisations at the centre holding out a hand to walk together in unison with all. No one dominating, no one feeling left out and ALL working together.

This sits so consistently with all I have sought to achieve for many years, in both education and dementia. I know that my friends who have contributed not just to this chapter but to the whole book would totally support this vision.

Please do not infer anything from the order in which these friends' contributions appear - they are 'all my favourites!'

Steve and I enjoy talking over a range of issues like all friends do; we discuss politics, dementia care and policy, family and, of course, music - and he is a man of great taste in all of this!

The first time I worked with Keith was on the first warm day of summer a few years ago. Keith and I were speaking together at a conference. I was telling people about DEEP, and Keith was talking about his experience as a carer for his mother. With us were two other people with dementia who had recently joined the Forget Me Nots.

Against our better judgment, we had agreed to be among the final speakers - never a great idea, especially for people with dementia. As the day wore on, the room became warmer and warmer, the speakers' power-points and technical jargon became more and more indecipherable, and nerves among our party, some of whom had no experience of public speaking, started to jangle.

When the time came though, everyone spoke with power and passion, and clearly articulated both the potential and imperative to live well with dementia. It was a refreshing and insightful session, clearly appreciated by the audience who were more than ready to hear what people with dementia had to say.

This said a lot about the bravery and commitment of those on stage, but there was something else. Throughout the day Keith had quietly and gently reassured his friends, and once on stage had very subtly supported and encouraged them to have their say.

I have worked with Keith on many occasions since then - and have always been struck by his ability and drive to support others to have their say. Several of those we shared that stage with have gone on to become themselves powerful advocates for people with dementia.

Of course, it's something of a cliché that great leaders are those that produce more leaders, but as with many clichés, there is more than a grain of truth within.

Our work at Innovations in Dementia is all about supporting people with dementia to have a say in decisions that affect their lives. When we started in 2007 there were relatively few people with dementia speaking out. Nearly ten years later there is a growing chorus of voices around the UK and beyond bearing witness to the potential to live well with dementia, and as Keith and others are showing, a diagnosis of dementia might be life-changing, but need not be life-ending.

Steve Milton, Innovations in Dementia

I first met Dawn Brooker in London in March 2012 at the Alzheimer's Disease International Conference, when I was introduced to her by our mutual friend Reinhard Guss. Over the past four years I have developed a liking and great respect for what she writes, says and stands for. I always respond positively to her requests for involvement in pieces of work and projects.

In December 2015 I had the sad honour of co- presenting with Dawn a tribute to our mutual friend, the late Peter Ashley at the DAA annual event. I think Peter would have been happy with the words and sentiments we each expressed (these are included later in this book).

Dementia has been part of my life forever. My earliest memories are of my grand-dad (or Pap as grandads are called in my family). Pre-school, he was my constant companion. He had lots of love and time to spend on a boisterous but lonely little girl. He always called me Joan (my mum's name) and would play endless rounds of pat-a-cake-pat-a-cake: I loved him.

When he died suddenly (probably of pneumonia, I think now) all my aunties said it was a blessing – him being how he was. They obviously didn't know how nice our life was! I was furious with them.

I have worked in dementia care now since the 1980's and the biggest change and biggest blessing is that people living with dementia now have a voice so we can tell the story together.

Meeting Keith at a DAA meeting a few years ago I thought, what a great guy - I want him in my corner! Having someone like Keith who can talk directly from his experience is so important in combatting stigma and fear.

Because of Keith I don't fear getting dementia as much.

I don't want the little memory slips I experience to be early signs of dementia but, if they are, knowing that Keith has coped makes me think maybe I could too.

Dawn Brooker, Professor of Dementia Studies, University of Worcester

Alongside time spent in conversation with Toby Williamson at every DAA meeting we attend I also gained an enormous amount serving with him on the Truth Project, which met every two months for a period of over a year between 2014-15, and its report is eagerly awaited.

The project was excellent, and Toby's facilitation skills ensured that I and all others involved were fully engaged throughout. We have also worked together on a number of DEEP projects which I've found very rewarding:

Social movements need activists – people with lived experience of what the movement is all about, who are prepared to stand up and speak out about what needs to change or happen. There is a growing social movement of people with dementia, influencing and improving how society understands and supports people with dementia. Keith Oliver is one of those activists.

I work for the Mental Health Foundation; a UK social research, service development, public affairs and information charity. I'm responsible for work we do on mental health in later life and dementia. We have a strong focus in our work on the involvement of people with lived experience; we helped set up, and continue to support, the Dementia Engagement and Empowerment Project (DEEP), a network of influencing groups involving people with dementia.

Keith has contributed to the Foundation's work in a number of ways, including as both participant and advisor. His contributions have always been made thoughtfully, drawing upon his life experiences (not just as someone with dementia), and where appropriate, with compassion and humour. His description of living with dementia, involving 'clear,' 'sunny days,' and more difficult 'foggy days' has stuck in my mind as a simple yet very effective way of explaining the condition as he experiences it.

No activist is effective on their own – Keith is supported by Rosemary, his wife, and others. Long may his activism, and their support continue.

Toby Williamson, Head of Development & Later Life at the Mental Health Foundation

Most of the projects I have served on with Toby have also involved Philly Hare, who brings similar but different skills to the project. What is common to both is their sincerity and admirable level of commitment and genuine desire to see their efforts - alongside those of people affected by dementia - make a positive difference:

I am a programme manager at the Joseph Rowntree Foundation, and I have led their work on dementia for the past five years. My background is in social work with people with disabilities and carers - I am currently on secondment with Innovations in Dementia CIC and also an Exchange Fellow with the University of Edinburgh.

We have come a long way in the last few decades - but there is still such a long way to go! Most exciting at present is the new role which people with dementia are playing - as activists, educators and influencers. I am confident that hearing their individual and collective voices is starting to have a huge impact on attitudes, policy and practice. We can no longer get away with tokenistic involvement and, directed by people like Keith, we are moving into the land of co-production and genuine collaboration.

I have known Keith and his wife Rosemary for a number of years, but only since his diagnosis of dementia. My main contact has been through the group he belongs to, East Kent Forget Me Nots, and the important role they play in the DEEP network. I have also seen Keith in action as a formidable and thoughtful public speaker at numerous events; as a very competent member of advisory groups (for example on the Mental Health Foundation's Truth Enquiry); as an audio reporter for Dementia Diaries, and as a founder member of the Dementia Policy Think Tank. I am in awe of Keith's talents, and in particular of his ability to talk honestly about the emotional impacts of dementia.

Philly Hare, Lead: Dementia Without Walls, Innovations in Dementia

One person who knows how much the concept of life story work means to me is Rachel Thompson, who, again came into my world via the DAA, and has gone on to work with me on a range of projects. Rachel, Jess Amos (when she was on placement) and I met to discuss life story work prior to a Truth Project meeting, and I learnt so much from her wisdom and experience. Whilst it is frustrating that some of this cannot be utilised by myself at this stage, much of her advice and signposting is contributing towards my writing within this book.

In September 2016, I accepted without hesitation an invitation from Rachel to speak at the annual Admiral Nurses' conference in Nottingham, partly because it was Rachel who asked, and partly because the Admiral nurses such as, Sinead who supports Rosemary, do such a fantastic job, and this is a small way in which I can express my gratitude.

Dementia care has been my interest, passion, and driver for many years and I continue to be constantly delighted, challenged, inspired and humbled by those I have met along the road.

Keith is one of those people who fits *all* the above and is an important reminder that people with dementia must be not just listened to, but respected and genuinely heard. I will always remember first hearing Keith speak at an event and being moved by his genuineness and honesty.

I sometimes reflect on changes since I was a student nurse some 32 years ago. My experience of dementia care was in a psychogeriatric ward for those in the latter stages of their condition. Care was institutionalised and it was seen as a dead-end job. At that time dementia wasn't discussed but I chose the path less travelled by. I wanted care to be better.

Thankfully much has changed: attitudes have shifted significantly and there is a drive for rights, inclusion, compassion, positivity and hope. I am encouraged by an increased thirst for understanding and enthusiasm for working in the field.

As an Admiral Nurse, I am reminded though that we still have a long way to go in ensuring all people get the support they need. My hope is for increased partnerships and investment in services, less competition and a real understanding of the issues faced by families affected by dementia.

To transform dementia care we must learn from those who are living with it, including their family and friends. Keith is an exceptional teacher!

Rachel Thompson, Admiral Nurse Professional Lead, Dementia UK

As I mentioned in the Acknowledgements, Tim was a very early and sincere supporter of this project, as indeed he has been of every project he and I have been lucky enough to be involved with. In his piece (which follows) he sensitively and articulately gives me and other readers greater insight into his story and thinking, which so enriches the writing.

I forget when I first got to know Keith. I've been at Alzheimer's Society for six years now as Knowledge Manager; I look after much of the information we produce for people affected by dementia. I just can't recall a time when Keith was not there: sitting opposite me at a Royal College of Psychiatrists executive meeting, speaking before me (and much more eloquently) at a British Psychological Society event, championing the cause of Young Onset dementia on a national steering group...

I've personally been delighted to support Keith's (first) writing project, the unique *Welcome to our World* book. The risk was reduced by having seen Keith's blog and knowing him through his many advisory roles with Alzheimer's Society, including as a longstanding member of our reader panel which comments on Society publications such as our flagship *The Dementia Guide*. More recently I've also supported with interest Keith's work on dementia friendly cinemas in Canterbury.

But these are items from a list that could easily be five times longer: Keith's interests are very broad, his energy is humbling and his influence towards the greater cause is clear and tangible.

One of the many things Keith has taught me about dementia is interdependence. We've grown used to the idea of promoting independence, part of the 'living well with dementia' mantra.

With characteristic good humour Keith has more than once challenged the idea that people with dementia crave independence, as if anyone (dementia or not) exists in a vacuum. He talks and writes about being part of a broader web of interdependencies where he is (like the rest of us) at times dependent on others but at times able to offer succour. Terms like 'carer' evaporate in the face of this.

I took interdependence as a theme at my late mother's funeral in 2015; she'd had vascular dementia (but never embraced 'the D word'), diagnosed in 2010 soon after I joined the Society. (My private and professional lives over the past five years have been irrevocably and at times painfully intertwined, as I learned about dementia and its impact on the individual. The abstract and the concrete melded in the 5ft 2-ness of my mother's gritty Yorkshire resilience.) At her funeral I quoted John Donne's famous poem that famously opens with 'No man is an Island, Entire of itself.' There is surely something important in here as we think about dementia in the 21st Century which goes beyond dementia-friendly communities and promoting personhood, vital though both of these are.

To me it is partly about adjusting to dementia as the new normal. I don't mean to imply that dementia is normal ageing or to downplay the way it changes people, relationships or futures. Just that, as more people develop dementia and are diagnosed, we as a culture need to understand and adapt our thinking. Done well, a dementia-friendly society is surely also a good thing for any older person, or anyone who happens to be vulnerable at that time, or, indeed, *anyone*.

Like rediscovering the person in nursing care, we're belatedly realising all this, but the fact that we need to perhaps indicates how bad things have become. If only out of self-interest, we would all do well to recall how Donne's poem ends: 'And therefore never send to know for whom the bell tolls; It tolls for thee.'

Dr Tim Beanland, Alzheimer's Society Knowledge Manager

Moving on from professional friends linked in a way to the DAA, I now want to turn to other friends who are also affected by dementia.

Firstly, to Chris Roberts who is a great friend not just to me but to many, many other people affected by dementia, and whose efforts are gigantean in advancing causes, and I am delighted to follow in his wake. Chris combines that rare talent for displaying wisdom, humour and bravery, never better shown than during the *Panorama* programme entitled 'Chris's story.'

I first met Keith at a MSNAP Peer Reviewer course, where people with dementia are trained to attend memory clinics as part of a professional team to review their services and environment to make it a better experience for people with dementia. It was a great pleasure to meet him in person as I had seen his story and advice to people with dementia in lots of places and sites on the internet during my searches for info on my own diagnosis (mixed dementia at age 50.)

Keith was, and still is, an inspiration to me and many others. Following his lead, I have become involved in lots of groups and committees regarding dementia. We work on a lot of projects together and have become very good friends as we understand each other. We have also spent a lot of time together at DAA events, conferences and as friends. Peer support at its best!

Dementia services, support and understanding have come a long way in recent years, but we still have a way to go, there needs to be better signposting and rehabilitation. We need to have a UK recognised dementia pathway so the different health authorities have a standard to achieve and adhere too, to stop services being a postcode lottery.

People with dementia need to be included in every decision that is being made for them,

We are experts by experience after all, 'Nothing about us without ALL of us.'

Chris Roberts, husband to Jayne and person with dementia, Affiliate on DAA

Jayne is Chris's wife. An important statement to make. They are an excellent team, equally engaging either individually or as a couple. They support each other and what is clear is their love for each other despite the bloody challenges that dementia throws at them, some of which only folk like Rosemary and I can understand.

Jayne delivered the best 'carer' talk I have ever heard at the DAA annual event at Westminster hall in December 2014, and it was nothing less than a disgrace that around a third of delegates had left early and missed the highlight of the event. She always cuts to the key issues, and then brings insight and understanding to allow others to see what it is really like to live with someone who has dementia, especially someone with Young Onset.

We met Keith on a MSNAP training day, and then at the MSNAP conference, where I was also introduced to Rosemary, his wife, after seeing each other around on 'the circuit' doing conferences, DAA meetings and the like, including the launch of the Mental Health Foundation's Paper on Dementia, Rights, and the Social Model of Disability. My husband could not attend this one so I went over and spoke to Rosemary, as the most familiar face to me there. We struck up a friendship from the bond that is being a spouse to a person with dementia: we 'get it.'

Keith and Chris are both regular speakers at events, conferences, and meetings, and this has led to us collaborating on some of the activism that is happening in the UK.

It makes the work less difficult with more than one lone voice. As a by-product, I have been invited to give my opinion, my voice, on the role I now have as 'carer' to a person with dementia. As this connection between us all has developed, we have become more than fellow advocates or activists; we have become firm friends, despite the geographical distances. And I am delighted by that. From terminal stigma, to a whole new world of articulate, engaged activists, who happen to have a diagnosis.

Dementia today is a very different scenario than it was just five years ago. People with dementia are now being heard, being listened to, with their opinions and advice being acted upon. But only in pockets. Care and services differ widely across the UK. We live in Wales, and ironically (as it is the poorer country) we seem to have it better, certainly in some respects. In others, less so.

What I would like to see is the best practice in one area, rolled out to another; a level playing field for all, regardless of postcode lottery, with the fear and stigma around residential care fading. Sometimes we need the professionals to do the job that they do best, and hope: I would like to see more hope for the fearful, and the lost, and for those for whom it may be all they have to hold on to. *Jayne Goodrick, wife and carer of Chris and affiliate on DAA*

Whilst I do not blog I know many who do and some of these such as Kate Swaffer are quite prolific. Whilst Kate blogs in Australia, closer to home my dear friend Wendy Mitchell is both a keen blogger and a keen talker especially if the audience is one of young, eager to learn university students. Wendy, like me, knows the great value and importance of speaking to the 18-22 year olds in our universities, for they are the workforce of tomorrow who will take on the mess or the highlights that we have left them, and hopefully make the world a better place in the future. Dementia care needs to be a part of this, and Wendy does 'up north' what I try and do 'down south' - we are a good pairing - similar yet different, as all good partnerships and friendships should be.

My name is Wendy Mitchell. On the 31st July 2014 I was given the devastating diagnosis of Young Onset Dementia. I was 58, otherwise healthy and working full time in the NHS. Although it was truly shocking to hear such news, it was also, bizarrely, a relief. A diagnosis finally puts an end to all the uncertainties.

I first came across Keith whilst trawling the internet for confirmation and reassurance that this bombshell of a diagnosis was in fact a reality for others in a similar situation to myself. After all, I, like many others, incorrectly assumed dementia only affected the elderly. Keith's video on YouTube finally gave me that reassurance that there were others out there experiencing the same symptoms and surviving the experience!

I soon realised that services were sadly lacking for people with Young Onset, so it was to others in the same situation as myself - like Keith - that I turned for support, guidance and inspiration. I have since met and collaborated with Keith on many projects. We made a wonderful short film for the BBC2 Victoria Derbyshire Show, entitled 'Living with Dementia,' each showing our struggles, strategies and more importantly our humour in living with this bummer of a diagnosis.

Wendy Mitchell, person with dementia and affiliate of the DAA

Whilst the first time we met was in the BBC studios we have since spent a lot of time together both at the DAA and other dementia events and meetings, some with the Alzheimer's Society, others led by Young Dementia UK.

Our last get together was at St James' Palace where I was absolutely thrilled that Wendy was awarded the same accolade that I had received the previous year by the Alzheimer's Society - no one deserved it more.

The last word in this chapter goes to a dear friend who I know better than anyone else included here, and have known since three months after I was diagnosed. Melvyn Brooks used to work in a brewery, and I guess at one time I probably kept him in a job! Melvyn and his wife Jan are good friends to Rosemary and myself, and I think they feel the same about us. Melvyn really wants to do things which will help others connected to dementia, and whilst not a member of the national DAA he is very active in the local group near his home in Kent. He and I are like chalk and cheese - total opposites in many ways, but that is part of why our friendship works so well. Melvyn is a founder member of the Forget Me Nots; although he was not keen when he first heard about the idea, very soon no one could have been a more vocal and passionate supporter of the group.

Sometimes his passion does overtake him at meetings, this is because Melvyn cares. He cares deeply about Jan, he cares deeply about the underdog, and those less able to fight the battles he sees and feels need fighting.

If I was in a tight corner I know who would be my side, and that is Melvyn Brooks. There is so much meaning in his piece that I hope the real Melvyn shines through.

At the age of sixty I was finally diagnosed with frontotemporal dementia and was pointed in the direction of a group meeting of patients and carers. This ran twice over a period of a few weeks. There, amongst others, I met Keith and his wife Rosemary, and this was the start of our friendship. Keith encouraged and inspired me to join a group of people with dementia and psychologists with the aim of improving the lives of people living with the illness.

We try to put the world to rights there, showing that life is different, but that it's still a life worth living and we can still be productive. Keith has done this. He has taken the bull by the horns and shown us all by example how to get out there and do what we each believe in.

I remember on one occasion we were both asked to give a talk at the local hospital. Keith was so eloquent, and I wasn't, but I learnt a lot from Keith that day. He gave me the confidence to carry on and to hopefully improve. We have met up socially and had lunch together, the four of us with Rosemary and Jan included. Keith and I don't always see eye to eye on things, but that is what a good friendship is all about.

He has told me that he's been at conferences to do a talk and afterwards a member of the audience has approached him and introduced themselves as a former pupil, how fantastic is that? He is still teaching indirectly along his and their journey in life. He's a good communicator, a special person, and a cherished friend who inspires me and others.

Melvyn Brooks, person with dementia and member of the Forget Me Nots

Intergenerational working

This chapter is dedicated to the young people who have supported me as part of their university placement year over the past five years. Whilst I hope I have been able to teach them new things which have helped during the year and beyond, I am thankful for what I have learnt from knowing them. To Ian, Heather, Alex, Sophie, Lewis, Jennie, Charley, Jess, Ingrid, Ellie, Michael, Kai, Briony, Vishy, Nicki and Pat – thank you.

I have been very fortunate to get to know these 15 individuals over the past five years. Working with young people is second nature to me, and I so enjoy the youthful enthusiasm which they bring to any kind of professional friendship.

One consequence of dementia is, at times, a feeling of disconnection with one's past. Working with placement students helps me considerably to reconnect to my professional former self, because for many years I was responsible within schools for training and supporting students on teaching practice, and then more latterly as an educational advisor helping, training and supporting newly qualified teachers navigate what could be for them a tricky first year in teaching.

All these listed young people were students following a four year Applied Psychology degree at the University of Kent. The third year of the course for these students is in the workplace, and the one chosen in this case was to work under professional supervision with Kent and Medway NHS Partnership Trust with people like me who have dementia. Some, such as Sophie and Alex, came to the year having done voluntary work previously at St. Martin's Hospital, but most began the placement either with knowledge gained from a family member who had dementia or little knowledge at all.

The number of students supporting me varied from year to year. Initially Ian was the sole student and I was the sole service-user. This was also the case with Heather who was the student from the following year. During Heather's placement the Forget Me Nots was established. In the third year of this working arrangement an exceptional group of students was recruited by the Trust, and I, like a number of others within the Forget Me Nots, benefitted greatly from this.

The three who worked most closely with me were Alex, Lewis and Sophie. During their year and overlapping into their return to university we attended many conferences in Kent, London, Brighton and Glasgow as well as writing a number of articles for dementia journals. Their support for me was exceptional and consequently a warm professional friendship developed. Here are the eloquent thoughts of Alex and Lewis:

It's rare to remember the first conversation you have with someone. Our first meeting with Keith, however, stands out in our memories.

As part of our undergraduate psychology degrees, we were able to undertake a year's placement in the local community mental health service for older people. Both of us had different prior experiences of dementia. Alex had volunteered on older adults' mental health wards, and her work with people with dementia in this context involved those with more complex needs, often in the more advanced stages of the condition. Lewis, on the other hand, had no experience of working with people with dementia outside of family relations.

Neither of us therefore really knew what to expect. We felt daunted by the prospect of supporting a person with dementia so early on in our placement, and felt the weight of responsibility accompanying this. To our surprise, we came face to face with a man who, in our minds, did not look like he had dementia. He had no difficulty talking with us, and led the meeting himself. The weight of responsibility lessened. The only indications that he had dementia were that, firstly, he told us he did. Secondly, he wrote down everything we said in his notebook. We were surprised by how much he wanted to get to know us as people. We had expected this to be a one-way relationship, with us providing support and Keith receiving it. Again our prejudices around dementia were challenged. He asked us to do an exercise in which we identified three things about ourselves: something each from our past, present and future. He duly wrote our answers in his notebook.

Our work with Keith spanned our placement year and beyond. We were involved in supporting Keith in a myriad of projects, including work with the Alzheimer's Society, the Dementia Engagement and Empowerment Project (DEEP), the Dementia Action Alliance (DAA), and even the upper echelons of government. This involved liaising with project organisers, arranging travel, accompanying Keith to and from events, and supporting him during the day however was required. This could include finding the venue and relevant people, taking notes, IT support, et cetera. Although we were there to support him, we found that support was reciprocal. Keith always ensured that we were introduced to the big cheeses of the dementia world, encouraging us to make the contacts which could be so helpful in the development of our own careers. When we co-wrote with Keith, or were involved jointly in projects, he always ensured that we were recognised as collaborators, and that we were always included in communication channels. We've even had the opportunity to present some of the projects we have worked on with Keith (most notably, *Welcome to our World*) at national and international conferences.

All of this greatly challenged our preconceptions about what dementia 'looks like,' one evident example being the age at which people can experience it. We learned about Young Onset dementia and the distinct difficulties and challenges that younger people with dementia (such as Keith) face. We began to understand the positive impact of timely diagnosis, and providing appropriate support and information in the early stages of dementia.

We discovered the Kitwood model of person-centred care for people with dementia, which puts the psychosocial needs of people with dementia at the centre of how we understand and support them. Kitwood, and ideas that followed, also represented a departure from purely medical models of dementia, which focused primarily on the limitations and disabilities imposed by the condition. It is now becoming increasingly acknowledged that a focus on strengths and personal value, while being mindful of the reality of disability, is a far more enabling approach.

Using these ideas allows many people with dementia to compensate for their disabilities and to lead full, active and meaningful lives. Valuing people with dementia also allows us to learn from the wisdom that comes with age and experience. Whether or not you have dementia, there is much to be learned from how the people affected by dementia that we have met approach loss and uncertainty, and how they are able to find positivity despite huge challenges.

An important element in our work with Keith was the relationship and rapport between us. We were a good match because we as students had genuine interest and enthusiasm in the projects we supported Keith with. This, in combination with Keith's own drive and passion, led to lively and constructive conversations between us.

Through these discussions, we realised that a large part of the support required from us was emotional, as well as practical. Debriefing after an event gave both parties the opportunity to discuss opinions and process emotions. This often seemed more important in terms of providing good support than briefing and organising before events. One thing we learned from this is that, for Keith (and for many other people with dementia), how an experience made him feel afterwards was far more salient than the cognitive content and specific details of a project. This may, in part, be why emotional experiences became so much more prominent in our work with Keith.

As we neared the end of our placement, we needed to think about the end of our work together. The disadvantage of having such a good working relationship was that the prospect of this support no longer being available for Keith was challenging for all involved. However, since we finished our placement we have kept in touch with Keith regularly, and have had the opportunity to support him with several projects that stemmed from our placement work. Now that we have progressed to the position of assistant psychologists in older peoples' services, we can more fully appreciate how Keith has shaped who we are professionally, and who we hope to be in our future careers in clinical psychology.

Once a teacher, always a teacher!

Alex Bone and Lewis Slade, Assistant Psychologists KMPT and formerly placement students with KMPT from the University of Kent

Also in the group with Alex, Lewis and Sophie were Jennie and Charley who initially I worked with in the general Forget Me Not group but who I got to know much better when they joined and supported the *Welcome to our World* project.

Within the writing course I often wrote with Jennie's support which was then built upon in producing the book with the diligent help of Sophie. Charley's contribution was gratefully noted at the book launch by A. Charles, the author she worked closely with. Alex worked with two authors who required considerable help, and being the modest person she is didn't tell me until after the book was printed exactly how much work she had needed to put in in order to achieve the success that was realised. Lewis ably supported his two authors and led the writing of the insightful student preface within the book.

Bringing to a close such a successful and happy placement is never easy for all involved. Nor is it easy for the next group coming in who feel the additional pressure of filling these large footprints. As co-chair of the Forget Me Nots I don't think I handled some aspects of the transition well. I remember distinctly the handover Forget Me Nots meeting where the five students I have mentioned were attending for the last time and the five new students were joining us for their initial meeting. On this occasion I wanted to celebrate what had gone before and to use this to inspire and motivate the new group. I think I went over the top and probably embarrassed the departing students and caused some anxiety to those about to begin their year.

It was only through working closely with Jess, Ingrid and Ellie that I think we overcame this. I remember saying to them, 'You will only get out of this year what you put in.'

Michael, who is assisting me as I write this, has reminded me this year that I said the same thing to this year's group and it's true, and he agrees!

As with those affected by dementia, students are also individuals who are uniquely different, and the working relationship works best once both parties get to know each other. Many of the events I have attended with a student have been in London.

Whilst I guess, if the transport system behaves itself, I can get there and back safely, the support of the student allows me that extra security and good conversation, much of which relates to the day's project. This entails discussing the meeting on the upward journey in order to brief the student so they know better what to expect and this enables me to be reminded of what is planned. At the actual event the role can be a passive one of sitting, listening and note-taking but can also be active.

Most students have attended the service-user involvement training workshop at the Alzheimer's Society delivered by Lisa Bogue and myself, and on this occasion, have become for the day a quasi-Alzheimer's Society member of staff. Ian, Alex, Sophie and Lewis have all co-prepared and co-presented at major conferences with me and I was immensely proud of the confident and competent way they presented.

On the return journey, talking through the day's events goes some way towards helping me remember and understand.

During the year with Jess and Ingrid, whilst I know they were a bit disappointed to have missed out on the *Welcome to our World* book, a number of other exciting projects came our way. They both helped Rosemary and I with filming for a BBC2 programme, *The Victoria Derbyshire Show*. Jess picked up where Sophie left off on the Truth project and Ingrid supported me with the VALID project, which is seeking to transform Occupational Therapy treatment for people with dementia.

As the title of this book suggests, Keith not only inspires people through his words, he does so through his deeds. His work to fight what he calls the 'fog of dementia' has shown me how someone can truly effect change when they have determination and resilience, even during times when they themselves are struggling. As a Kent University Psychology undergraduate, I worked with Keith on a number of projects during my year in industry. One, which stands out in my memory, was reviewing the film *Still Alice* for the Alzheimer's Society.

The film was good, but what I really valued was being involved in the discussions which Keith led after the film which gave me a unique insight into the daily difficulties of living with dementia beyond what the film could offer.

I had the pleasure of listening to a number of Keith's speeches. I remember him ending one saying: 'I don't know how much of this speech I will remember, but I hope it will stick with you for some time and be helpful,' and I can confidently say that his words will not only stick with me for a long time but they have shaped my career aspirations to go into dementia research and care.

Jess Amos, formerly a University of Kent student on placement with KMPT, now research volunteer at MHF

This illustrates overlap between the groups of students because the evening we watched *Still Alice* together at my home, present were: Reinhard, Elizabeth, Lewis, Charley, Jess and myself. This event was supported by the Alzheimer's Society with an advanced copy of the film on DVD (care of the British Film Institute) for us to watch. Our time together was arranged by me and resulted in an article on the film in the national press (*The Guardian.*) My feedback on the film was sought but I wanted the thoughts of others on the film to be included. I remember distinctly Charley's comment which was, 'It was a good film but not as inspirational as working with real people with dementia.'

When I attend a meeting, a conference or an event with a student, the other professionals in attendance are always impressed by the way the student conducts themselves and supports me. This gives us a springboard to explain the placement project and how it is of benefit to all parties and hopefully can lead to a career for the young person. This gives me a sense of usefulness and helping, and adds a legacy to our friendship.

I have used the thoughts and words of former students in this piece and for the closing words to the chapter I want to turn to Dr Pat Chung, a lecturer at Canterbury Christ Church University with whom I have collaborated on a number of occasions with her Occupational Therapy students and who I am delighted to call my friend.

Worldwide dementia is one of the biggest health care issues. It is crucial for health and social care professionals to develop deeper insights and understanding of the experiences of people living with dementia, to enable them to facilitate a true person-centred approach.

With Keith's commitment to contribute towards the learning of the future generation of professionals, I have been very fortunate that he has become a regular speaker on a final year Occupational Therapy module since 2012.

A key objective of the module is to promote the wellbeing of service users through meaningful occupations. Keith's talk aims to share with the students his experiences, aspirations and challenges. I really do appreciate the enormous amount of time, commitment and energy he puts in to prepare each talk every time. He is an educator who wants to use materials and strategies to enable learners to understand the subject matter. Keith always ensures that his talk meets the specific learning objectives of the occupational therapy module.

Keith is also an inspiring speaker. The feedback from our students has always been very positive. The following quote from a student which captures the impact of his talk on his audience: *'Pat, I found Keith's talk emotional but truly inspirational, and it has given me a huge sense of passion and drive to become an Occupational Therapist to help people... I found his topics very helpful, not only about dementia but food for thought concerning other patients who experience similar feelings. This has been a huge highlight to the occupational therapy programme and I thank Keith for sharing his story and making us better occupational therapists!'*

In summary, I feel privileged to have the opportunity to work with Keith in supporting students to develop a deeper understanding of how a person-centred approach could be implemented in dementia care.

Dr Pat Chung, Senior Lecturer, Occupational Therapy Pathway, faculty of Health & Wellbeing, Canterbury Christ Church University

It is always a pleasure meeting and working with Pat, and a privilege to have the opportunity to talk to, and with, her students. This is my comfort zone as an ex-teacher, and allows me to feel valued, purposeful and hopefully able to help encourage and steer the next generation of professionals.

This chapter was written with the support of Michael Blackburn KMPT placement student 2015–16.

My Christian faith

This chapter is dedicated to Eric and Jen who have come with me to this door, unlocked it and, with God, helped me to walk through it.

I grew up in a non-Christian home, where God was never encouraged to dwell. My mother was an atheist and my father an agnostic. As a teenager I was really into music, and like most contemporaries I enjoyed rock music, and one favourite band were Jethro Tull whose album *Aqualung* was a favourite of mine. I remember the sleeve design having an old man looking quite fierce with the statement, 'In the beginning there was man, and he created God in his own image.' For several years from my mid-teens to my mid-twenties I did believe this.

I never went to church until I met Rosemary, my wife, who was a practicing Christian. This led me to being baptised at the age of 25, and then confirmed at 28. As a primary school teacher and head teacher I always saw myself as a caring, spiritual person keen to do the right thing for other people and myself and lived my life accordingly.

Around 20 years ago I lost my way with regards to faith and would express myself as 'spiritual but not religious,' whatever that meant!

If someone had said to me a year ago that I would be where I am now spiritually or with regards to my faith, I would not have believed them. Over the past year my eyes, my mind and my heart have been opened to the gospel in a way which has been both transforming and liberating.

Part of the reason for this has been meetings every three weeks or so in a local cafe for about an hour with Eric (a local pastor) and Jennie (a friend) both of whom share wisdom, care and patience which has served to open doors for me around theology I didn't know existed. They have encouraged me to read a variety of books some of which are linked to C.S. Lewis, and it is a quote from him which I turn to often these days.

'I believe in Christianity as I believe that the sun is risen - not only because I see it, but because of it I see everything else.' C.S. Lewis quoted by Alister McGrath in the introduction to his book *Mere Theology*, page xi.

At these coffee shop meetings, the three of us chat over a range of issues connected to faith, and both Eric and Jen have been loyal, patient and sincere in helping me understand better both myself and my place in this world. We do this through our conversation, through reference to the Bible and my broader theology reading. We celebrate the work of C.S. Lewis and other Apologists whose thoughts I can readily relate to. Eric often sets homework to be done before the next session and we discuss this. It is usually Bible-related and I do sometimes find this hard as my Biblical knowledge is not good.

I look forward to these meetings and value the sense of comradeship we share. This is good for me as my other links with the church at this stage are through the podcasts from Eric's church rather than through active attendance, although Eric and I did do a double act on the theme of 'This Time Tomorrow,' during one Sunday service which I really liked. I do enjoy listening to the podcasts and find them helpful.

It could be said that what I have described has changed me; I would agree to a point, but prefer to think that I am still the same as I was before we met, but that through this a part of me which was dormant has been allowed to grow and develop positively.

Here's Eric's and Jen's separate accounts of how we came together. I used to believe in fate, and I am not going to argue against this, but now I do genuinely feel that a more heavenly being guides such friendships as these for they do happen for a positive purpose.

I am not looking forward to this, I thought to myself, as I approached Café Nero for the first time to meet Keith. All I knew was that a man with dementia had been asking questions about faith and, as the minister of a local evangelical church, I had been asked to help him.

My view of dementia was at that time limited to pastoral visits I had made over the years to care homes. In those situations, meaningful conversation had been a challenge and I wasn't sure how I could help in this one. I was relieved to see Jennie, a friend of Keith's, there too, as I thought she could help me if it all became difficult.

I really didn't need to worry! Keith was articulate, funny, friendly and very easy to talk to. I wasn't sure he had dementia at all by the end of our first meeting. It showed me how wrong my understanding of living with the condition really was.

Over the past year the three of us have shared a journey of faith and friendship. I now really look forward to our meetings in Café Nero. It has been such a joy to see Keith grow in his understanding of what it means to trust Jesus in every area of life and to find that promise of eternal life beyond this one.

Eric Harmer - Pastor at Barton Evangelical church, Canterbury

I'm privileged to have met Keith whilst on a placement year with the NHS.

Keith was acting as the Dementia Envoy for Kent at the time, working as an advocate for people with dementia and chair of the Forget Me Nots network.

If I were to sum up my year in one phrase it would be, to quote CS Lewis, 'surprised by joy.' I went into the year thinking that working in the context of dementia would be emotionally heavy and draining. What I found however was an extraordinary positive attitude from staff and service-users alike. Extremely dedicated staff ensured that no patient sustained the belief that a diagnosis of dementia meant their life was now over. Rather, the emphasis was to live as well as possible with dementia and to maintain their personhood. This became the mantra adopted by the Forget Me Nots group and was a philosophy I could also apply to myself in the face of adversity.

I'm a person of Christian faith and my relationship with Jesus feeds into everything I do, especially so in my love of music, which I write and perform. Keith and I connected particularly over this and began to have conversations about the content of my songs, namely, spirituality.

After listening to an interview I did for Premier Christian Radio, Keith told me about his disillusionment with religion due to past experiences, but that listening to the music and interview had allowed him to 'keep the door open.'

I said to Keith that I knew of a local church pastor who meets up with those who are struggling with faith issues or disappointment with religion, and perhaps this conversation was the beginning of this delightful journey which Keith, Eric and I are now on.

We meet regularly to discuss matters of faith in Christ, theology, and humanity. This trio has been incredibly rewarding, not just for Keith in finding the relationship with Christ he had not found previously in institutional church, but for all three of us. We have been regularly inspired and challenged by each other.

I personally have been made more aware of how spirituality takes a different shape for each of us, and that it is linked to the shape of our personalities. Moreover, it has emphasised to me the importance of community. People are made to be connected with one another. It is in relationship that we grow and in relationship that we gain understanding. Each of us is different in many ways, but when we come together we can go further than we would by ourselves. No man is an island, nor is he created to be.

One of the key building blocks for Keith's newfound faith was becoming able to pray. In our initial meetings he expressed how he found it difficult, as if he were talking into the ether. As Eric and I listened we encouraged him that there is not one set way to pray. Eric suggested he try going to a place which inspires contemplation – for Keith this is by the sea - and to try writing down his prayers. It was like an old door unlocked! A real sense of connection with the creator was finally found and Keith remarked that prayer was now for him as much about being with God as talking to him.

It is this openness and humility to confess that we don't know it all that carries these meetings, I believe. We can bring our strengths and weaknesses to the table and come away encouraged and blessed. For myself, these sorts of connections are what I get up for in the morning!

Jen Holland (nee Russell), former placement student now a friend.

Using my metaphor of the open door, I feel that Jen put the key in the lock, and Eric turned it and together we opened the door and the light shone in. For that I am eternally grateful.

I usually use Mindfulness to help me clear my head and begin to focus, and this is especially useful before beginning to write or to pray. When I first started to try and pray I found it very hard so I decided to go somewhere that I thought would help inspire me and allow me to focus; where better, as a resident of Canterbury, than our wonderful Cathedral, I thought.

It didn't work, and at first I was surprised and quite frustrated that this amazing setting didn't inspire me to connect with God. It was only through talking this through with Eric and Jennie at our meetings that Eric encouraged me to start and keep a prayer journal and this really helped me a lot. I use it maybe two or three times most weeks.

Whilst having Alzheimer's Disease does present me with a range of challenges some of which can be frightening at times, I am guided to seek any positives. I now know that my faith has given me an opportunity to utilise my remaining skills to continue to serve him and to help others.

I don't know how my Alzheimer's came into my brain or indeed why, but I do know that now I have a purpose and a desire to make use of the skills

I retain for as long as I retain them and in doing this I know that God is watching over me and helping me along this pathway. When delivering talks, or helping to lead projects and seeking to advise professionals working in this field I know God is with me and guiding me. So often I think to myself that it is amazing what we are achieving - is this through our own endeavours or something above and beyond human control?

A few years ago I remember hearing talks by a number of other people with dementia and hearing them talk of their faith and how much they drew from this and thought how fortunate they are, but that it wasn't for me - now I am so pleased to think differently.

I also was asked by the Alzheimer's Society to present two talks at their Christmas Carol services - in 2013 in London at St Paul's Knightsbridge, and then in 2015 in St. Margaret's Church, Rochester. I was in a very different place spiritually at each event. At the end of the first one I remember saying to Rosemary that despite the wonderful occasion and the uplifting service it had not re-engaged my faith. I went into the second event knowing that God was with me. You can read these talks on page 309.

Mindfulness and therapy

This chapter is dedicated to Jane Roberts, whose tough love was the start of picking me up and thus enabling me to live well again with dementia through therapy; then to Yvette Kusel, who has picked up the challenge of helping this bloke, and has helped me better understand both myself and others, and to Richard for making it all happen.

My first experience of what is, for many people, a helpful strategy to relax and deal with difficulties was not a success.

I was with Reinhard, Charley and Chris Ryan in London at a dementia conference, and on the agenda was a taster for Mindfulness delivered by Rachael Litherland, a dear friend and ally. Rachael gave each delegate a raisin to hold in our open hand. The idea I discovered was to feel, smell, think about and then place it on one's tongue and let the taste gradually come through and then linger.

I didn't do this. No sooner was the raisin in my hand than it was in my mouth, and no sooner was it in my mouth but it was being chewed and eaten. Not the idea at all!

From this unpromising start I have listened to people advocate its use, I've read two helpful books - *The Little Book of Mindfulness,* edited by Tiddy Rowan and *Mindfulness and Christian Spirituality,* by Tim Stead, two very similar but very different approaches to the subject, and I have drawn much from these two books. I have also been encouraged to download and use the app *Stop, Breathe and Think,* by Yvette Kusel, as a part of a really helpful course of compassion-focused therapy which she is leading me through during 2016.

The story of Mindfulness goes back to the 1970s in Massachusetts when Jon Kabat-Zinn developed a meditation-based programme to help support people suffering from chronic pain. Kabat-Zinn had previously been introduced to the benefits of meditation by a Buddhist teacher. He soon realised that it not only helped ease chronic physical pain but also the stress and distress patients were living with.

There is some misunderstanding around Mindfulness and its association with Buddhism. It is fairer to associate it with meditation and a sense of peace, both of which should apply to any religion.

Mindfulness for me can be enabling in a cognitive, emotional, psychological and spiritual sense. It helps me to pray and to be able to better understand my own Christian faith. It is for me a means to a number of ends - not an end in itself. It helps me make space in my life for so much that matters to me.

For me the best way to summarise Mindfulness is to say it sets out to make one more fully aware of one's own experience in a non- judgemental way. It does this through four strands: awareness, experience, the present moment and non-judgementalism.

For anything like this to work one has to be honest and invest something of one's self as well as time and effort into it. I know an eminent member of the dementia world who said at a meeting recently the time that therapy starts to work is when the person starts to pay for it!

I wonder if he meant cash or payment by way of oneself? In my case it is very much the latter.

As one starting point to access Mindfulness more positively I bought and read *The Little Book of Mindfulness* edited by Tiddy Rowan. The idea of being mindful, rather than having your 'mind full,' particularly resonated with me.

I think we spend a lot of time doing exercises for our body and eating well and thinking about physical well-being, but not enough time and energy focusing upon both our mental and emotional health.

I think it was Einstein who wrote that 'Imagination is more important than knowledge.' I agree, and by using Mindfulness I see this even more so. I know much is written about the benefits of puzzles and enjoying mental games etc, and they do help, but only if one's emotional health is on an 'even keel.'

Mindfulness can help give you the time, space and encouragement to think clearly and more calmly about living in the moment and valuing what really matters. Like all exercise it needs encouragement and training, and there is a plethora of books available for those who respond to this approach. I value books and find them supportive, but I also need a person to help and encourage me with this (or anything for that matter.)

Linked to this, it helps you be more at ease with yourself, and then in turn with others. I really dislike judging people. I dislike people judging me or hearing them judge others, especially negatively. I always walk away from conversations where this is happening and Mindfulness provides strategies to help avoid falling into the traps which result in being judgemental of others and oneself.

I always said at school and at home that for every negative comment it required four or five genuinely said and sincerely meant comments to help restore and maintain the targeted person's self-esteem.

Some would say you cannot teach kindness and compassion, and whilst there might be some truth in this, I would dispute this stance. Often we focus upon trying to encourage people, especially children I guess to be kind and thoughtful towards other people, and I am aware and told by others that I am often very kind to others, but what I, like a number of others, am not good at is being kind and compassionate towards myself. Mindfulness and therapy are helping me to address this in order to live better.

As a driven person who is always happiest when busy I don't find this approach easy, but it is helpful and does enable me to reflect upon both my own needs and those of others - the former I find harder, especially when I am busiest. I suspect that some of the Mindfulness rubs off on me when I am walking, because often that is when I do my deepest thinking and decision making.

Increasingly making decisions is becoming harder, although I am fortunate to have retained at this stage the ability to not pick over thoughts and re-visit and question the thinking and decision once it is made. I think this is my headteacher background coming to the fore because as a head I would consult, listen, think, discuss, put my point forward and then make a decision which I (and others) would then seek to make work.

I still do this and sometimes Rosemary will be keen to check that I am okay with a decision I or we have made. I always try and put her mind at ease that the decision is made and now it is down to us to make it work. I used to say that I had no regrets and regretted nothing. That is now not the case, but I do try, and the only regrets I ever have are when I feel or fear I have let someone who matters to me down.

In my case Mindfulness grew from a course of Cognitive Behavioural Therapy which is now accepted as a treatment which can, through the NHS, help people to deal with difficulties and to avoid relapses. My therapy with KMPT clinical psychologist, Yvette Kusel, now has moved to compassion-based therapy and I am looking towards Mindfulness with Yvette's help and encouragement to help me with this.

I understand that to feel well inside I need to develop more effective self-compassion. I cannot do good work if I don't feel good, and this includes improving feelings towards myself. There have been times when I have been nominated for awards which I have declined because I did not feel worthy and have a problem with competitive individual awards. How can one be judged against another very worthy person?

Yvette has worked very hard to find ways to encourage and assist me in developing more effective self-compassion and I was delighted when she kindly agreed to write a piece for my book, and even more delighted that she approached the task in such an innovative and 'outside of the box' manner. I do like good stories; telling, listening to and reading them, and I hope that you enjoy Yvette's...

My first memory? It's late April, possibly the first few days of May, 1971. I am, or am just about to turn three. I'm trying to stand up straight but that's hard to do when you're so young and standing on a mattress.

I have a vague recall of white vertical bars in front of me; they can't be prison bars, so perhaps the bars of a cot?

There is a woman walking around the large room in front of me, stopping off here and there for a moment, but gradually making her way towards me, bearing a container in her hands. As she reaches my destination she offers the container over the top of the bars of my cot side but the contents of the container are not to my liking, marshmallows I believe, so I decline and sink back to sitting on the bed, disappointed.

A seemingly uninteresting memory you may think, but it is retained due to its personal significance. I know, from my Mother's repeated retellings that I was in hospital at that time. I had suffered repeated ear infections and tonsillitis in my first few years of life and the required tonsillectomy was not permitted until I reached the advanced age of three years.

Memory, as we learn in psychology lectures, is a funny old thing; so little of it is static and permanent. Personal memories like the one above are vulnerable to change just like in the childhood game of Chinese Whispers. As we retell our memories, and as others retell us their own versions, our memories change, the details may become somewhat inaccurate, the sensory details may become a little lost in translation - but the narrative, the personal meaning, gains in strength. Mundane events lie forgotten, whilst unusual, unexpected and personally significant events are re-explored and may evolve over time.

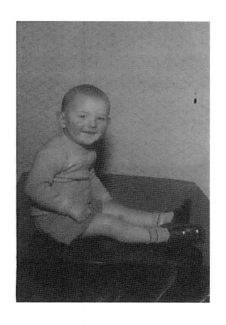

Clockwise from top left:

Keith as a baby, Meadows Nottingham 1957

Crazy night, Jersey, June 1967

Student days in Marshall Hall, Sheffield 1976

Keith, Dad, Cousin Jane, Mam, Jersey June 1967

Tats and Keith, Agde, France. August 1979

36 years later, October 2015

Tats and Keith going to see *I Believe in Miracles – The Forest Story*

"Where's Keith?" Celebrating Forest's winning goal in the European Cup Final, Madrid. May 1980

Celebrating winning European Cup in Madrid, May 1980

Wedding day, March 1981, Crewe.

Gareth, Rosemary, Keith, Karon

Lounge in Fordwich with "Sweet Baby James". November 1982

Keith and Bev Endersbee, staffroom, Norwood primary school, Adelaide.
Handing over "The Ashes"! August 1989

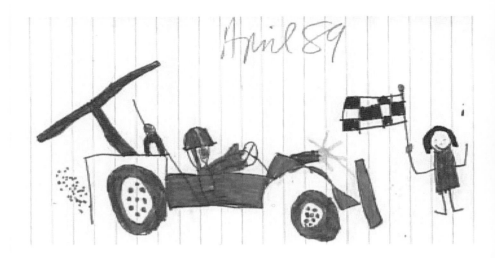

James's way of looking forward to the Grand Prix. April in Adelaide, 1989

Keith, James and Rosemary at Uluru (backdrop is feature called *The Brain*) July 1989

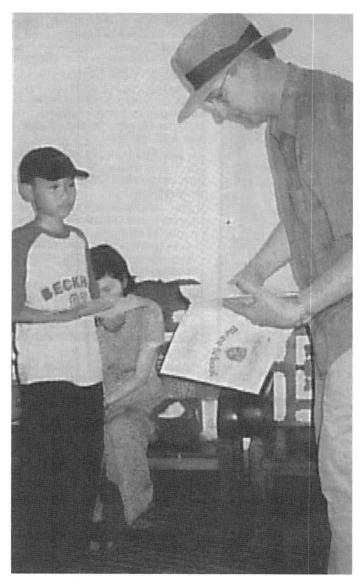

Keith handing over gifts to Liem. Ho Chi Minh City, Vietnam.

Kentish Gazette April 2003

Keith in his classroom at Pilgrims' Way Primary School, Canterbury.

Kentish Gazette October 1988

Keith's retirement assembly at Blean Primary School, Canterbury.

Kentish Gazette April 2011

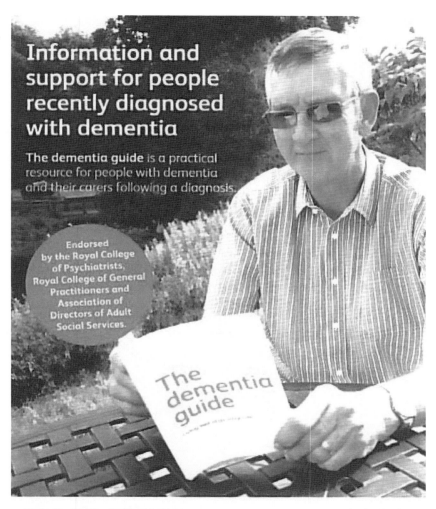

Keith on Alzheimer's Society poster promoting their Dementia Guide.

June 2013

Keith with professional and personal friends at the MSNAP conference, London - September 2014.

L to R: Rachael Litherland, Chris Roberts, Chris Norris, Rosemary, Keith, Reinhard Guss, Janet Britt

Photograph of Keith taken in June 2014 by Charley Massingham and used for conference publicity

The whole family, gathering to celebrate Keith's 60th birthday at *The Parrot* in Canterbury. December 2015

Keith delivering a talk on behalf of DEEP at RHS Hampton Court Flower Show conference.

July 2016

Rosemary and Keith at Scotney Castle.

Summer 2016

I have a related memory, a few years later I believe (the time stamp not quite so well defined). I think I was about five or six now, and we had regular trips to the library, particularly during the school holidays, trying to complete the holiday reading schemes.

On this day though, I could not read for myself, as I had to lie on my side and keep very still. Reading in that position is not easy I had discovered. My father kindly read to me to try to keep me occupied, as medication was placed in my ear, first one side, then the other, treatment for yet another ear infection. It was a nice plan, to have my father read to me, but unfortunately his voice appeared to fade away, as the medication blocked my ability to hear. I felt an increasing sense of isolation as I 'lost' my hearing for those long minutes of treatment – a personal meaning that has remained strongly attached to this particular episodic memory.

As well as the stories that my father read to me at that time, there was another, more fearful story going around. A member of the family (no one I had ever met) was reported to have gone deaf, the change occurring rapidly one night.

Understandably, my family had retold this story many, many times and without a good medical explanation for this poor woman's plight, there was fear lest this storyline be repeated.

My parents clearly worried about my repetitive ear infections – could I be vulnerable too? Audiology check-ups ensued but no permanent hearing loss was found and eventually my ear infections subsided; perhaps I was going to be ok after all.

I was reminded of these childhood memories and their personal meanings this week by the unexpected and uninvited return of an ear infection (two infections, to be more precise).

Having enjoyed a wonderful fortnight's sailing holiday, frequently swimming in the warm, crystal clear sea in Croatia, I had tried to continue the seaside theme with a few dips in the sea near my newly-adopted home in Kent.

Sadly, though, my ears had decided to retain this murkier British water for a week and infections in both ears eventually arrived.

My hearing was muffled, pain was beginning to radiate into my face and jaw; hearing, talking, eating and sleeping were all day-to-day functions that I was beginning to struggle with. At work I had been startled when a colleague had sat down in the armchair next to my desk; I had not heard her entry into my office and she sat there grinning at me until my peripheral vision took up where my hearing had left off.

Later that day back at home I had been startled by my son on two occasions in the kitchen; how could I not hear his 6ft frame walking over our yet-to-be-renovated and oh-so-noisy Georgian floor boards?

Over dinner my husband tried to tell me something funny but I missed the key word, the punchline. 'Don't worry,' he said. I wasn't worried about the content of what he said, but I was frustrated that I had not heard it, and that he did not want to keep repeating himself.

I was also worried though – what was wrong with my hearing, how long would this last for, would I recover or would I be left feeling isolated again? The application of prescribed ear drops and olive oil just left me reliving the sad isolation of my father's story-telling.

I am very lucky with my local GP practice. If I get up early enough and queue up, I can get to see a GP that morning. I know that many other people are not so fortunate and so I greatly appreciate this. Despite this prompt service, it can still be hard to be a 'patient' patient.

Sitting in the GP surgery, I did not want to see the projected images of the insides of my ears; these images were unfamiliar to me and therefore meaningless. I just wanted my diagnosis, reassurance that all would be well, and if necessary a suitable and quick-acting treatment to cure me.

It took a second appointment to get the infection recognised and my treatment changed, a week later a third treatment was offered – hopefully this would finally resolve my difficulties. Two weeks of muffled hearing, a week of pain and decreased confidence in communication.

The personal meaning of these ear infections is a fear of permanent hearing loss, repetitive experiences of social isolation and a fear that if this was to continue, my roles in life (particularly in work) could be in jeopardy.

As a healthcare professional, particularly as a Clinical Psychologist, it is essential to be able to communicate, especially to listen. We can listen in a literal sense, processing the sound vibrations, parsing the grammar and so on, but it is also important to hear the personal meanings of what is being said, to try to imagine what our clients and their loved ones are going through when they are referred to us. Not only do we need to find out what difficulties they are experiencing, we need to explore with them the personal meaning of these. Whatever their difficulties or diagnoses, it is the personal meanings that we also need to pay attention to.

In my clinical work, I see a very wide range of difficulties that people are facing. A significant number of people are referred to me if there is concern that they might be developing a dementia, or there is uncertainty about the type of dementia that they may have.

Other people may have already have had a clear diagnosis, and now need some time and support to help them come to terms with this diagnosis, perhaps to tackle the personal meaning that this poses to them.

I am fortunate, in that I do not have a dementia diagnosis, but I hope that through reflecting on my own health difficulties and the personal meanings attached to these, I will be prepared to take a more individual, person-centred approach to the meaning that dementia (and other conditions) may have for the clients that I am privileged to work with.

Keith kindly invited me to write an article for this book. I wondered what I could write that would be useful. Then the ear infections arrived! I hope this piece will help me (and others) to reflect on the process of assessment for possible dementia and - just as importantly - the personal meanings associated with the changes dementia can bring.

At the beginning of this piece I outlined my first memory and the recognition that memories can be reconstructed. In talking therapy we sometimes make positive use of this process, helping clients to rescript or reconstruct part of any traumatic memories, in order to help them cope with them and to process them more comprehensively. If memory can be reconstructed, perhaps we might also benefit from reconstructing our roles in life.

As we age, develop health conditions, or find ourselves in difficult situations, we may not be able to carry out our old roles - but perhaps there are elements of these that we can still carry out, or new roles we can take on. Keith is an excellent example of this reconstructive process, using many of his headmaster-related skills in his dementia envoy role. Keith continues to demonstrate a keen willingness to explore new skills in order to see what more he can learn, what skills he can master, and in the process, teaching us all a thing or two.

Dementia is not just about memory loss, so let's explore the personal meanings attached to dementia (and other health conditions) and find ways to work with these in order to help people have a more meaningful and comfortable future.

Dr Yvette Kusel, Clinical Psychologist KMPT

Although I have known Yvette for barely a year, during that time I have come to respect, trust and have faith and confidence in her both as a professional and as a human being (the latter for me is even more important than the former.) Whilst rightly our therapy sessions, which she leads me through, focus upon my needs and feelings, this piece helps me enormously to get to know the person who I am sharing this time and space with, and to see them outside of the professional vacuum.

One thing my life has taught me, and the sessions with Yvette along with the writing of this book has reinforced, is around the distance - either real or perceived - between friends and letting them go. People seldom leave our lives completely, and I think social media such as Facebook can help with this. If we cannot see them as much as we would wish they often remain in our mind or in the background, seldom is it that they are gone forever.

Dementia and depression

There is no question that dementia is a wretched condition to live with and that, irrespective of age, depression is also extremely challenging for the individual and - as with dementia - it is really tough for those close to the person. So, to have the toxic mix of dementia and depression is extremely difficult, and to be given little support often sends people spiralling downwards.

On the day the neurologist first suggested that I had Alzheimer's Disease, the next thing he offered was a prescription for antidepressants. I do know that these work for some people. However, I hate taking any tablets, so I refused them then and have done so a couple of times since. Initially this was because, although shocked by what he was telling me, I was not depressed by it. Challenged - yes; determined to confront it with Rosemary - yes; confused – yes; but I was going to learn about Dr Alzheimer's legacy and do my very best to keep it at bay; I thought I was bullet proof and the first two or three years after diagnosis did little to disprove this. When offered antidepressants by both Dr Richard Brown, my consultant Psychiatrist, and by my G.P. my response of no was accompanied by the explanation that, 'If I am going to go down, I want to do so with my eyes wide open.'

Thankfully, they accepted this and, in Richard's case, he referred me for a course of fortnightly psychotherapy through the local NHS Trust (KMPT), which, whilst challenging, did help. It enabled me to talk issues through with a very skilled and experienced practitioner. I did though find it a bit one sided and I found the silences to be very difficult and uncomfortable: I would wonder if I was being given time to think around the issue or was there a sense that I was holding back? One feels the need to fill a silence which I found draining mentally and emotionally.

When the therapist retired in September 2015 I was handed over to Dr Yvette Kusel who steered me in a slightly different direction through the use of Cognitive Behaviour Therapy and Compassion-Focused Therapy both of which I found very helpful, especially the latter. My understanding of myself has improved through our dialogue at these sessions and our focus has been on trying to seek ways and strategies to support my greater self-compassion. For so long my focus has been on the needs of others and seeking their well-being, I guess for both their benefit and if I'm being honest, for mine as well, because if those around me are happy then I am, too.

This therapy is taking a slightly different line whilst holding onto the positives around showing care and compassion for others. It does seem to link quite closely to Mindfulness with the person at the centre, and explores areas such as threat, compassion and drive. I see myself in all three, but clearly drive can be the predominant aspect for me, although when I was really low I felt VERY scared and threatened, which, for me was a totally alien and frightening experience.

At my lowest points when the toxic twins of dementia and depression were taking hold I did feel scared and frustrated - these were the two paramount emotions - and many days had the feeling of being hit by a tidal wave which would metaphorically and almost physically knock me off my feet. I was not sleeping much, was losing weight, and felt very agitated and at sea. Rosemary and I would sit on the settee together in the evening which would help settle me, and thus helped us both.

Since then we have generally turned the TV off at about 9pm most nights and rather than me get fidgety or agitated and Rosemary fall asleep we play a card or board game instead for the last hour of the day. This works well for us both. I think only Rosemary saw me at these low points; I tried very hard to screen family and friends from them, and a 'mask' came in useful here.

The first time I thought about a mask was at a Canterbury Christ Church University dementia workshop in 2013. I was the only person with dementia there, all others were professionals or academics working in the field.

At one session the course leader, Jan Dewing, gave out A3 paper or mask templates and asked us all to illustrate how we saw dementia. Interestingly in the feedback at the end I was the only person to choose the mask! At that time I felt quite well - challenged yes, frustrated certainly - but not at all depressed. My mask was made with the colourful collage junk available and felt pens. It had brightly coloured, feathery hair, tears coming from the eyes but a strong line through the tears, rosy cheeks and a bruise on the chin. I think that says it all!

The mask attracted a lot of interest in the discussion after the practical as I was asked to explain the features, which I did. I kept the mask for about a year afterwards until I threw it away in a clear out of my office. I wonder what my mask would have been like when I was at my lowest, and what it would look like now that I feel more positive again.

I, like many people, am a very complex individual. I think there are few who really know me, indeed there are times now that I sometimes wonder how well I know myself! I am multi-layered and it is only when a person takes the time to talk with me that these layers can be peeled back to reveal the soul of the person at the centre.

I have never wanted to mask the symptoms of dementia, or depression, or to hide from them. My way of dealing with them is to work with them and, if necessary, to confront them. To do this I need help and support and people to talk with who try to understand me. I have been very lucky to spend time with a number of people over the past few years who have been able to do this with me, and I feel that the treatment - for that is what the intervention with Yvette is - has built upon this. I still find some days hard, a few are very hard, but I now have some strategies that are helping me to restore the sun without having to resort to a bottle of pills.

After my mother died in 2014, I thought I handled this quite well. As her main surviving family member most of the arrangements fell on me, which presented lots of challenges not just connected to my dementia, but due to the distance between Nottingham where she lived and died, and where I live in Canterbury. The care home where she lived and died was of little or no help.

The emotional impact hit me a few months later, and this along with changes in support structure and the stress but also euphoria of getting *Welcome to our World* onto the shelves took a heavier toll on me than I would have expected, or had the resilience to contend with. I did think back to the depression and mood assessments I had sat through at the Memory Clinic back in 2010 when I was far more confident, and as I said earlier, bullet proof (or so I thought). I also thought of a conversation I had with Reinhard following a comment made to Ian Asquith when he was supporting me at a conference where I was speaking in 2012. One of the delegates had expressed concern about me to Ian at the end of the day, saying that, when no longer able to deliver talks such as this people like me often become extremely depressed and even suicidal. I didn't know this, or that this conversation had taken place.

Reinhard raised it quietly with me a week or two later when we met in my garden at our monthly meeting. I guess he wanted to check me out on how I felt about this. I was very pragmatic, and re-assured him that he need not worry, and I asked him not to share this with Rosemary or anyone else as I didn't want them worrying unnecessarily. Two years later I felt differently.

My approach was to try and take control of my declining mental health and mood, to not just lean on others but to do something on my own.

I have heard one of the country's most eminent dementia experts say at a meeting that, 'Therapy only works for people when they start to pay for it.' I agree if he means payment in time and effort and shared responsibility but not solely if he is referring to cash payment.

I wrote down the Samaritans' phone number and placed it in my wallet where I knew I could access it if it was required. I never did, but doing this helped, and I shared this strategy with the psychotherapist who thought it was an excellent idea. One seriously considers the impact any decision or action will have on others close to one. It is tempting to think that certain actions can be seen as selfless, but actually they are often selfish. My mother would tell me a number of times that she had tried to commit suicide and was so upset that she had failed in this - what she saw as - selfless final task. I remember hearing Melvyn Bragg speak on the TV about the suicide of his first wife, an event he fictionalised in his novel, *Remember Me*. He was asked if writing the novel made dealing with his pain and sense of loss easier, to which he answered without hesitation that it in fact made it harder. I know what he meant, and was keen to talk to him about this when I met him at a book signing event at Waterstones in Canterbury a little while later. Time didn't allow for this as we talked more about my Alzheimer's and he was interested in how it affected a younger person and what medication I was taking for the disease. As I have written earlier, my mother had very severe mental health issues and needs and I am sure that this has influenced the way I see this crucial aspect of both my health and that of others.

For far too long mental health has been a taboo subject. It is a totally toxic mix when dementia and depression form an alliance which not just affects the person, but those closest to them. Thankfully with the help and support of Rosemary, Yvette, Eric, Jen and other family and friends - many of whom have so kindly written in this book the waters of life are calmer now, and there have been very few large tidal waves for a little while.

Gardening and dementia

One of our favourite pastimes is gardening, and one of the next favourites is sitting in the garden enjoying what our labours have created. There is no question that hobbies such as gardening are fundamental in encouraging and enabling both Rosemary and myself and many, many others to live well.

Gardening is good for our physical health as well as our emotional and psychological well-being, and when family and friends visit us we share our garden which then becomes a social benefit.

We don't just share our garden with people, we encourage wildlife to visit and enjoy our garden as well, and we enjoy watching their busy antics.

Being in the garden also gets us outdoors, into the fresh air and able to benefit from vitamin D in its natural form rather than through a tablet or supplement.

We do also try, within a limited space, to grow some fruit and vegetables naturally without chemicals, which always taste better - especially when they are freshly picked. Our garden overlooks the river and farmland which is an added bonus as we get the view and the pleasure without the work required for its upkeep.

Our passion for gardening was one reason I was so pleased to accept the invitation of the RHS, through Rachel Niblock at DEEP, to speak at this year's RHS Hampton Court Flower Show. The event was organised on the day before the show opened to the public, and with Rachel's superb support we were able to have a preview of the show and listen to some excellent speakers on the subject of 'Gardening with Disabilities.'

Originally the line-up consisted entirely of professionals. Rachel took this up with the RHS and the outcome was a five-minute slot for me to represent the many people in the UK with a disability such as dementia, who enjoy either actively gardening or the chance to sit and benefit from the labours of others.

I was asked to close the conference. They did not know what to expect as this gathering was outside my usual remit. I think I did a reasonable job, and the audience was extremely kind in their feedback and response.

More importantly to me; what I said hit home and did form a part of the RHS charter, and consequently Rosemary and I were given honorary membership of the RHS for the year, something we were delighted to accept and will enjoy over the next twelve months.

I think the organisers learned a few lessons from this experience, and hopefully next time they organise a conference of this sort, a service user from an aspect of the disability range will be included. That would please me immensely.

You can read the talk I delivered at that event on page 350.

One of the lasting memories I have of this experience was the wonderful friendship and support given to Rosemary and myself from Rachel as always, and now I will give Rachel the opportunity to share her thoughts:

I first met Keith and his wife Rosemary in person (for they do indeed come as a pair, two sides of the same coin) at a conference a couple of years ago. I had heard so much about Keith, I had also seen him on various pieces of film on YouTube - so warm, kind, passionate and determined to make a difference for all people, not just himself. He's very knowledgeable, intelligent and I can absolutely see that he would have been an inspiring, colourful (in more ways than one) teacher - the kind who really motivated me as a child. He's also extremely humble, considerate and caring. He fondly signed my copy of a book he had contributed to.

I recently spent a very lovely 24 hours with Keith and Rosemary, again this was at a horticultural conference, where he presented as well and powerfully as he has done before - but this time he confided that he found the process stressful and that it made him feel very anxious. You would still never know. I felt honoured and privileged to be by his side. I was also especially honoured when he told me that he had focused on my tearful face at the conference where we first met as a 'friendly face in the crowd' - a great tip for anybody presenting or teaching!

What I have not mentioned thus far is that my work and my relationship with Keith came about because of dementia - Keith has a diagnosis of dementia and Rosemary his wife lives with dementia as a very loving and supportive partner.

First and foremost, people living with and caring for somebody with dementia are human beings. Somewhere along the line this got lost and now we are working so hard to ensure social justice for all people living with dementia.

My eyes were tearful when Keith focused on me at the conference a couple of years ago because they were filled with pride and admiration. The power, the passion, the voice of people living with dementia WILL be the change we wish to see for the world.

Rachel Niblock, Innovations in Dementia

Later the same day I was asked to deliver a similar talk within the show complex for the Abbeyfield Care Home Group who had commissioned a lovely dementia-friendly garden which would, after the show be lifted, transported and reinstalled at one of their homes.

This also went well, and one outcome was an invitation to speak at their annual conference in Manchester in October 2016 (a month away at the time of writing). Again, I am delighted about this because so often care homes do have lovely green spaces outside which unfortunately for a variety of reasons are quite sterile and uninspiring. I have stated that these spaces should be colourful, attractive and engaging for residents and staff alike. Residents should be helped to enjoy this outside space, and wherever possible to have some input into its use. There are few people who are not uplifted by the sight of a beautiful flower even if, as our dementia progresses, we cannot smell it or talk about it. We can still enjoy it and share the experience with a staff member or volunteer. Indeed, one consequence of my dementia is that my sense of smell is now quite poor - this can be a blessing - but in the case of my love of sweet peas and old-fashioned roses it is something I miss terribly.

Another consequence of the Hampton Court speech is that I came on to the radar of the charity THRIVE who do sterling work associated with gardening. Sean from the charity visited my home in the summer with Nada Savitch to make a short film about gardens and dementia, and how care homes can better meet the challenges associated with using their outdoor space more creatively and constructively. THRIVE spoke to, and filmed, care home staff, university researchers, volunteers from homes and me. The film is one which I do commend to you via either the THRIVE website, DEEP's site or that of KMPT.

One fear of moving to a care home for me is to have a sense of imprisonment or confinement indoors. Already my world is shrinking, and this for me would be the ultimate limitation. I dread giving up our garden and the pleasure we derive from it, and hope and pray that wherever I move to has a garden and one that can be shared and enjoyed.

I am going to close this chapter with the closure to my interview for this film:

INTERVIEWER: What role does the garden play in your life now that you live with dementia?
KEITH OLIVER: An absolutely crucial role - as indeed it has done for the past 35 years. When I was working it was my relaxation and space to play with our family. It now gives me a great sense of achievement in seeing the results of

our labour. It is a great way of sharing recreation and physical exercise with Rosemary. It is lovely to sit and admire colour and the nature that comes as visitors, too, share our garden by way of bees, butterflies, hedgehogs, moths and damselflies. It allows Rosemary and me to see changing roles within our partnership and to support and encourage each other, and then to share relaxation in our garden, usually with a cuppa.

INT: One of the goals of this project is to develop 'dementia-friendly' gardens in residential and dementia day care settings. What do you think makes a garden 'dementia friendly?'

K O: Being accessible, interesting, colourful, changing with the seasons, multi-sensory, giving as much ownership and responsibility as one can, being a source of stimulation to conversation with the resident(s) and staff, and opportunities for quiet time in the garden for both residents and staff: happy staff equals happy residents.

INT: What advice would you give to someone with dementia who was interested in taking up gardening?

K O: Go for it! So often people with dementia are seen as in a downward spiral - this need not be the case. If one has always gardened then it allows the person to retain their selfhood and self-esteem, if it is going to be a new recreation then it can inspire them to try something new and show that they are still, with support and encouragement able to achieve something worthwhile.

INT: What are the benefits of gardens and gardening for people living with dementia?

K O: Well-being. Physical, emotional, psychological, and spiritual. A sense of retaining one's self esteem and purpose. Patience. Organisational skills and time management - both of which I now find much harder. Being outdoors means increased Vitamin D. Harmony with wildlife. Appreciation of colour and looking beyond one's own needs in order to care for the plants we try to nurture. And, like today, to be able to share and celebrate what one tries to achieve.

When gardening yesterday, I was thinking about the flowers in our garden and likened them to dear friends. Friends who come into our lives - sometimes fleetingly - make a positive impression upon us and then leave, but what remains behind is the positivity, memories and emotional engagement that the experience has brought. This remains until the next time they re-appear and then it happens again.

Dementia in the media

At the time of writing many people are trying very hard to shift the emphasis on how dementia is portrayed in the media from one of fear and sensationalism to a more grounded, fair and accurate portrayal. No one would deny that dementia is a wretched condition which starts bad and progressively gets worse, but not all the time, and not without resistance and fight from those affected.

Occasionally the media do capture this, usually through the efforts of individuals such as Chris and Jayne Roberts whose brave fly on the wall documentary on BBC Panorama in June 2016 was honest, sincere, accurate and rounded in the way it portrayed the family and the impact dementia was having on them all.

This in depth film featured one section following Wendy Mitchell, Christopher and Veronica Devis and myself made as part of a BBC TV documentary for the *Victoria Derbyshire Show*, and aired in April 2015. As with Chris and Jayne, they gave us each a video camera and asked us to film events and everyday life over one month. The Roberts family were filmed for much longer than this. Wendy and I were then brought together with Joy and Tony Watson, and filmed in a TV studio discussion around dementia to accompany our films. Again, because we were central to the piece, it was well presented.

I write elsewhere about the wonderful people I have had the honour of working with from the Alzheimer's Society, and it was one these outstanding professionals who supported me during the *Victoria Derbyshire Show* project: Katie Bennett from their central media team. Here's Katie's recall of this and another one of the many successful projects we have worked on together:

Working in the Alzheimer's Society press office, I listen to a lot of media interviews, but it's rare to hear one that makes you stop short, sit down and just listen.

When Keith spoke openly and candidly to Radio 4's consumer affairs programme, *You and Yours*, about his dementia diagnosis and its impact on his life, routines and relationships I did just that.

One of the primary purposes of my job, as I see it, is to change perceptions of dementia among society and tackle misconceptions. Helping people with dementia find a voice in the media is instrumental to this. A favourite project of mine - one that I collaborated with Keith on – achieved this by supporting people with dementia to keep a video diary for a month, with the footage aired on BBC Two's Victoria Derbyshire Show.

From witnessing the coping mechanisms Keith has in place to complete his morning routine, to seeing the place where another Alzheimer's Society Ambassador, Wendy Mitchell, first realised she was experiencing the symptoms of Alzheimer's, this window into the private and personal lives of people with dementia gave real meaning to our mantra 'life doesn't end when dementia begins.'

Unlike many people who work at Alzheimer's Society, I don't have a family connection to dementia. I suppose this meant that on joining the charity I didn't really know what to expect. The friendship I have built up with Keith has taught me that the best projects here at the Society are collaborations between staff and people with dementia, and that we all have a great deal we can learn from each other.

Katie Bennett, Alzheimer's Society Media Officer

I have appeared a number of times on the BBC Radio 4 show *You and Yours,* and was most moved that its presenter, Winifred Robinson, specifically asked for me to be involved in an interview with Alistair Burns when a major

Government investment in dementia was being announced. This link arose partly from the *Welcome to our World* book, which featured on Radio 4 in August 2014, but also from an interview on dementia with me and David Cameron (then Prime Minister) a month previously.

Winifred handled the interviews with me sensitively and was both encouraging and supportive towards me. (I describe this experience on pages 143-146 in *Welcome to our World* in the chapter titled *An Amazing Day*.) Again Katie went the extra mile by coming down to Canterbury for the book launch we held, which I much appreciated.

People are surprised when they know that I turned the BBC and the Prime Minister down to meet three Kent University placement students, Lewis, Alex and Sophie, but that was typical of my loyalty and commitment to meeting them and to supporting their work. It did make the BBC think, and they arrived at a solution to please everyone: how? Well you need to read it in *Welcome to our World*!

I was once interviewed by ITV South East News, and rang Reinhard and asked him to come around to help me as it was only about a year after I was diagnosed.

The interviewer started - before filming - to discuss what he could film that showed me trying to do something I found too hard to do which previously I'd been good at.

I told him to forget it if that is what he wanted.

After a conversation, in the words of my hero Brian Clough, we talked for a few minutes before deciding that I was right and the filming focused upon what I felt was right, to project around living well despite the challenges. I remember one question being, 'What scares you, what are you frightened of now?' My answer was straight to the point and honest: 'Nothing!' At that time that is where my mind was.

Since April 2011, with a little help from Celia from the Forget Me Nots I do keep a press file of dementia-related newspaper cuttings, hers generally from *The Times* and mine from *The I,* both of which cover dementia quite frequently and reasonably well, despite often slipping into phrases such as 'sufferer' which most folk with a diagnosis object to. These papers do cover investment in dementia and initiatives either from the Government or the third sector charities.

Despite great efforts and inroads from *Dementia Diaries* it is still quite rare that the voice of a person affected by dementia forms the leading part of the piece, an exception being two articles involving me - one in the Guardian in February 2015 around the time that the film 'Still Alice' was released to much media attention, and one was my story in the Reader's Digest in October 2014. The latter was a straightforward person story; what is less common is when we are treated as equals in commenting upon a breaking story - they still too often go to the working experts rather than the experts by experience.

Occasionally if in a cafe I'll read the Express or Mail and buy it if they have a dementia-related story in that day. Most of their stories revolve around eye catching headlines about 'wonder drug found' or 'dementia and diet,' and are either rehashed old stories, common sense or nebulous research involving, say, ten mice!

Sitting here in September 2016, writing this piece, recent headlines in my file include:

'New drug offers fresh hope in battle to beat Alzheimer's' - **Daily Express** 20.08.16
'New Atlas reveals postcode lottery in care for those with dementia' - **The I** 17.08.16
'Period pain drug could reverse Alzheimer's' - **The I** 12.08.16

'High street eye test can provide early indication of dementia' - **The Times** 27.07.16

'Loss of smell could be early sign of dementia' - **The I** 27.07.16

One of the best projects I have been involved in with the media is one I originally turned down and walked away from. Gee, I am glad I reconsidered. This is the *Dementia Diaries* part-funded by Comic Relief and supported through DEEP.

It has brought together around 20-30 active people with dementia, who, with an electronic device and the support and encouragement of Paul and Laurence from *On Our Radar* send in reports on issues which mean something to us as individuals. We also respond to prompts from Laurence and Paul around what might be useful for the media to consider when reporting dementia and living with the condition.

One example is when *Dementia Diaries* early in 2016 did a very good job with the *Mirror Online* around Young Onset dementia. This piece did some good in challenging stereotypes, and more of this is needed, both for the younger people with the condition, and for the older age group. Here are the thoughts and words of Laurence:

As a journalist and project co-ordinator of *Dementia Diaries*, over the course of the past two years I have worked closely with Keith Oliver on numerous campaigns and media projects.

Keith has been an active member of our project since its genesis, and together we have worked successfully to amplify the voices of over 50 people with dementia and further challenge preconceived notions of what it is like to live with this varied condition in the UK.

Keith's contributions to articles for the Mirror (a selection of first person diagnosis stories), the Telegraph (advice for communicating with people with dementia), journalism.co.uk (tips for reporting on dementia) and others, have brought real-life experiences of dementia to new audiences, helping to drive forward better practices and shape understanding.

My personal views on dementia care have been informed by the views of people like Keith, and through thousands of conversations with others with dementia. In short, regardless of financial complications, the individual needs of people living with dementia must be placed at the centre of all forms of dementia care.

Keith's leadership, erudite and calm nature endears him to all who cross his path. However, it is his unrivalled, empathetic approach to supporting everyone with dementia, irrespective of age, class, gender or race, that leaves me honoured to call him my friend.

Laurence Ivil, Editorial & Engagement Co-ordinator, On Our Radar

Sometimes the journalist will share the story with the person in the piece before publishing and sometimes they don't, the former always works best, largely to check for factual errors. Never can I recall seeing a piece with the headline prior to publishing, which is a great pity as sometimes good stories are spoilt by thoughtless headlines which at worst are both offensive and bear little relevance to the article itself.

Back in 2013-15, I was asked to advise Channel 4 on a ground-breaking documentary series about caring for people with dementia which went out in three parts under the title of *Dementiaville*. I really liked the collaborative working with the two producers involved and the four professional experts, and my views were considered and did inform the programme makers.

One debate I did lose though was with the title, which I hated from the first time I saw it. It conjured up in my mind a place I do not want to go to! Channel 4 loved it and thought it would attract viewers; I remain unconvinced, although the programme was successful and Rosemary and I enjoyed attending and speaking at its launch at the Houses of Parliament.

Along with *Welcome to our World* the other media project I am most proud of is the film *Keith Oliver's Story* which was brilliantly made by the talented film maker, Mycal Miller, who, at the time the film was made in August 2012, was working as a trainer for Dementia UK. I'll handover to Mycal to set the story up:

I first met Keith in 2012 when I was asked to collaborate with him on a 'Dementia Awareness' course for library staff in Kent. The aim was to provide staff with a better understanding of dementia in order to assist anyone coming to the library looking for information. As Keith had recently been diagnosed with early onset Alzheimer's, the idea was that he would talk about his own personal experience. In order to give some background, we also made a short film to be shown to the group.

Initially, I imagined the plan would be for Keith to tell his story at the start of the day, after which he would be free to go - rather than sit through the whole session. From experience, I knew the sort of questions people often asked, particularly about the long-term prognosis and end-of-life issues. In my heart, I felt this could be upsetting for someone who had just received a diagnosis, so was quite reassured that Keith would not need to sit through all of that. But Keith would have none of it! He told me if he was going to be there, he wanted to participate for the whole session. Of course, I said, it would be up to him. So, that was settled!

It turns out I needn't have worried - Keith was fully aware of the issues, and as he said himself in the film, 'I feel that I have a window of opportunity to speak to people about dementia and make a contribution to raising public awareness.'

We agreed that Keith would not be introduced to the group by way of 'Here is a person with dementia.' He was simply part of the group, and when we asked people if they wished to talk about any personal experience of dementia, Keith talked about his mother who also had Alzheimer's. It was only later, after showing the film, that it was revealed that Keith had recently received a diagnosis himself. Up to this point, no one would have known - and this was in itself a powerful message. We need to see the person, not the label.

For so many people, a diagnosis can come as a terrible shock, often followed by despair. Keith's tireless work and invaluable contribution have given hope to so many, demonstrating that it is perfectly possible to enjoy a good quality of life, living with dementia. Keith is an excellent communicator - once a teacher, always a teacher!

Although Keith and I began as colleagues, we are now friends. I feel very privileged to be part of the journey.

Mycal Miller

Mycal is too modest about his talent and the success of the film is largely down to him. We were a team and it was a true collaboration and I think that shines through in the piece of work. A year later, in April 2013, he placed it (with mine and Kent County Council's agreement) on YouTube where it stands to this day. I was pleased when it reached 100 views and emailed this to Mycal; delighted when it reached 500 views and then absolutely astonished when 1,000 was reached. At the time of writing, 23,000 views have been recorded and rising at well over 140 per week, which I find utterly staggering. More importantly I know from written and spoken feedback the film is helping other people, both those living with dementia, especially Young Onset, and those helping to care for us.

Alzheimer's Society Dementia Awareness Week launch event
Savoy Hotel, London, 11ᵗʰ May 2013

This piece was written by me in May 2013 as a thank you to Jane Cotton, Maria McDonagh and their colleagues at the Alzheimer's Society for firstly hosting and inviting us, and then for looking after us so well. Many of the Society staff present on that day have become good friends since, and I have been blessed to meet Carey and her mum a couple of time since. In addition to which we have seen all of Carey's growing body of excellent film roles since this first meeting. I hope you'll enjoy this story:

One consequence of Alzheimer's Disease is that my former clear memory for dates is much diminished. Having said that, I am confident that Saturday, 11ᵗʰ May 2013 will remain as crystal clear as the sparkling chandeliers which so caught our eyes at this amazing event.

I was delighted and surprised when Emma from the Alzheimer's Society phoned to invite Rosemary and me to an afternoon tea with the famous actress and Alzheimer's Society Ambassador, Carey Mulligan, at the Savoy Hotel in London. As the event got closer I got even more excited, and was so pleased that Rosemary's initial shyness about the event was replaced by positive expectation. Our anticipation was further heightened when we heard that Carey's fellow celebrity ambassador, Julian Fellows, would also participate in the event. Amazing.

As always the pre-event preparations were so thoughtfully conducted by the Society staff, details were clear and concise, so could easily be understood and followed, train tickets were arranged with no fuss or bother, and follow-up friendly, supportive calls were made from Emma, Jane and Maria from the Society. Excellent.

On the day, we arrived a little early, and used the time to walk along the Strand doing some window shopping – I was nearly drawn into Stanley Gibbons to add to my Australian stamp collection, but alas had forgotten my 'to buy' list; probably a blessing. We also really enjoyed admiring the spring flowers in the Embankment garden before making our way into the hotel through the Riverside entrance.

Our breath was taken away by what we saw as we entered the hotel; the decor, the ambience and the beautiful fresh flowers, including one of our favourites – the fragrant sweet pea. What a fitting setting for an event which linked into Carey's new blockbuster movie, *The Great Gatsby* - such a glamorous film, set in the heady days of the 1920s. I have to say that since being diagnosed and striving to raise awareness by speaking at various events I felt nervous for the first time. I am pleased to say that these nerves were short-lived as we were immediately met by staff from the Society who made us feel most welcome. Memorable.

Moving through into the room for the afternoon tea, we were treated to a feast of delicious sandwiches and tempting cakes and scones. We all enjoyed these whilst talking with fellow people affected by dementia and society staff; this needed to be done quietly because Carey's first task was to be interviewed in the same room by Channel 4 for a forthcoming programme linked to Dementia Awareness Week. Immediately she had concluded this, there was no hesitation from her in coming over to chat with us all at our tables. Meeting celebrities and stars is not something one does frequently, so expectations can become quite jumbled. Carey came over so positively and in no way as a star-struck diva. She was relaxed, interested in us and interesting and open in her conversation. I was extra thrilled when she kindly signed a photograph I had so fortuitously spotted in that morning's newspaper with a special message to Rosemary and myself. Brilliant.

The next highlight of the afternoon was to be entertained by a very engaging, relaxed question and answer session between Julian Fellows and Carey, where he led her through her career to date, from an aspiring teenager who contacted him about being an actor to which he advised, 'Marry a banker or a lawyer.' Whilst, frustratingly, some of the content of this session has dimmed, the overwhelming sense of enjoyment from this session is still shining brightly. The trailer from *The Great Gatsby* was just enough to whet our appetite for more. Previously we had intended to see it, now we couldn't wait. Enjoyable.

The concluding part of the afternoon was spent in the delightful company of Jane from the Society, who Rosemary and I really felt we got to know. We spoke not only about Dementia, but about family and something of our pasts, and never did I once sense the difficulties of holding a lengthy off the cuff conversation, which is becoming a little more pronounced. Relaxing.

I first met Keith and his lovely wife Rosemary in May 2013 at an Alzheimer's Society event in London's Savoy Hotel. We were hosting a Q&A with our Ambassadors, actor, Carey Mulligan, and writer, Julian Fellowes following an in depth interview for Channel 4 with Carey for Dementia Awareness Week.

I was there to support the event in my capacity as celebrity liaison and found myself in conversation with Keith and Rosemary as the event came to a close. We discussed many things and the dialogue flowed freely.

As we said our goodbyes Keith remarked to me that this was the first time for many months that he had been able to engage in a conversation for that length of time without being confused or unable to keep up with what was being said. I left the hotel feeling very moved by that statement but also happy that I had been part of something so important to Keith.

As the time passed by Keith and Rosemary became more and more involved with Alzheimer's Society and I was made the key worker for our ambassadors who live with dementia alongside my celebrity liaison post. I was delighted when Keith accepted our invitation to become an ambassador for Alzheimer's Society. This enabled me to get to know Keith and Rosemary very well, and we developed a great friendship. Keith's talks for the Society grew in content and humour and I felt really honoured to have been asked for my opinion and support.

I have seen how confident Keith has become in speaking out on behalf of people living with dementia, and he shows that it is still possible to develop and expand one's talents and dreams in spite of the disease. This he has proved by becoming an author of not just one, but now two books.

I am indebted to Keith and all the people living with dementia that I work with as they have inspired me and proved that with grit and determination anything is possible!

Jane Cotton, Senior Celebrity Liaison Officer, Alzheimer's Society

It always amazes me how a chance meeting and conversation can reap such rich rewards as the treasured friendship that has ensued between Jane, Rosemary and myself. Thank you, Jane.

So now to close this chapter. Thank you from Rosemary and myself to everyone involved in organising this marvellous event. The most positive thing about being diagnosed with Alzheimer's and being engaged in the varying aspects of voluntary work I do associated with this is the wonderful people I've met. There are days when Alzheimer's causes a metaphorical fog to descend, but Saturday 11th May was one of those bright, sunny days when everything is positive.

Alternative routes to wellbeing and healthcare

Around 23 years ago I went to see an osteopath because I had a painful shoulder, and had been recommended to do this by my GP. I saw her for around six months, and after a series of appointments she seemed to help with the pain and I ceased to continue the treatment and used the money for something else.

Meanwhile, over many years, Rosemary had suffered significant amounts of pain from sciatica and other pain associated with spinal problems. She went everywhere she could to seek help, relief and hope. Eventually the options narrowed and after some hospital treatment she walked through the door of BodyWell and into the care of Christian Farthing, a spinal health specialist.

Rosemary, like most of us, will give whatever helps a fair chance but she, like me, isn't easily taken in. The treatment given her by Christian and his team led almost immediately to improvement in both her well-being, her mobility, her confidence and constant pain, and the need for tablets almost disappeared and certainly became very manageable.

I am lucky; to date my back has not given me the problem that often tall people encounter, especially those working at desks or leaning over to help little children. However, I had suffered from a series of infections since 2003, and we thought maybe me seeing Christian might help. I wanted a quick fix. I saw that paying money for my health care was not something I had been brought up to anticipate. I saw medical people as 'fixers,' not carers or 'preventers.' So I went to Christian for a year and then dropped out.

I stayed outside of this loop until Dr Alzheimer came to reside inside my head. Then, like Rosemary with her back those years before, I needed to seek ways of treating what was confronting me and, at the time, giving me a lot of health issues. I was 'wearing a mask' to convince the world that I was coping with my dementia. I still do this at times. Christian saw this and encouraged me to lower the 'mask' and put trust and faith in his approach, and I haven't regretted this for one moment since returning to his practice in April 2011 soon after my confirmed diagnosis. I was delighted when Christian agreed to write a piece for my book and here is his contribution:

I believe everyone should lead a life in the best of health. Inspired by this vision, my search for what makes us well took me into the realms of nutrition, fitness and mental health.

One overriding factor dominated my learning – the Central Nervous System. Everything related to the optimum performance of your body relies on having a nervous system that functions at 100% as Mother Nature intended. Every cell in your body, every organ, every bone and every muscle is served by the nervous system carrying messages to and from your brain and spinal cord. I have now been in clinical practice for over twenty years and have helped many thousands of patients.

When I first met Keith, he was immersed in his career as a successful and very well respected head master at a primary school, just 200 yards away from our Centre. His wife, Rosemary, came for a consultation and once Keith had learned more about the body, he soon followed for a check-up and continued treatment for twelve months. After this, he felt so well that he stopped his treatments, and decided he would get back in touch as and when he felt he needed to. Rosemary often spoke with me about how concerned she was about Keith. She had noticed his health deteriorate. I knew he had a lot of responsibilities and stress as a head teacher.

Keith did return to see me for a consultation nearly four years later. I'll never forget that day.

'Christian, I have been diagnosed with dementia, can you help me?'

'Yes,' I answered.

Together, we looked at ways in which I could support and help Keith.

In my eyes, Keith has never changed. That is because I am taking care of Keith the man - and not dementia. I feel confident that, by Keith's returning to BodyWell, I am making a positive contribution towards helping him to live well now - a view endorsed by both Keith and Rosemary.

I believe the true secret in helping Keith - and anyone with a condition - is to focus on supporting their health rather than managing the condition.

When I look at Keith now, I don't see someone with dementia. I see a man who is aging gracefully and enjoying a full and active life. He is proactive with his chiropractic programme, deep tissue massage, nutrition advice and his mental outlook – all to reduce stress within his nervous system. We work together, always towards the best of health.

I have seen Keith not only stabilise his condition but also improve in terms of his physical and emotional health. As a teacher, he had a passion for teaching children; today, he continues to teach, but a different audience of adults, inspiring them to take action and be proactive with their health. Nothing has been lost, but more gained from his experience. His passion continues.

With that in mind, always look at the person with the condition rather than the condition within the person.

For the best of health,

Dr Christian H. E. Farthing, BAppSC (ClinSc); BCSc
Chiropractor (Australia) Wellness Doctor and Spinal Health Specialist (UK)

In the five years since returning to this practice I have learnt an awful lot about looking after my own health, taking greater responsibility for my health and ensuring that I maximise my health potential. My weekly spinal adjustments are at the core of the treatment, supplemented by a fortnightly deep tissue massage and frequent workshops which have been immensely enlightening. Through the workshops I have been introduced to a wellness food intake, part of this has been a passion for juicing fruit and vegetables - not a diet, as that to me suggests a fix-it approach. He taught me about Steven Covey and his work which has so enriched the way I now problem solve. I have shared this in a number of my talks, and this was picked up by dear friend Tanya Clover...

I first met Keith Oliver when he supported the first Excellence in Kent Programme 2012/13 that I was leading for the University of Bradford School of Dementia Studies.

We had attracted funding to provide a wide range of coaching and support to 12 selected care and nursing homes across Kent. Keith came along to spend a day with the participants within the Leadership in Person Centred Care element of the project. In the morning he spoke about his role as a son supporting his mother who lived with dementia in a care home. Participants thought he was there to talk to them as a carer.

After morning coffee, he spoke about his life and experiences teaching and introduced Covey's concepts of interdependence. The participants thought then that he was there to talk to them as an educator and leader. After lunch he showed a video that discussed his diagnosis with dementia. You could have heard a pin drop. It was an incredibly powerful experience.

Participants were moved by his intelligence and his openness when talking about living with dementia. For many it was the first time they had met a person living with dementia as an equal. Even now, four years later, participants tell me of the enormous impact listening to Keith made in their practice.

I now have a new role as an independent consultant and have been thrilled to be working with Keith and his colleagues from the Forget Me Nots group. We have been presenting to GPs, practice staff, receptionists and community teams, talking about dementia. I don't want to give too much away, but we are proud to be talking about how these sessions have changed practice procedures and approaches to front line support for people living with dementia at this year's UK Dementia Congress in Brighton.

At a recent session, a GP said to Keith that he held back on seeking a diagnosis for an individual to avoid 'depressing them.' Keith answered levelly and logically, but from his heart, that to deny diagnosis was to deny that person's opportunity to live well, to prepare for their future and to live the life they wanted. That GP, and others in the room, said that Keith had changed their minds, and that they would be more active in seeking diagnosis.

I have been privileged to see Keith use his extensive knowledge of leadership theory, his own life experience, his humanity and his sense of humour to change beliefs and overturn prejudices. I know that Keith has, and will continue to, directly influence local and national attitudes and approaches and therefore the care and support for people living with dementia.

I also know that my life is the richer for knowing him.

Tanya Clover, Lead at Clover Care Consultants

Christian also recommended that I saw a nutritionist through BodyWell which I did, and that is explored in the chapter on diet and dementia.

As I have explained elsewhere, one's physical health is closely entwined with one's mental health, and another useful strategy Christian has taught me involved compiling a 'Bucket List' - not to do before I leave this world for my maker, but one which states clearly what one is determined to try and achieve in the forthcoming year.

I have NEVER believed in New Year's Resolutions, but this is different. I made mine look quite eye catching and appealing, and then printed and displayed it on my board in my office, where I see it most days to remind me what I see as important to achieve this year. I will repeat this for 2017, and hope that when I review it in December, I am content that I have tried and hopefully succeeded with as much as possible. Mine follows. Rosemary did a similar exercise.

My Bucket List for 2016

1.   To be happier and to help to make those close to me to be happier

2.   To get a better balance between humility and healthy self-esteem

3.   To remain as healthy as possible and as medication-free as possible

4. To share and include Rosemary in decision making at stage one all the time, rather than most of the time

5. To be a positive role model for others seeking to live as well as possible with major health conditions and diseases such as Alzheimer's and other forms of dementia

6. To walk and exercise more in 2016 than in 2015

7. To write words which people can draw strength from once again by attending a writing course/ group

8. To go further along the pathway of knowing God, Jesus and theology in order to better understand life and to be a better person

9. To know when is the time and place to lead and when to follow, and to be a better follower

10.   To read even more widely, to develop better ways of remembering what I've read, and to take more from what I've read and the thinking it has inspired

Keith Oliver, 16th January 2016

Diet and dementia

The statement, 'What is good for the heart is also good for the brain,' contains a lot of truth.

Whilst most of the research I have examined has focused upon the use of diets to prevent dementia, most of these being diets rich in omega 3 fatty acids - largely from oily fish and certain nuts (walnuts come to mind) - or a Mediterranean style diet - I feel those already with dementia could equally benefit from trying these. There is also some research which concludes that diets high in sugar carry a greater risk of bringing on Mild Cognitive Impairment which can lead to dementia later. Alongside this a reduction in carbohydrates is also to be encouraged.

In my case I feel my diet has always been good, but having said that I have over the years examined what I eat and have modified my intake of certain foods in the light of advice gained from professionals, friends, books and to a much lesser extent the media.

We have always enjoyed lots of fresh fruit and vegetables and have tried to focus upon local and in season. When we lived in Fordwich we grew about half of our fruit and vegetable intake because we had the land to do so. Since leaving there in 1995 this has much reduced although for the past ten years or so, as visitors to our home will vouch we have made creative use of an old fridge freezer which Rosemary ingeniously converted into a raised vegetable bed to grow lettuce, beans, radish and spring onions alongside half a dozen tomato plants grown in pots up a cane. When we go to the fridge to get veg it can mean in the kitchen or in the garden!

We are cautious about fats and too many sweet foods, although both of us like an occasional cake or biscuit to accompany the daily cuppa or two or as a dessert.

I write this for a number of reasons, one of which is that I do not conform to the usual model of someone being old with dementia, nor the model of developing it through a poor diet. What I am seeking to do is to use my diet as one strategy to help me to live as well as possible for as long as possible. I am sure this does help.

Linked to this we have taken the advice given by Christian Farthing. Upon his recommendation we bought a juicer and have juiced very happily for the past four years, initially following a 'super Juice diet' devised by Jason Vale in his best seller *7lbs in 7 Days Super Juice Diet*, and then used juice to accompany our main meal. We both felt very well and energised when following this programme and have enjoyed the fruits of this since.

Early in 2016 I saw a nutritionist who conducted various tests on me including DNA, intolerance tests and a range of others. The outcome of this was that I was lactose and gluten intolerant. She recommended I removed both from my diet. I haven't completely, but what I have done is to significantly reduce both cow's milk and gluten - in bread, cereals and cake. This has helped me to feel better physically, and therefore emotionally and psychologically.

Not everything, though, worked positively: taking of turmeric curcumin with black pepper (recommended to help brain function by reducing inflammation) gave me Irritable Bowel Syndrome (IBS)-type symptoms, so I had to stop taking this and the IBS disappeared.

I do though feel that I am actively doing something to help myself, and in most cases at little extra cost financially. I drink coconut milk as much as cows, and gluten free cakes are even nicer than those with gluten. I am not as keen on the bread, and the crackers are very expensive so I pass on them but I have given them a try.

Nowhere has advice on this been forthcoming from health professionals within the NHS, and whilst the Alzheimer's Society does a fact-sheet on diet it is in nowhere near enough depth. Perhaps both these points are worthy of consideration by those in a position to do so.

I also spoke with friends who also have dementia, one of whom is Charles Ryan who, as a fellow Forget Me Not, was a co-author of *Welcome to our World*. He and his dear wife Pauline are keen followers of the work of American Dr Bruce Fife. Charles writes and talks about what he refers to as 'his battle plan' which is connected to this.

On their recommendation I bought and read Fife's significant book, *Stop Alzheimer's Now!* The book is very clear in its hypothesis that, whilst Alzheimer's has no cure and is progressive, individuals can proactively help themselves to either delay its onset or slow it down once diagnosed.

The science in the book appears sound and well researched, and is supported by detailed, verified case studies. He examines causes including diet and how these can be changed to good effect, partly by the use of coconut oil/ milk. Now, I am not going to precis a 300-page book here - why not look it up and make up your own mind on this? Maybe with a little encouragement not only from me but also from A.Charles and Pauline:

I was diagnosed with Mixed dementia in August 2012, after six months of testing by a Clinical Psychologist. This was following a referral from my Stroke Consultant. I had a stroke in April 2009 followed by a heart attack in October 2009. I had had a quadruple heart bypass in October 2001.

It has been very helpful to have had the diagnosis of dementia and to be part of the Forget Me Nots Group. I am involved with various research projects with DEEP and IDEAL, and was part of the recent Dementia Friendly Film Club project. As a member of Forget Me Nots I have been involved with interviewing second year psychology students for placements with the Forget Me Nots and been on other interview panels. My wife and I have given a talk at The Memory

Clinic on our experiences post diagnosis. I have given several book readings from *Welcome to our World*.

I have not experienced any dementia care other than the regular appointments with a Consultant Psychiatrist. My wife is my carer. We need to explore what my care plan would be for the future.

I have chosen an unusual path for treating my dementia by following the recommendations of Dr Bruce Fife's Coconut Oil Diet, when the Donezepezil medication ceased working. It is said that the Medium Chain Triglycerides in the coconut oil, linked to a diet low in carbohydrates, but rich in proteins, vegetables, fruit, nuts, seeds and pulses can help to halt the progression of Dementia.

I also exclude dairy, wheat and gluten from my diet Added sugar is to be avoided. Further information is in my Battle Plan published in the *Welcome to our World* book with regard to acupressure, acupuncture, reflexology and exercise, all helping to live well with dementia. Listening to choral music is very beneficial and I am exploring the benefits of reading poetry to stimulate the brain. I have meditated for some 40 years.

I am a retired lawyer and a published writer, having contributed articles to the *Dictionary of National Biography*, *Catholic Life* and having published in 1997 a book *The Abbey and Palace of St. Augustine*, to coincide with the 1400th Anniversary of St. Augustine's arrival in England. I am also the Chairman of the Kent Recusant History Society and have contributed to their regular publications.

It is very exciting to follow and be part of the numerous research projects currently being developed around the world all with the aim of combatting this disease and helping those with a diagnosis to live better.

A. Charles, Forget Me Nots, written with his wife Pauline Ryan

More recently, following an appointment with the nutritionist, I purchased and read *Grain Brain,* by another American doctor, this time a neurologist Dr David Perlmutter. He approaches Alzheimer's prevention and to an extent treatment again through diet, this time identifying gluten as the villain of the piece. He argues that the inflammation brought on by gluten in the brain is at the core of the growth of harmful proteins which in turn can lead to tangles, amyloid and atrophy resulting in Alzheimer's. Again he argues his case in a reasoned, scientific way which I think carries a lot of sound sense.

At a time when much research is in the very rudimentary stages, the work of Fife and Perlmutter should be more widely read by professionals who are then in the position to suggest that there may be useful strategies here for people to consider which are helpful. Often I think of Bill Clinton's famous quote, 'If you always do things in the same way, you will always get the same results.'

Whilst no one wants to promote crackpot schemes or quirky fads, sometimes a little creativity and thinking outside the box is necessary to help people, and to address key issues when, on the surface, answers do not seem to be emerging.

Shopping

When someone says to me, 'I don't like shopping either,' I recognise this is said to empathise and to display a shared experience, but what then comes to mind is the parallel with someone saying, 'I forget things as well' when they ask about my dementia. Often well-meant, but less often illustrative of understanding of what it is really like for someone like me who lives with dementia to varying degrees day in day out.

Shopping has never been a favourite occupation of mine. I have seen it as a function and, if clothes or food buying, I would go in the shop with something in mind to buy, look at a few options and then either make the purchase or leave the store and go into another one. I would do this on my own quite comfortably, and - if with Rosemary - we would discuss what was available to buy before making a joint decision. If we were together in the supermarket she would have the list, and I would gather some items, and she others, in order to do the task as efficiently as possible.

Now all this is very different. When clothes shopping I often get confused and overwhelmed by the choice available, and the changing location of items in stores such as M&S. Sizes seem confusing as well. My sense of colour has changed, sometimes for the better, as I do like brighter colours than the more sober business colours of yesteryear. But sometimes I am at risk of looking over the top, or choosing colours which simply clash rather than complement. If the 'fog' then descends, as it does at times, then it is like a panic attack and I cannot flee the shop quickly enough. Rosemary is very understanding and patient, and is always keen to come and choose clothes with me. This is good and does help, but also at times leaves me with a sense of dependence which I am less comfortable with.

In the case of supermarket shopping, I now very seldom venture into our local supermarket. The old way of helping became a problem because I would walk off, not find the items and then not find Rosemary and become fretful; conversely she would, understandably, get concerned as to where I was, as getting a bottle of milk shouldn't take *that* long. I would also question what we needed, which did Rosemary's confidence no good either. So now we make the list at home together and she does the supermarket shop on her own. A mixed blessing, but in the circumstances it does work. Browsing together around gift shops and the like is still ok, provided that they are not too busy, and even then I often get agitated and feel the need to get into the fresh air or to sit down.

Some stores, such as M&S, have encouraged their staff to become Alzheimer's Society Dementia Friends, and this is good. The Flight Centre in Canterbury have been outstanding in their support and service to Rosemary and myself, and from this to other travellers who have dementia. Other stores who haven't completed the awareness raising often still provide consideration from staff especially if I need to tell them that I have dementia. On other occasions the level of service has not been so good. I do often use the phrase in this context, 'What is good for someone with dementia is good for everyone.'

Amazingly, on the day I wrote this chapter I received a newsletter from the Alzheimer's Society signposting people to a new fact sheet in their extremely helpful series which is available from their website. This one is in the section on Dementia Friendly Communities and is entitled 'Becoming a Dementia-Friendly Retailer.' There is as always excellent advice given, which illustrates some of the issues I have raised from my experience.

One shop I do seek sanctuary in is the local Waterstones bookshop in Canterbury, which I love browsing in, talking to the staff who I know quite well and making a purchase of a book which hopefully I haven't bought before. This does sometimes happen, and the understanding staff will exchange it the next time I go into the shop. Maybe this goes some way to help explain why our house is so full of books.

Labels and dementia

I have found all of my adult life that labels are often taken for granted and once thought of can be applied both positively and negatively. This judgement can be by the person themselves or by others who make the judgement of the individual.

As a teacher and head teacher, I encouraged children, parents and teachers not to use negative labels. Telling somebody they are naughty, bad at maths or spelling – or that they are hopeless or rubbish at something - does stick, especially when someone is told repeatedly. The next stage was almost always that the person lived up to this label because that was what was expected of them. So often I heard the individual say to me, 'What is the point trying if I cannot make the person believe that I am trying at something?'

The same is the case with some adults outside the world of education and there is a parallel with the world of dementia. Many people with dementia hate to be referred to as 'sufferers' and find this promotes stigma and pity neither of which are helpful. When 'sufferer' is used as a noun it also defines us and people then do not see the person beyond the dementia.

If professionals use 'sufferer' with all its connotations, then they almost certainly fall into the trap of treating the disease and not the person. My experience leads me to think and hope we are moving away from this situation. 'Sufferer' often then leads to the use of words such as 'burden,' 'trouble,' or 'encumbrance' - who would want labels such as those attached to them? But I have seen and heard them used. Some days I, like everyone else with dementia, do suffer and feel frustration at what dementia causes, but I will not give in to it and let it control and then define me negatively.

Moving onto the label 'carer.' This can be the most positive of words and in most cases I have experienced this is very much the case and is easy to justify. We are generally a caring society with compassion and generosity of spirit at its centre. It is not an easy label though to live up to. Training and support is not consistent, in some cases it is non-existent either in perception or reality. Most carers take on the role out of love for their family member - husband, wife, parent, grandparent, partner, aunt, uncle or whoever. Without this army of good people, the situation in this country would be dire. They need more recognition and more support. Few, if any, come to the role with any preparation.

Having said all that I also make the point that the first label for a family carer should be their long term role which they had before the dementia arrived and afterwards. In our case, Rosemary is my wife who cares for me, I am her husband and I care for her. Neither of us see ourselves primarily as 'carer,' and I am pretty sure that no matter what the future holds for both of us health-wise this will always be the case. I do not speak for Rosemary and she does not speak for me, although I expect that as the dementia progresses this may change, and indeed that is the other point: relationships and support for each other does need to be dynamic and responsive. There have been occasions when both of us have been at meetings talking quite happily to a person with dementia who has then become quite mute when their partner has spoken for them and about them.

Guilt is a dreadful emotion for anyone to feel, and I know a number of people, myself included, who have felt it at times connected to dementia. The person, like me, who feels at times that the disease is almost getting the better of them and that they are at risk of becoming a burden; the carer who feels, wrongly, a failure because perhaps they feel they have contributed to the person's dementia or not done enough to stop it in the early stages, and then feel guilt at not performing the carer role in a super- human way. Again all emotions I recognise, which deserve better understanding and support from the professional community beyond a cuppa and a tissue. I also understand the currency and leverage that the 'carer' label can have upon Government and other official bodies in securing funding for people who need it, and of course I respect and support this.

For those of you who have heard some of my talks you may recall I have in the past stated my unease with the expression 'being on a journey,' in relation to living with dementia. This is not entirely because the 'journey' word is an overused cliché (which it is) but because of what being on a journey encourages one to think.

Most journeys are either chosen because they are enjoyable or a means of getting from A to B usually as fast as one can, and then settling down at journey's-end. I do not want my dementia journey to come to an end as things stand at the moment - there is no cure which would be the ideal conclusion. I want to do everything I can to slow the 'journey' down.

Reading this book could be seen as 'a journey;' I hope you are enjoying it and finding it interesting. If not, then you can put it down and bring the journey to either a temporary or permanent end. The word 'journey' does have its uses, I recognise this, but beyond being bored with hearing it used, please consider the broader issues around this word; otherwise I fear another useful word will lose its usefulness. I have included in the talks section of this book further reference to this.

I think often people get over-concerned about political correctness and a sense of inertia related to fear of causing offence, and the simple, thoughtful response is often the best one to use. In a similar vein once I was interviewed on BBC Radio Kent as part of a programme about dementia, and towards the end the presenter said it didn't seem like I had dementia. Tempted though I was to give her my full and usual answer on this occasion I decided not to, and simply said, 'Thank you' which caused her to stop and then take a different thread to the interview.

I have met people with dementia who do not like being identified with the condition and still refer to it as 'the D word.' Whilst I do understand this, not naming it doesn't actually help remove it from one's life but maybe it helps the person live as normal a life as they can. I have heard people with dementia also refer to dictionary definitions of dementia using phrases such as 'without mind,' and then to be even more depressed because of this. Linked to this I recently researched what the word 'nostalgia' meant, as it is something which I have mixed feelings towards - looking back as I have done to write this book can evoke a range of emotions. It comes from two Greek words - *nostos* which is memory, and *algos wh*ich is pain. There is a certain beauty in this, but there can also be difficulty.

Perceptions and labels can be misleading and unhelpful. I think back also to when I was a child. I was always tall for my age, and I remember my mother defending my often displayed ineptitude to do something I was expected to do because the person asking thought I was older than my real years. Understandable, but frustrating especially when accompanied by 'You don't look such and such an age,' or now 'You don't look like you have dementia.' That should have been my catchphrase; 'You don't look like...'

The surprise either of my age or me having dementia is much better dealt with by all concerned if the person directing the initial surprised comment follows it with something positive and then learns from this that not everyone with dementia is over the age of 80 and in the late stages of the condition. Indeed, I know many people in their eighties who have not long been diagnosed with dementia who do not present in a way consistent with the stereotype label. A friend of mine recently mentioned to me at an Alzheimer's Society training workshop I was co-delivering with Lisa Bogue, that he had been asked, 'How do you refer to a person affected by dementia?' His response was, 'By their name!' I couldn't have answered this better.

Stigma and dementia

Whether real or perceived, stigma is a very significant issue and concern for many people affected by dementia, both those living with it and those living with us. One could say that stigma exists in a range of ways within our society not just connected with dementia, but where it is particularly noticeable is when one thinks there is stigma around being old, around mental illness and around dementia - usually those with dementia fall into all three categories, and those people termed as having Young Onset often also experience disbelief and mistrust around their difficulties.

Everyone with dementia is different, and there are many different types of dementia. What, though, is consistent is the progressive nature of the condition, and the fact that currently there is no cure available. Consequently, this combination contributes to fear, both from those affected, and from Society generally. Often this is allied to misconceptions, half-truths and misunderstandings, usually fueled by a headline-grabbing media which serves to reinforce negative perceptions, which in turn feeds views associated with stigma.

I feel that fear is at the root of this issue. Fear from the person with dementia that their life is changing for the worse, and that there are no interventions and/ or support to help them to live as well as possible, and that they are somehow to blame for the negative changes in their behaviour and personality. This often provides challenges to loved ones, family and friends who at times reinforce the stigma, often unwittingly by talking about their 'declining,' changing or now more challenging loved one/ friend, often without understanding the changes which the person is confronting.

Stigma then obstructs the person's ability to continue to make useful contributions to family or the broader society. One early casualty of this is the person's self-esteem, which is hard to recover once tipped into downward mode. People don't always know what to say to the person with dementia: do they feel sorry for them? Do they fear upsetting them? Do they fear an aggressive/challenging response to something they may say or do? The stigma is internalised (often in both the person with dementia and their loved ones) and then it feeds on itself, leading to someone who previously may have been trying to live well, feeling now depressed, helpless and socially excluded.

All, though, should not be doom and gloom!

With support, understanding and tolerance, stigma can be kept at bay and dealt with as rationally as possible. The Dementia Friends initiative is potentially a powerful force in raising awareness, and in turn friendly support for those of us with dementia. Service user involvement groups such as those coordinated by DEEP give people comradeship and a real sense of continuing to make a useful contribution to society. The *Dementia Diaries* project is leading the charge with this and I do commend this to interested readers. The Alzheimer's Society through its service user involvement plan, panels and associated activities encourages people with dementia to live well in spite of the difficulties being confronted. The Society is also committed to working with the media to try and reduce stigma in its portrayal and language used to describe dementia and those living with it. The Dementia-Friendly Communities initiative is starting to make a real difference in some parts of the country.

These views are based on the real experience of one person, and the experiences of many people with similar experiences whom I have been privileged to meet and talk with about this and other related issues in the past five years since I was diagnosed with Alzheimer's disease.

Young onset dementia: a personal viewpoint

This chapter is dedicated to Chris N, Chris R, Melvyn, Anne, Alan, Mark, Anne-Marie - youngsters at the Forget Me Nots, and to Chris and Jayne and Wendy and her lovely daughters, along with all other younger people who live with the 'embuggerance,' as Terry Pratchett would say, which is Young Onset.

The very first contribution I received for this book came in within one hour of being asked and that was from Adrian Bradley from the Alzheimer's Society. Here is Adrian's very thoughtful and thought-provoking contribution.

An English tourist, so the joke goes, finds himself lost in the rolling hills of rural Ireland. Seeing a local farmer in a nearby field, he walks over to the man and says, 'Good afternoon, I don't suppose you know the way to Lisdoonvarna.' The farmer looks up, leans on his gnarled wooden crook, and replies 'I do, but if I were you I wouldn't start from here.'

Many people diagnosed with young onset dementia feel lost when they receive the news. They want to find help, find answers, find their way through the new landscape all around them but cannot find the friendly farmer. There are no maps. Sat-navs can't be relied upon.

Keith and Rosemary have chosen to travel along their journey in a way that helps others to find their own way, pointing out obstacles, pot holes, wrong turns, cul-de-sacs and even the odd short cut. More than that, they also highlight the points of interest, sights, sounds and smells of life along the way.

In doing this they are not alone, but they are special. They help us with their local knowledge. As paid supporters of Keith and Rosemary, and the tens of thousands of people in similar situations, we at Alzheimer's Society must help to plot a path which helps them to find their way, find each other and find themselves once again.

In health and social care there is too much jargon, far too much complexity, and there are quite possibly too many elaborate metaphors. Churchill wrote a letter to a friend in which he apologised for its length; 'If you had given me more time,' he explained, 'it would have been shorter.' As someone who does not knowingly use one word when three will do – enough; no more. I will stop and leave the rest of the page to Keith.

Adrian Bradley, National Lead – Younger People with Dementia, Alzheimer's Society

Here are my thoughts on the subject of Young Onset dementia, used in an article I wrote:

For the past five years I have knowingly been increasingly sharing my brain with an unwelcome and unwanted guest: Dr. Alzheimer. As someone diagnosed with Alzheimer's Disease on New Year's Eve 2010 at the age of 55, I am host to this insidious visitor. Others who share my life are so much more welcome and friendly amongst whom are my wife, my three adult children and my three grandchildren. Others who have entered my life since being diagnosed, and have made such a positive impact upon me include other service users and some wonderful professionals working in the NHS and in the voluntary sector.

When diagnosed I had the typical impression that dementia was solely the domain of the elderly. My mother developed Alzheimer's in her mid-70s and she was typical of how I imagined people with dementia. Never had I met someone affected by dementia below the age of 65 (which is the threshold for someone to be referred to as Young or Early Onset). My diagnosis was very unexpected by both myself, my family and our GP who had sent me for a scan and a neurologist appointment to rule out a brain tumour. Dementia wasn't on anybody's radar until after the scan and the appointment, following which I was referred to the memory clinic in Canterbury for what turned out to be an in-depth six-month assessment period which culminated with a confirmed diagnosis. During this period, I was extremely well supported by the professional team who explained to me the testing and the results of the tests which, at best, I was performing at average and at my worst at the lower fifth centile. The pacing and the approach were both person-centered.

I wanted information and needed this to understand what I was living with, and subsequently this served to allow me to come to terms with moving from a suggested diagnosis to a confirmed one with less of a shock and then to begin to live well with dementia.

No one - especially someone in their 50s - wants to be diagnosed with dementia, but because of the impact the disease was having on me by way of my ability to undertake my work, remember conversations and reading, TV programmes, films etc., changes in my behaviour and concentration and difficulties with balance, there was some peace of mind in knowing what the cause of these problems was.

From this, one is then able to move forward by sorting out a smooth exit from work, financial support, lasting power of attorney and wills and beginning to meet other people who are sharing the same or similar experience.

I then felt that information was exerting power over the disease and I also realised that I wasn't alone. Indeed, one morning I woke up to open the newspaper and read that my understanding of there being 16,000 people with Young Onset dementia was incorrect and that the Alzheimer's Society were suggesting the figure is 42,000. Some would say this is an underestimate and I have heard figures around the 65,000 mark, (SCIE) which is probably more accurate as many people either don't or won't come forward or are mis-diagnosed.

The vast majority of people in their 40s, 50s and early 60s who display symptoms of dementia are still in work when they or a family member realise they have a problem. Sometimes mortgages still need paying, dependent family members rely upon this person and there is a real fear that a diagnosis will bring little gain and lots of loss. Young Onset dementia specific treatments, interventions, or support are a postcode lottery and are few and far between. So many services place younger people in with Late Onset service users, which is often inappropriate and doesn't engage or meet the needs of the younger person.

Usually younger people with dementia don't present with the same co-morbidities as older people. Often we are physically fitter, have enormous amounts of physical energy - sometimes too much (!) and it's our cognitive functioning which lets us down, frustrates and at times leads to depression. Depression and dementia are a truly toxic partnership and having experienced both after a period of feeling 'bullet-proof' it is sometimes difficult to know which is having a greater impact on my ability to feel that I am living well.

I have drawn great support from professionals in KMPT, the Alzheimer's Society, Young Dementia UK, DEEP and Age UK which alongside my own reading, especially works such as those by Tom Kitwood, *Still Alice* and *Dancing with Dementia* have helped.

For the past year the Alzheimer's Society have had Adrian Bradley in post as National Lead - Younger People with Dementia to champion and coordinate the Societies' provision for young people with dementia, and this again is a very positive innovation. Alongside this I serve on the National Network for Young Onset Dementia which has a range of agencies involved and is co-ordinated by Young Dementia UK (YDUK).

In the case of Kitwood, I refer often to his illustration of a flower which has love at its centre surrounded by: attachment, comfort, identity, occupation and inclusion. When these are in place I live well.

Unfortunately there are times when, as Kitwood describes, 'Malignant Social Psychology' makes my life much more challenging. Aspects of this which negatively impact upon my self-esteem and well-being and result in fear replacing positivity are: treachery, disempowerment, infantilisation, intimidation, labelling, stigmatisation, outpacing, invalidation, banishment, objectification, ignoring, imposition, withholding, accusation, disruption, mockery and disparagement. I have experienced most of these in the past, especially in the past two years as slips and dips in my mental health have occurred.

The Royal College is acknowledging the needs of younger people with dementia, and sitting on the Royal College's Executive Board I am pleased to see that the need for age appropriate services to MSNAP standards are being introduced. This I am sure will help raise awareness amongst professionals and help provide better services for younger people with dementia.

I also am a member of the Alzheimer's Society Research Network and sit on their Grant Advisory Panel. We do receive applications for projects linked to care and wellbeing of younger people with dementia, but not enough. One major relevant project the Society is funding is PREVENT which is receiving somewhere in the region of £600,000. Part of my role in the network is to help monitor this project. It is based in West London Mental Health NHS Trust and at Imperial College London and Edinburgh University and is focusing on people in their 40s and 50s. Its aims are: to find the very earliest signs of changes in the brain while we are still in good health, to propose prevention strategies and to monitor these strategies over time to evaluate their efficiency in slowing down the progression of biological changes in the brain.

To conclude, whilst neurologically there are many similarities between Young Onset and Late Onset dementia, the impact on the individual and their families and presentation of the condition are often very different. Consequently, the type of treatments, interventions and support need to be person-centred, and fit for purpose in order that the person can live as well as possible for as long as possible.

This article appeared in the Royal College of Psychiatrists' Newsletter for the Faculty for the Psychiatry of Old Age, dated May 2016.

Alongside this I would like to include the thoughts and words of two more professional friends whom I have worked closely with on projects connected to Young Onset dementia - Tessa Gutteridge and Julia Burton-Jones.

Call Keith - one of my first thoughts when developing the first national Young Dementia Network. Together with over 42,000 others in the UK, Keith's experience of dementia in mid-life and its different impact on him, his wife Rosemary and his family has led to his deep understanding of what is needed if life is to be fully lived. Keith's choice to use this to effect positive change now and for the future means that our efforts to improve on the scarcity of support at every level benefit from Keith's contribution.

It is important to us at Young Dementia UK that our work is founded on a positive approach to the reality of living with Young Onset dementia. So the call to Keith, and his willingness to share his first-hand experience and knowledge in determining how we, through a successful network, can influence nationally and create support locally brings us so much of value. We all learn from Keith's insightful contributions, well-considered and fair commentary, and wise observations.

But more than that really; the call to Keith brings us to the core of Keith, which is his humanity, compassion, humour and determination. And with dementia or not, those qualities would help all of us to have fulfilled lives.

Tessa Gutteridge, Director YoungDementia UK

Julie Barton Jones has also kindly written here:

I was first asked to make contact with Keith by Kent Library Service when preparing a training programme Dementia UK delivered for their staff. The trainer, Mycal Miller, is also a film maker and was commissioned to make a film of Keith to be shown on the course; the film is on YouTube and has been used with great effect in many training contexts. Keith contributed to a project I delivered for Dementia Pathfinders on young onset dementia, speaking at the launch of a publication to raise awareness called 'Approaching an Unthinkable Future.' I have heard Keith speak at many regional, national and international events and never fail to be impressed by the intelligence and impact of his presentations.

My passion is for a world where the views of people with dementia are valued. Keith has demonstrated people with dementia are more than capable of setting the agenda, however, I feel the skill and commitment he invests is sometimes under-estimated. I would like to see people like Keith recompensed realistically for the time and expertise they offer. This is especially significant for those with Young Onset dementia who have taken early retirement from previous employment.

Keith has become a friend I value for his warmth, humour and honesty. He influences those around him as much by the person he is as by what he says.

Julia Burton-Jones

Care today, cure tomorrow:
Dementia research

Seldom does a week pass without the press reporting something connected to dementia research, usually with an eye-catching headline around a 'wonder drug' or a 'miracle cure' for the condition. Of course the first error with the headlines is that they refer to the umbrella term 'dementia,' when in fact they usually only mean Alzheimer's, which is only one form of dementia. Then when one reads beyond the headline it is clear that the headline is misleading, and that whilst trials may be underway, they are usually in their early stages and that only some indications are proving potentially hopeful.

Since joining the Alzheimer's Society Research Network in 2011, I must have read many hundreds of applications and proposals for funding written by British Universities and submitted to the Society. Many are well thought out, and have at their centre a genuine desire to add to the bank of knowledge connected to dementia within this country.

Over the last two years as greater funding has become available - from around £2-3million pounds per year, to around £8 million - with an aim of reaching £10 million per year in the next year or two. The Society has then declared a commitment to spend £100 million in the next decade. Consequently, in 2014 the Society wisely split its portfolio into two sections, these being 'Biochemical' which sets out to find the causes of different types of dementia and a cure, and 'Care, Services and Public Health,' which funds projects focusing upon caring for people affected by dementia now and in the immediate future. I know that these funds have got to be raised in order to be spent and that a range of tactics will be used to attain the necessary money.

All evidence suggests that dementia is the most feared health condition amongst the 40-plus age group and of course this section of the population is best placed to pressure Government and contribute towards fundraising. Maybe the money you spent on this book will help here, as the proceeds raised from sales goes to either Alzheimer's Society or Innovations in Dementia.

In order to give you greater insight into the significant work of the Society's Research Network I invited Anna Grinbergs-Saull to write a piece outlining her role within the Network:

In my role with the Research Engagement team at Alzheimer's Society, I have the privilege of working with the Research Network.

All Research Network volunteers are either living with dementia or are carers or former carers for a family member or friend. The volunteers' role spans the whole Alzheimer's Society research programme, from setting our funding priorities to making funding decisions and monitoring research projects as they progress.

Increasingly, Network volunteers are helping to develop or design research projects – giving researchers advice before they apply for funding. In my time at the Society, I have been able to see first-hand the impact of this relationship between people affected by dementia and researchers on the research we fund as well as the individuals involved.

Researchers from a range of disciplines tell us that listening to the experiences and ideas of people with dementia and carers has allowed them to see research from a new perspective, both in terms of the subject itself, and the benefit that involving people affected by dementia can have. So much so that Research Monitoring, where we match three volunteers to each project we fund, has in some cases encouraged the development of lasting partnerships between researchers and volunteers.

It has been fantastic to see the involvement of Research Network volunteers extend beyond our own funding programme, and seeing volunteers acknowledged or named in grant applications and academic papers illustrates the impact that they have had.

On a personal level, I too have learned a lot from the Research Network. The volunteers' generosity in sharing their experience and knowledge has helped me to gain more understanding of what it is like to live with dementia. There is always more to learn, and I feel very fortunate to work with a group of people who constantly inspire and challenge me to promote the meaningful involvement of people affected by dementia.

Since being formed in 1999, the Research Network has ensured that our research is informed by people affected by dementia. Without it, the Research and Development directorate would not be what it is today.

Dr Anna Grinbergs-Saull, Research Engagement Manager, Alzheimer's Society

I feel the Society is fully justified in its claim that the Research Network is one of the numerous 'flagship elements' within the organisation, and this is because of the outstanding efforts of staff and volunteers allied to the funding allocated by trustees and the quality of applications which we are working with.

In addition to the funding I have outlined, the Alzheimer's Society is supporting the establishment of a Dementia Research Institute in London by 2020. I was honoured to be asked to join the panel to help interview for the director of this centre. A massive £250 million will be invested in the Institute - £150 million by Government, £50 million by the Alzheimer's Society and £50 million by Alzheimer's Research UK. One reason I was keen to be involved is because part of its focus will be care and cure programmes.

One drug which in August/September attracted a lot of media hype was Aducanumab and the facts on the story as described by the Alzheimer's

Society can be found in an online series called *Behind the Headlines* - www.alzheimers.org.uk/behindtheheadlines - shared via a newsletter issued on 31st August 2016 to its Research Network volunteers.

I applaud this factual, no nonsense way of conveying information by the Society, and I was able to share this very usefully with a group of fourteen people with dementia who were interested and concerned by the news stories and were then, like you I hope, encouraged to look at 'Join Dementia Research.'

Personally, a drugs trial project is not something I wish to be involved with. However, I do recognise and applaud that in order to provide a cure or effective pharmaceutical treatment, volunteers do need to come forward. It is just that I hate taking ANY medication and steer clear even of taking a headache pill. I am happy to test any non-medication treatment, and to sit on boards and committees linked to research projects especially, though not exclusively relating to care programmes.

Projects I have been heavily involved with include:

The Truth Project which is multi-agency, and is seeking to better advise professionals as to how they should address issues around telling the truth to people affected by dementia in the later stages. Inevitably its findings will be of interest to a wide range of professionals, but also to people living with dementia either with a diagnosis or helping with our care.

The IDEAL Project which again is multi-agency, and is examining ways people can live well with dementia over a long period rather than as a 'snapshot.'

The VALID Project which involves a number of health trusts and universities and is seeking to substantially improve occupational therapy care in this country based upon a model devised in the Netherlands.

PREVENT Project which is funded by the Alzheimer's Society and is looking in depth at risk factors of developing dementia amongst the 40-60 age group.

Reading Well is funded by the Big Lottery and co- ordinated by The Reading Agency, and this project is looking to move people from being isolated and lonely to being engaged and happier through the use of books and a network of 'reading friends.' Not exclusively for those with dementia, but a sizeable element of the participants will have dementia.

There are more I am involved with, and heaps more out there which I am not a part of. What is important is the 'So what?' question: I do not want to support research for research's sake; funding and time is too precious. Projects have to add to the knowledge base AND make a difference to the lives of those affected by dementia. There still needs to be additional investment into care and cure, and a greater focus upon areas such as other dementias than Alzheimer's. Also, for the younger age group who develop dementia, 'The Angela Project,' which is about to be funded by the Alzheimer's Society to improve diagnosis and post diagnostic support for younger people living with dementia and their caregivers will, I am sure, be very useful.

A third neglected area is gender and dementia. Gender has long been ignored, and until recently there was very little on women with dementia despite more women than men having it - one reason being that they do tend to live longer and as age is a big risk factor it figures that more women in the older group will develop dementia. As for men, when I recently Googled research on men and dementia and there was virtually nothing, and certainly nothing worth sharing with you the reader. For the many hundreds of thousands of men with dementia I hope that this is soon addressed.

In September 2016, six people with dementia had an excellent Service User Review Panel (SURP) meeting in Canterbury with the Alzheimer's Society, where we spent 90 minutes discussing at some length dementia research, and many of the points within this chapter were covered at that meeting. Clearly, more money is going into this research but when compared with other major health concerns such as cancer we are moving from a very poor starting point.

I want to close with something I wrote for the press release when the Dementia Research Institute was announced in a story featuring me in Summer 2016 edition of the Medical Research Council's publication entitled *Network*:

I feel that this potentially very significant institute will go a long way towards attracting, recruiting, retaining and then celebrating the successes of those involved in dementia research at all levels.

It's great to see the Government, charities, the research community and key universities about to work together to bring about this exciting venture. I am thrilled and excited and would love to still be around to add the expression delighted when its potentials are realised. So at the moment... I will be delighted when I see the results of its success.

We shall see, and I do obviously really hope so, not just for me, but for everyone with dementia now, and the hundreds of thousands who are likely to follow in years to come. It is all our needs that this research should seek to address.

Welcome to our World

This chapter is dedicated firstly to Liz, Janet and Sophie, each of whom contributed enormously to supporting me in making this book happen and without you three it would have remained an unrealised ambition. Then to Alex, Charley, Jennie, Lewis, Chris N, Chris R, A Charles and April for your full commitment both during and after publication. You all talked the talk, and walked the walk and were very welcome in my world.

Despite two years of writing virtually nothing other than talks for dementia events, in many ways this book begins where *Welcome to our World* ended.

Welcome to our World was a very unique book which resulted from a very unique project. I hope that time will remove the word unique and replace it with the word 'first,' which will mean that others have followed in our footsteps, have learnt from our successes and mistakes and taken the concept to another level. This would please me greatly and add to the project's legacy.

Before describing how the book came into the world it is important to explain the background. It arose from a writing project which was funded by the Alzheimer's Society/Lloyds Bank Innovation Fund and DEEP (Dementia Engagement and Empowerment Project.) The £5,500 grants paid for Liz Jennings to plan and run the course and to devote time to the book, payment to the students to support writers after their placement had finished, publishing costs for 1000 books, and refreshments to keep writers and students focused during the writing course.

Eight people with dementia, most of whom had never written before, joined the course; all were members of the Forget Me Nots group in Canterbury. Five University of Kent students who were on placement with the Trust were able to join us to offer their support. This same team then went forward to work on the book. After months of planning between Liz and I the course ran from April - June 2014 and featured the following programme -

- Introductions
- My family and other animals
- Life changing moments
- The world I've known
- Red-Carpet occasions
- My favourite things

It was a great success for all involved.

I first met Keith when I was invited to join the Canterbury Forget Me Not Group in the Spring of 2013. This was after attending an excellent programme of talks organised by The Memory Clinic at St Martin's Hospital. He was the then Chairman of this group which meets monthly. It is a very proactive group.

We both joined the excellent creative writing course sessions at The Beaney Library in Canterbury. I believe that he was responsible for setting up this group and finding the funding for it. These sessions led to us collaborating and contributing stories with eight others, which led to the publishing of the book *Welcome to our World,* funded by The Alzheimer's Society and launched in November 2014. This was a very inspiring project. Keith was very proactive in bringing it to completion.

A. Charles, author and member of Forget Me Nots

The course encouraged writers to write about their life experiences, including - if they so wished - their thoughts on living with dementia. The quality of pieces from folk who had never written before was outstanding, add to this the fact that we all had dementia is really quite extraordinary. Homework tasks were set by Liz and reminders issued by the students, everyone completed these tasks willingly and enthusiastically.

As the course moved towards completion it was evident to us all that a book could result from this, and we had the funding and I had a date in mind to achieve publication by - early October - to be able to present and sell the book at the biggest Dementia conferences in Europe - Alzheimer's Europe in Glasgow in October and UK Dementia Congress in Brighton in November. Few thought this possible, but I knew it could be achieved if we rose to the challenge, and we did and it was! Of the 70 books we took to each conference only six on each occasion remained unsold!

The book was a team effort. I will refer here to the team - the most proactive members of which were the eight authors, all of whom have dementia, the five psychology students who supported us with our writing, Liz Jennings who taught us and then led the editorial process, April Doyle who advised and encouraged and was our initial contact with the publisher and this process, and Janet Baylis who was our connection with the Alzheimer's Society. Hereafter I will refer to us as 'the team.' Janet and April's roles in the project were fundamental to its success - they worked tirelessly behind the scenes and were my constant 'go to,' which I so needed. Here are their thoughts:

You can lead a good life after a diagnosis of dementia and Keith Oliver is living proof of this. He's a great role model for anyone wanting to know how to live well with a serious long-term degenerating condition. He's determined to get things done and does; able to articulate the big picture, also generous and kind, always acknowledging the contributions of others.

We first met about five years ago, when Keith got involved in the User Involvement programme at the Alzheimer's Society. I was working for the Society and wanting to get people with dementia to contribute to the review of print information including published books about dementia. Keith was fantastic in this role and later we contributed to a national project - the Reading-Well

Books on Prescription Scheme Dementia List which led to recommended books being made available in all public libraries in England.

Keith had the idea for the ground-breaking Kent Forget Me Nots writing group project for people with dementia and the book that followed, *Welcome to our World*. Partly funded by the Alzheimer's Society Innovation Fund, it was a big challenge in lots of ways: encouraging people with dementia to take up a new interest - several of the contributors hadn't written before; collaborating on the production of a book, promoting and selling it; people with dementia managing a complex project that grew in ambition as their collective confidence increased; having a plan and working to tight deadlines.

It also challenged the Alzheimer's Society's internal ways of working. It was the first time our Innovation Fund panel funded a project suggested and submitted by a person with dementia, and giving support to the project encouraged cross-departmental collaborative working with many staff involved. 1,250 copies of *Welcome to our World* were sold with the proceeds coming back to the Society, way exceeding the original grant.

For me, being involved in this project was one of the highlights of my time at the Alzheimer's Society. What was most important was demonstrating what a group of people with dementia could achieve when given the opportunity to do something new, enjoy social contact and have something to look forward to.

Of course, not everyone with dementia will be able to take part in something so innovative, but, given an opportunity, most can continue to do some of the things they've always enjoyed doing.

On diagnosis, I would encourage people with dementia and carers to stay as active as possible in what's important to their sense of self and involve family and friends whenever possible. Focus on 'can dos,' rather than things that are no longer possible, and put arrangements in place for the future before it's too late.

Several of the Forget Me Nots are among the estimated 42,000 people in the UK of working age with a diagnosis of dementia. The symptoms are similar to people who develop dementia in old age but they often have different needs and require different support services. I strongly believe that there's an urgent requirement to do more to raise public awareness about younger people with dementia, as most people still associate dementia only with someone much older.

I worked as the Manager of the Dementia Knowledge Centre at the Alzheimer's Society for 11 years. During this time, I cared for my mother who had Alzheimer's disease. Drawing on my professional and personal experience, I am an advocate for access for all to quality standard patient information together with personal stories of the lived experiences of people affected by dementia, in print and on film. Alzheimer's Society website www.alzheimers.org.uk is a good starting place for information.

Janet Baylis, retired manager of the Alzheimer's Society Knowledge Centre

I first met Keith when he was a student in my Life Writing class in 2013. He was an enthusiastic member of the class, keen to share his pieces of writing with fellow students for feedback, and always contributing to class discussions. I enjoyed his concise, unsentimental writing style, and was very pleased when he signed up for subsequent terms of life writing and creative writing classes.

Keith was always very open with the group about his Early Onset dementia, and his honesty is something which has continued to impress me, along with his drive and determination to raise awareness and spread a positive message.

In 2014 Keith invited me to join the *Welcome to our World* book project and I was honoured to be a part of it; from helping with the initial discussions over how to turn the collection of life writing pieces into a book to assisting with proof- reading, editing and getting the book ready to go to the printers. I loved being part of the team – and was very pleased when Keith contacted me again to talk about working with him on this book.

April Doyle, writer and writing tutor on the Community Arts and Education programme at Canterbury Christ Church University

Between course and book, we had regular meetings to which all members of the team were invited and which as many as possible attended. At one we were joined by a reporter from BBC Radio 4's *You and Yours,* and he taped an interview with many members of the team present which was then broadcast. Everyone was encouraged to submit between eight to 12 pieces for the book, and these pieces were chosen by the writer. Liz, who had done a splendid job with teaching and encouraging the writers, then subsequently became editor for the book. The students were at times a scribe for the writer, asked prompting questions, and assisted Liz in supporting both the learning and the writing in the group using very much a person-centered approach. Examples of this are where one student used a Dictaphone to record the stories and wrote them up herself; another visited the writer five times rather than the suggested two in order that writing could be successfully completed; another accompanied the writer on two memory walks during which the subsequent writing was discussed.

Through Jane Cotton at the Alzheimer's Society a wonderful, moving foreword was written by Jo Brand as a tribute to our team which gave everyone a real lift and so aided our attempts subsequently to sell the book.

The original plan was to publish 1,000 copies and to sell them over a period of one year, taking them to conferences and meetings, selling them to family and friends beyond the five complementary copies I secured for the writing and back up team. It became clear that demand would exceed supply and I was encouraged by the Society and our team to commission another

250 copies for sale and 250 copies for the Alzheimer's Society to use at an annual awards ceremony as a gift to all nominees.

A most enjoyable local book launch was kindly hosted by Waterstones, Rose Lane, in Canterbury on 6th November 2014, and their former manager, Claire, became a loyal supporter of the project. Apart from £2 from every book sold by Waterstones through their chain, all the money raised from the sales went to the Alzheimer's Society. Overall, the project raised close to £6,000 for this very worthy cause. All this made me immensely proud when I conveyed this information to the team.

At this point there are only a very small number of copies remaining to sell via the Alzheimer's Society online shop. Copies are available from the Kent Libraries if you live in the county, or if you have access to the library at the Alzheimer's Society Knowledge Centre they too have copies for loan. Whether I, the Alzheimer's Society or someone else is happy to arrange for more to be available only time will tell!

I now want to turn to significant others involved for their thoughts on the project; Liz Jennings, our amazing co-leader, and the fantastic student supporters to express some of their thoughts on the project: the students' thoughts are taken from *Welcome to our World* pages 15-19.

When I think back now to the life writing group, I cannot help but smile. Those were good times, thinking and writing together.

I was introduced to Keith through our mutual friend, Elizabeth Field. I had run writing groups before at Age UK, but had no clinical understanding of dementia; in retrospect this probably worked to everyone's advantage. I had no preconceived notions of 'can't,' and approached the group as any tutor would, excited to meet these unique people with their own interesting stories to tell, who appreciated the space, creative stimulation and encouragement to do so.

Life writing is really about taking some time to acknowledge the worth of each other's lives, experience and opinions. Through it, people who start out feeling they have nothing in common find they are identifying and empathising with one another – this happens so quickly with life writing, it's a wonderful thing. If you've never tried it, I'd really encourage you to find a local course and give it a go: it's so life-affirming, and definitely time well-spent.

Liz Jennings

The medical definition of dementia tells us that it is degenerative, that cognitive and social function diminishes over time. This seems in direct contradiction to our own experience.

Over the course of the sessions we saw people, some initially sceptical about their own writing skills, become increasingly confident, coming into their own sharing more of their experiences and bonding as a group... we hope that you will find the same inspiration and joy reading these pages as we did helping to put them together.

Alex Bone, Charley Massingham, Sophie Razzel, Jennie Russell, Lewis Slade, at time of writing, psychology students at University of Kent

Never, in my experience, have the diverse elements of a project come together and produced something so significant. I remain puzzled how and why this was so, however, I no longer dwell upon this, I merely reflect and remain thankful that it happened and that I was a part of it.

Creative activities with people who have dementia

Creativity is certainly not something which stops when people develop dementia, in fact, from my experience and for many others, it is quite the reverse. But what is required to allow this to happen are appropriate resources both in terms of personnel to lead and support, an engaging subject matter, an accessible location and a level of commitment from the person with dementia. When these are in the place the sky is the limit.

Welcome to our World is a good example of all these elements coming together, as was the *Cabinet of Curiosities* which I attended in the latter stages. These are both writing projects. Another project in which I was not involved as a participant, but did advise on and view afterwards, I would like to describe to you now.

In November 2015 I was asked to attend with Liz Jennings and with the support of Briony Russell (one of the year's placement students) a Southwark Dementia Action Alliance meeting on the theme of the creative arts. I shared a session with Liz on the *Welcome to our World* project, and hopefully we encouraged others to consider doing something similar. I also sat in on a really good workshop led by Veronica Franklin-Gould from Arts4Dementia which looked at drawing from all the creative arts especially music and dance.

The range of projects being covered was most impressive and I was delighted to see at least one enthusiastic commissioner there to learn more first-hand about the projects in his 'patch.'

The project, *'Sculptural Revelations,'* took place during the first half of 2016 and culminated with a display of the group's work in Canterbury's Beaney library/ museum during July 2016. It involved a group of seven older people with dementia - the age group was approximately 75-84, working with Sumita Chauhan, a sculptor and doctoral researcher at the University of Kent.

They explored a range of traditional physical and very modern digital sculpture - something that none of the group had done before, or even imagined doing. The course was, I know, both challenging and stimulating for those involved, be they the sculptors with dementia, or Sumita and her helpers.

The work they produced and displayed over a two-week period in the Beaney gallery was magnificent and inspirational. I don't think anyone could fail to be moved and impressed. When Rosemary and I saw the work and spoke with Sumita I was moved to tears and I still have a lump in my throat thinking of it now and writing this piece. The project was extremely uplifting and challenged every stereotype there is about the limitations on one's creativity which might occur for this older age group upon developing dementia. It would have been quite amazing if it was the 55-70 age group in the early stages of the condition producing these pieces, but some of the group are really quite well into what would be seen as the mid-stages of this condition. I would love this work to be more widely viewed and for longer, but I guess like most art its impact is greater if relatively short lived. Maybe.

Here is Sumita's account:

I came into contact with Keith Oliver for the first time two years ago through a common friend regarding my PhD research project which involved people with dementia. His response through email was very spontaneous and enthusiastic, and helped me overcome any diffidence I felt at that initial stage of my research. He warmly welcomed me to his house and we discussed about my art background and proposed research at the University of Kent. Coincidentally, we found that my supervisor's two sons were students in Blean Primary School when Keith was the Head Teacher.

He gave me a list of relevant books and contacts of people involved in dementia related projects which proved immensely useful and very beneficial.

His advice to contact Beaney House of Art and Knowledge and St. Martin's Hospital helped me very much to plan my study of my PhD. As an artist and researcher, my research aim is to investigate the ways in which the creative potential of people with dementia can be explored through meaningful artistic engagement and co-creation. I worked with seven participants with dementia over a period of six months which culminated in a very successful exhibition of their sculptures along with my works in the Beaney House of Art & Knowledge in July 2016. The exhibition, titled *Sculptural Revelations,* was highly appreciated by a large number of visitors, not only for the displayed sculptures but also the determination and perseverance of the participants, most of whom tried some of the techniques for the first time.

I had sent an invitation to Keith for the Private View but he was away on holiday in Cornwall. He kept his promise to see the exhibition after his return with his wife. I was delighted to see them and show each exhibit. I explained the various processes of making sculpture undertaken by my participants and how each session working with them revealed something new about them and their personality, beliefs and emotions. I realised the importance of the efforts of each participant and the significance of such projects for creative enjoyment.

Keith invigorated me with his brilliant words and praises after seeing the exhibition personally and through social media. I am deeply appreciative and aware of his exceptional contribution to people affected by dementia and their carers and his active involvement.

Keith has enthused me immensely with his compassion and valiant attitude and I wish to pursue work in my chosen field with his guidance and support.

Sumita Chauhan

I do hope that Sumita will go on to work with people affected by dementia in the future, and that others reading this will want to find out more in order to consider similar projects. What I have described is now past, and looking to the future, through the IDEAL project the Forget Me Nots have been invited to take part in a multi-faceted creative project called *A Life More Ordinary.* I think this may involve exploring in a group the potential for writing poetry and using photography and drawn cartoons to support this. I think this project will also be undertaken with some other groups around the country and will inform the IDEAL research project which is examining ways in which people can live well with dementia over a longer period.

I am on both the ALWAYS (Action on Living Well: Asking You) advisory group and the main IDEAL Project Advisory Group. IDEAL stands for 'Improving the experience of Dementia and Enhancing Active Life,' and is led by Prof Linda Clare from Exeter University. Nada Savitch and I are leading a workshop on the IDEAL project at the UK Dementia Congress in November 2016.

There is a growing body of anecdotal evidence to suggest that the creative arts have great potential to support living well with dementia and I am pleased that commissioners are helping to drive the cause for more research to provide more in-depth evidence. Creativity has learning at its centre, and as teachers from my days at Blean will vouch we were as close to a creative school as you can get. All can learn from this sort of project - the participants with dementia, the professionals and their supporters/ helpers leading and facilitating the project, the public who view and celebrate its end products and yes, the commissioners, charities, and government - both local and national who often sponsor them. We just need more!

A bibliophile: my favourite books

As a head teacher, colleague, teacher, parent and person, I've never been someone to have favourites who took precedence over others or who received preferential treatment. I have always tried to treat people equally.

Having said that, when Stephen Spielberg was interviewed on BBC Radio 4 to promote the launch of his movie, *The BFG,* I reflected upon his refusal to be drawn on a favourite film - either from his own impressive CV, or from the encyclopaedic catalogue of films he has seen over the years. I have thought about this and, whilst it was tricky, I have come up with the following lists.

Dear reader - why don't you have a go yourself and make your own list of favourites. If you are like me, you might find the list does change - especially from around numbers 6 to 12.

1.*Tuesdays with Morrie* (Mitch Albom) Life changing in the insight of the author and the main character in this true story. I am not surprised that this is currently the biggest selling biography ever! Both Jocelyne and Sophie, who read it after my recommendation, said that Morrie reminded them of me which was kind.

2. *To Kill A Mockingbird* (Harper Lee) I read this as a teenager and it inspired so much of my thinking then and still does today 45 years later. I loved the film, but preferred the richness of the writing in the book. I couldn't bring myself to read *Go Set a Watchman*, the follow-up which was published in 2015, as the first novel was so special to me.

3. *Welcome to our World* (Liz Jennings (ed), A Charles, B de Frene, Chris, Chris, Keith, M.J. Saints, Rose, Tony) I was so proud to co-lead the project which resulted in this book. All the writing was superb and Jo Brand's introduction to the book was magnificent.

4. *The Seven Habits of Highly Influential People* (Steven Covey) Inspiring - I wish I had read this when I was working. I was introduced to his work via Christian Farthing for which I'm very grateful.

5. *Kes: A Kestrel for a Knave* (Barry Hines) I read this as a student when living near the setting of the book in Sheffield and was moved by the characters and the plot. I used the scene about the tadpoles in the wellies to encourage reticent children to talk and then write - it did work! If you've seen and enjoyed the film but not read the book, you are missing a classic.

Equal 5. *The Scarlet Raider* (Joseph B Icenhower) An unknown historical novel and the first book I owned which I chose. It was a present for my ninth birthday and helped fire my interest in the American Civil War, a subject I did my History dissertation on at University and could hold my own with on Mastermind!

6. *Letters to my Grandchildren* (Tony Benn) Loved the man and his writing and wish I had written this - so much for those of us who are grandparents to take from this, irrespective of politics, which are hardly mentioned in this book.

7. *Cider with Rosie* (Laurie Lee) Beautiful writing by a lovely man. His style is one which April Doyle encouraged us to consider when writing, she chose well!

8. *Dancing with Dementia* (Christine Bryden) Reading this was a turning point for me. Before this I didn't know how to live well with dementia but after Reinhard Guss steered me towards it in 2011, I could see someone I could relate to and from whom I could learn so much in my current situation.

9. *I Believe in Miracles* (Daniel Taylor) We did believe this miracle. This is simply the best football book ever about the best team ever, am I biased?

10. *The Long Walk to Freedom* (Nelson Mandela) The first person who truly inspired me, and I would say the greatest person of the twentieth century.

11. *Deep Magic, Dragons and Talking Mice* (Alister McGrath) A wonderful insight into the life, mind and works of CS Lewis. This book opened so many different doors for me, doors which Eric Harmer helped unlock.

12. *The Lion, the Witch and the Wardrobe* (CS Lewis) I have read this book many times over the years both to myself and to children in various schools without really understanding its meaning and subtleties, much of which only now do I understand. A true classic on so many levels which helps move us all from the 'Shadowlands.'

Books so often provide me with wisdom, which, if I remember or write down, can inspire some of my thinking. An example being Albert Camus, mentioned in the Sheffield chapter. He wrote: 'Real generosity toward the future consists in giving all to what is present.' Live for the day! Over to you: happy reading.

I learned to read with the aid of comics and the sports pages of my dad's newspaper, and have loved reading ever since. Books came a bit later as my parents never ever bought them. Although my dad was a keen library user he never bought me a book and there was no more than a handful to be seen in our house.

Oh, how different to how I am, and we are as a family. I now find that I still read a lot but I remember very little which can and does at times cause much frustration, although I do try and apply my rationale to it: 'Ok, so you can't remember the content, don't beat yourself up Keith take from the book the same thing as from conversations - hang onto how it made you feel.' This does help.

I also love talking about books and have spent hours doing so with Karon and various friends - one of whom is Jocelyne - here's her thoughtful contribution which fits into here so well but also foreshadows what this book is trying to address...

Keith and I have shared our time in many different capacities as friends, teachers, book critics, co-researchers, members of the Forget Me Nots and colleagues. To me, time spent with Keith is when we are all of the above, together, chatting in a sunny spot in the garden.

I suppose I should add 'avid gardeners' to my list although discussing the pros and cons of various species, wondering together why some plants are flourishing this year whilst others are not and how the state of a lawn can vary so much between Canterbury and Whitstable is more our cup of tea during these times than the act of gardening itself.

We are both generous to each other with our time. For different reasons, neither of us have the luxury of endless spare time now or in the future. Tuesday morning is our preferred slot. Like Mitch Albom's *Tuesdays with Morrie*, when and where possible, my Tuesdays are with Keith.

I knew nothing about dementia before I visited the Forget Me Nots in November 2012, only that I thought I might one day like to work in the area. To me, people with dementia are lucid, thoughtful, passionate, humorous, capable, remarkable and…I could go on because most important of all, people with dementia are individuals.

Some people think my view has been warped by these first encounters. They have been unlucky enough to only witness the sadness and despair that dementia can also bring.

As I said, people with dementia are individuals and different dementias affect people differently at different stages. This view has been reinforced by my professional work. As a trainee clinical psychologist working in a memory assessment service, I have assessed and helped to diagnose numerous people. I am glad to say that no two have been the same – if everybody with dementia was the same then my job would be very boring.

I like stories.

By the time this book is published I will (fingers crossed) be a clinical psychologist working in Swale Community Mental Health Service for Older People. Luckily for me many of my fellow trainees are somewhat baffled as to why I want to work with old people. But then, I struggle to see what draws them to moody adolescents, mad and bad criminals and those who hear voices, for example. I am glad that we all have different interests. The world would be very dull if we were all interested in the same things. It would make it even more difficult for us psychologists to get jobs!

Who knows what my life holds, but at this point in time I feel very privileged when those who have lived long lives choose to share their wonderful, thorny, dysfunctional and fascinating stories with me.

Jocelyne Kenny, KMPT (Trainee) Clinical Psychologist

The film project, my favourite films and why

Following the success of *Welcome to our World*, Liz and I were keen to undertake another project, which would need to be similar but different. As we share an interest in films, indeed she is passionate about films, this seemed like a good way to go, so in January 2015 we began to plan a film project. This took almost nine months to fund, again from the Alzheimer's Society, and to prepare detailed plans. We needed a suitable venue, a concept and supporters to implement it, an audience beyond just the Forget Me Nots and a programme of films. The project ran in Canterbury from January to April 2016.

The venue was tricky: we tried all the local cinemas – there were positives and flaws with each - before we settled upon a local church room, which was kindly available for free. This was near the centre of Canterbury, had some parking and was near public transport. Sorted, although we did adjourn half way through to a local community centre, which had more parking.

The concept was not just to watch films, it was to watch a range of modern films with good plots and strong characters. Liz came up with 15 made in the last six years and people with dementia voted for the top six which would form the programme: sorted.

The concept then was to relax and watch the films with refreshments provided and then to discuss the issues, characters etc that the film engaged people with. We needed help to do this and Liz had three or four friends who did a very able job. I enlisted some students from the local universities who also helped out – some of whom were really excellent.

The audience was to be both sides of the same coin - ie people with a diagnosis of dementia and a supporter - usually a family member/ spouse. We regularly got 28 people attending some of whom were not in any other group or activity relating to dementia, others were proactive Forget Me Not members - all mixed in together really well.

The films were wide-ranging and all proved popular, the most popular being *Mao's Last Dancer,* an Australian film unknown to all beyond Rosemary and myself, and one which challenged all stereotypes about what you might expect people affected by dementia to engage with: it was modern, political, half in Chinese with subtitles, sections of the story in flash back. It worked because it is such a powerful story, so well told. Second favourite was *The King's Speech*, which opened the project. The weakest link was *The Monuments' Men*, which was least popular due to its multi-protagonist storyline being rather poorly constructed, we decided after discussion.

The discussion element was extremely well received and went swimmingly with Liz's leadership and direction. We had spouses together some weeks, another week it was men/ women split up to discuss, and also we had people with a diagnosis and their companions separately. All worked well in their own way and gave everyone the chance to express themselves.

By choosing good modern films, we hoped to re-engage people with the idea of going back to the cinema, and the Odeon in Canterbury helped with this by opening their cinema for a special dementia friendly showing of *Eddie the Eagle,* just for our group. They offered this for a very small token fee and this was covered by the Alzheimer's Society. Numbers of people affected by dementia going to the cinema locally did increase and now everyone is asking for this to be repeated this winter. Canterbury Christ Church University are looking to do this in the city.

Here is an account of not just this project but also Frances' links to my story:

My name is Frances James and I work at the University of Kent (UoK) in the School of Psychology as the Placements and Employability Officer. I hadn't been in the role very long when I had a phone call from Keith. I didn't recognise the name at first (after all I had only known him as Mr Oliver!) but as soon as he mentioned Swalecliffe, I instantly recognised the voice from the Year 6 classroom next door: I was in Miss Hadler's class, and if you were ever *really* naughty you had to go to Mr Oliver's class room (he was at the time our Deputy Head.) I was a pretty compliant (some might say boring) pupil and never really did anything naughty (or exciting) enough to experience this myself but there were a couple of boys who I remember regularly had to visit Mr Oliver's classroom - who knows, maybe they preferred it in there!

Mr Oliver (sorry, I mean Keith) had previously run a really successful project with our psychology students creating a wonderful book written by Keith and some fellow Forget Me Nots. On the back of this success, Keith wanted some of our students to help run his cinema project. I was really excited about the concept and purpose of this project and not only was I keen to source some students for him, I was just as keen – if not more so - to get involved with the planning of the project. I was also really pleased that I was able to attend some of the film showings and help facilitate the discussions afterwards.

This of course was *very* strange at first. I'll be honest – nothing to do with the aspect of Keith's diagnosis as Keith was exactly how I remembered him, but there is something very strange about being bought a cup of tea by someone who you haven't seen since you were 11 years old and who thinks you're a grown-up!

As part of my role at UoK, I have attended some of the Forget Me Not meetings and as I've mentioned, helped with the film viewings. I do have some experience with dementia and an academic background in psychology so I felt I was confident in getting involved. I have also always been aware of the pressure this condition can put on relationships.

I don't know where I heard it but I have always been struck with the concept that when a partner, friend or family member has dementia that they can lose the person twice. In light of this, I have been impressed by the people I have met with the diagnosis of dementia and their partners. I have been impressed by how they don't seem to be fazed by this and have the attitude of taking it as a challenge – a challenge not taken lightly and this certainly includes Keith.

The passion, energy and determination demonstrated in general, but more specifically in changing how people perceive dementia is extremely impressive. If you could harness that energy – who knows - we could faze out fossil fuels altogether!

Although I have only dipped my toe into the world of the Forget Me Nots, I feel privileged that I have been involved at all. And Keith – next time we have a planning meeting – I'll buy the tea!

Frances James, Placements and Employability Officer, University of Kent

This project was 20 meetings in the planning – most of which we held in the cosy café between Liz's home and mine, Café Solo. I'll let Liz share her reflections here.

I'd seen Keith and Rosemary often across the cinema in the Senior Screen showings at Canterbury Odeon, which I go to most weeks for an injection of creative inspiration. The only thing I don't like about the screenings is that feeling afterwards, when I've seen a film that excites me, or gets me really thinking – and then, because I go alone, I've got no one to chat it over with.

I approached Keith; as a fellow film-lover, did he think a group could work, and if so, what should it look like?

Keith embraced the question with enthusiasm and vision. One of the many brilliant things about him is his determination to work a plan through to make it an actual reality: I can be a bit of a dreamer, so I really appreciate this! Our meetings at Café Solo with Keith, Rosemary, Frances and I working through the plans over a cup of tea, being chivvied along by Keith's lists (which always kept us on track) were really enjoyable times together.

Katy Hirst, of Bright Shadow, joined us for a session, and told me recently that what was refreshing about our approach was the way the discussion groups afterwards had nothing to do with reminiscing (we never asked, 'Do you remember King George?' for example) but were all about what individuals thought *today*, how they responded and engaged with a film's themes and characters *right now*.

The last film we saw was *Eddie the Eagle*. This week's session was entirely organised by Keith, who really had to push hard on some doors. He could have given up, but he refused to do so. The result was a wonderful final week altogether, with the perfect film to close the project. The message that runs through *Eddie the Eagle* can be summed up in one of Eddie's lines of dialogue, 'I love proving people wrong;' it's something Keith, and many other people I have met with a diagnosis of dementia, do every day.

Liz Jennings

Now to my top ten films...

1. **The Way** - starring Martin Sheen: Inspiring.

2. **Inside Llewyn Davis** - starring Carey Mulligan – I love the period and music set in the New York folk scene in 1961.

3. **Zulu** - starring Michael Caine. All boys of my generation watched and loved this movie.

4. **Midnight Cowboy** - starring Dustin Hoffman and Jon Voight. Hoffman at his best, a real classic - great acting and a very moving and engaging story. Put Hoffman on a pedestal as my favourite actor back in 1969 and he's stayed there since. First time I can remember crying at the end of a film.

5. **The Graduate** - starring Dustin Hoffman. A classic both by way of acting, story and musical soundtrack. Rarely do all three come together so well.

6. The King's Speech - starring Colin Firth, Geoffrey Rush and Helena Bonham Carter. How Firth and Rush didn't get an Oscar for their acting in this I will never know. We used this to start our Dementia Friendly Film Club project and it went down brilliantly. Cried again - well over thirty years since the last time I cried over a film.

7. Shenandoah - starring James Stewart. An American Civil War film with a difference, this time not glorifying war but portraying the human side. Also a childhood visit to the cinema with both my parents, quite a regular event for us in the 1960s.

8. Mao's Last Dancer - starring Chi Cao. Based upon Li Cunxin's memoir, which topped the best-selling charts in Australia. This challenged all preconceptions about the ability of people with dementia to engage with film when we used it so successfully in the Dementia Friendly Film Club project: an unknown film, subtitles with 40% dialogue in Chinese and use of flashback. It was voted the best film by most attendees. Rosemary's favourite film.

9. Billy Elliot - starring Jamie Bell. I loved the film so much and saw myself in Billy. Not the dancing, but the background and personality of us both as kids.

10. Swimming Upstream - Geoffrey Rush. Little known classic Aussie movie about challenges experienced in a relationship between a very strong father and his two very different sons, each trying to live up to their father's expectations, dreams and ambitions in competing in the swimming pool.

Equal 10. The Alamo - starring John Wayne. This along with Ben Hur were the first films I remember seeing at the cinema with my mother. I was five at the time - no Disney movies for us then!

I hope there are movies here you can relate to and perhaps some are favourites of yours. Also, maybe this will encourage you to check out some movies you haven't seen for a long time or maybe not seen at all before.

Favourites in the world of music

As John Miles sang, 'Music is my first love, and music is my last, music of the future and music of the past.' I used those words to open my talk at the 2016 Alzheimer's Show at Olympia in London. It is so true. Music is vitally important to enjoying a good quality of life.

In my case it is only though listening these days, as I no longer play the guitar (a pity) - or sing - a relief for others! It is seldom that when out walking or working in my office that there is no music filling my ears and lifting my spirits. As I write this I am listening to the excellent young band Rend Collective who were recommended to me by Eric and Jennie.

I think my taste is very wide and eclectic, and when looking to draw up a list of favourite albums and artistes I was reminded of this. As someone who was brought up listening to the Top Thirty on the radio with Alan Freeman in the 1960s/70s on a Sunday teatime the idea of ranking music is not alien to me. I did though find it very hard - how about you? Have a go!

My top ten albums which are the most frequently played when I am 'walking the walk:'
1. *Graceland* - Paul Simon
2. *Dark Side of the Moon* - Pink Floyd
3. *Babel* - Mumford and Sons
4. *Tangled up in Blue* - Bob Dylan
5. *Bridge Over Troubled Water* - Simon & Garfunkel
6. *Bookends* - Simon & Garfunkel
7. *After the Goldrush* - Neil Young
8. *Freewheelin'* - Bob Dylan and equal 8th *Rumours* - Fleetwood Mac
9. *Sergeant Pepper* - The Beatles
10. *Inner Visions* - Stevie Wonder and equal 10th *American Pie* - Don McLean

There are at least another ten I could so easily have included and if asked next week they might have been listened to more, or have inspired a memory which would promote them into this list.

My top ten musicians (I tend to go for the thoughtful singer - songwriter genre) How about you?
1. Paul Simon and equal 1st Simon & Garfunkel
2. Pink Floyd
3. The Beatles
4. Eric Bogle
5. John Williamson
6. Mumford & Sons
7. Supertramp
8. Neil Young and equal 8th Crosby, Stills, Nash & Young
9. Leonard Cohen and equal 9th Bob Dylan
10. Jennie Russell and equal 10th Sara Storer

I expect most of these might be on many people's lists but there could be a few you are not aware of - why not give them a try on iTunes or similar?

Often I use the music of Eric Bogle (along with his long-time collaborator John Munro) as part of my talks, especially *While I am Here.* In writing this book I wrote to Eric and John, both of whom live in Adelaide, and this is part of their response.

Dear Keith

I'm sorry about your early onset of Alzheimer's Disease, but admire your response to what must have been a pretty unpleasant shock when you received the diagnosis. Support and activism on behalf of those who have the disease, and advocacy to help inform those who do not, is a most positive and laudable response.

I'm pleased that my music has been of some support to you; music has supported me through some tough times in my life. I would point out though that *While I Am Here* was not written by me, although I sing it on the CD, it was written by my long time musical collaborator John Munro. However, knowing John, I would state without any hesitation that he would be delighted if you used the song in any capacity in your future talks.

Best wishes,

Eric

Hi Keith,

Sad to hear about your diagnosis but uplifted by the strength you are bringing to the next phase of your journey. Eric knows me well and is right to say you can use the song in any way that promotes your message.

My very best wishes,

John

You will find the amazing words for this song in a talk I gave which begins on page 315 - and I think you will see why they mean so much to me - maybe they mean something to you as well. I encourage you to download the song (and others of Eric's.)

Closing words

I suspect the two hardest parts of writing a book are the beginning and the end, and I guess I have opted out of this by using Richard Madeley and friends to open the book with me, and it falls to Karon, my daughter to close it alongside me.

I'm lucky. I have two fathers: my Dad who brought me into the world but sadly died when I was a little girl of seven, the other, Keith who has been my stepfather since he married my mum when I was 11. I use the phrase stepfather very lightly as the correct definition of the word is 'the man who is married to someone's mother but who is not their real father.'

Keith is most definitely a real father.

At the age of 33, Keith scooped up his family and took us to live on the other side of the world; an experience which has instilled in me a love of travelling and a great desire to see how others live. Experiencing new foods, being immersed in different customs, having my mind opened by others' religions and making memories with a diverse range of people all stemmed from that first trip when we all set off with a sense of excitement and trepidation.

That feeling of exhilaration as I set off into the unknown has never left me and I look back at some of my experiences with enormous pride and affection; traipsing along the Inca Trail in Peru, circling the summit of Mount Everest in a tiny plane, gazing with awe and wonder as I wandered along the Great Wall of China, swimming with sea lions in the Galapagos Islands and living amongst the clouds in Hong Kong are just some of my fondest memories.

Another huge love of mine is reading; something that Keith and I regularly discuss. Our tastes in literature may be different, but the emotion that runs through the experience I feel is the same for both of us. I read for pleasure. I read so that

I can share with those who have read the same thing. I read so that I can share with those who have had the same emotions and experiences. And to quote one of Keith's favourite authors, C.S. Lewis, 'I read to know I am not alone.'

So for me, the open road and an open book are two of life's greatest pleasures. Our journey now as a family will be a different one, but as Keith navigates his way through the challenges of dementia his enquiring mind and desire to do good for others does indeed mean that he 'walks the walk and talks the talk' with an honourable, positive outlook.

Karon Branch, (nee Oliver)

Well, dear reader and friend, after a bright, clear day, part of which I have spent sitting on our patio with the doors open wide, and the late summer golden sun shining brightly casting lengthening shadows, I am like a cat seeking the small patch of warm afternoon sunshine amidst the flowers which share the space with me. I look over to the river, which meanders gently past our garden with a sole occupant, a swan, gracefully gliding downstream.

I think I'll call it a day for today, and go for a walk.

Coming?

Part Two:

Talk the Talk

My talks about me: the person living with dementia

Whilst writing *Welcome to our World* I was co-leading a fourteen-person team. This is my first solo book, and for a number of reasons, largely related to my dementia, this will also probably be my last.

I say 'my book' but again I am sharing this effort with friends, this time around there are 72 of you who have 'walked' with me. Many of these good people have heard at least one of these talks, some returning for seconds or more; some have not heard any of them as they knew me better from 'my former life.' I nearly said 'former self' but that would be very wrong, because as Paul Simon wrote in an additional verse to *The Boxer*, one of my favourite songs - 'after changes upon changes, we are more or less the same.' So true and many associated with dementia would do well to please note this.

I hope as you read from the very first 'talk' delivered to one person, a researcher from Dementia UK - in my lounge - to the most recent one, coincidentally again for Dementia UK but this time in a conference hall to an audience of over 150 professional staff, that you will get a sense of how I am attempting to live well, and hoping to encourage others that it is entirely possible to do so, with dementia.

Being able to stand up in front of an audience comes, I suspect, from a career in teaching. I do see it as a part of my 'comfort zone.' That isn't to say it is easy, because it is not, and whilst I do not tend to get nervous I am always very keen to ensure that the talk is meeting the needs of the event and the audience. As you see from the range of talks here since I began this part of my life back in 2011, they are all different but with some key threads which are common to all.

I was keen from the start not to be seen almost like a living medical exhibit, wheeled in to demonstrate something vaguely connected to dementia. All my talks have something about me as a person - marriage, family, interests, professional background and so on. Then something around what, for me, living well with dementia entails and conversely some of the challenges dementia presents to me most days. I try to illustrate what living with the condition is really like and the impact it has on me.

From that the teacher then takes over and I often see my role as advising, encouraging and sometimes challenging the audience to address issues which need their attention. I am always honest and sincere, and have occasionally upset people because of discomfort they may feel about a message I convey. I make no apology for the message but do regret their upset.

When asked to deliver a talk I always initially ask myself these questions:

- can I make the date and location?
- what is the event about and what will be my role within it?
- what are the potential impacts upon myself and Rosemary by me participating?
- what are the potential positive impacts upon the piece of work of me participating?

If I/we see all these as positive then I say yes, if not then I am not their man.

In compiling this section of the book I wanted to avoid lots of repetition, so I have very slightly edited the talks and hopefully this will help the reader retain a sense of the event and the message I was seeking to convey.

Writing the talks has become harder. Not so much thinking of the ideas and what I wish to say, but the physicality of typing them up now takes me ages. Placement students have helped occasionally in the past and I am considering the use of computer software like Dragon, but haven't yet mastered it. Typing each talk from scratch with a little copy and pasting from previous efforts (about 25%) allows me to meet the needs of the unique audience, avoids me getting complacent or bored and stimulates my thinking around messages I wish to convey about how I am at that time.

Whilst writing is much harder, if anything, delivery of written pieces is a bit easier. My confidence is greater and sometimes now I am able to deviate from my script and enhance the talk, and even cut it short if I overrun, though that is much harder to do. On really very 'sunny days' the hardest aspect of the event is which shirt to wear for the day, although also getting to and from the venue can be hard, and I do need assistance with this along with increasing assistance with pre-event communication, which has varied from excellent to poor with everything in between. That adds to the relaxed or tense person presenting.

I know some people get very upset about others taking and using catchphrases or statements. This doesn't really worry me as plagiarism of this sort is a compliment, and I feel the more of us saying similar or the same messages then the more likely those in authority will listen and do something about the situation. Also for those new to presenting using statements of others which they can identify with can be a support to allow them to build their own confidence. I guess the ideal is where statements are acknowledged, as I do for example with my dear friend the late Peter Ashley who referred in talks to himself and his dear wife being the two sides of the same coin - his original thoughts shared and spoken by us both.

Whilst in essence I am still the same person I was six years ago, I have changed and this I feel is reflected in some of my talks. At first, once I had come to terms with what dementia was doing to me, and had developed through some very good support and some self-developed strategies, I did feel as though I was 'bullet proof.' I was wrong: no one is. My vulnerabilities became obvious to me, and this was covered in some of my talks.

Writing my talks - and this book - is an enormous challenge for me. Some days when the 'fog' descends I manage perhaps only a few words, often riddled with spelling and typing errors. Other 'sunnier' days are a little easier.

When I used to deliver talks as a head, adviser or a teacher I would do so with some key words or points on a card and then ad lib and speak around these; this is not possible for me now that I have dementia. All my talks are scripted and the font has increased from 12 to 16, I've said that when I need to go beyond font 20 I'll call it a day. The larger font helps me keep track of where I am as I do lose my place and concentration at times.

I did once try the technique shown in the *Still Alice* movie of highlighting the text in yellow with a felt pen as I read it but I found this too distracting and it confused me more than helped. It is only when I feel really well that I am able to digress and expand upon the content, sometimes this is a positive and useful ideas and points enter my mind, at other times I can go off at a tangent. Drawing another parallel with the BFG, he sums this up when acknowledging his problem with language, 'Words...is such a twitch-tickling problem to me...they is always getting squiff-squiddled around.' I couldn't express it better!

Putting this section together, I was amazed to see that since the first talk I have written and delivered 76 talks. This has grown over the years - five in 2011, 12 in 2012, 14 in 2013, 16 in 2014, 17 in 2015, 12 (and still more to come!) in 2016.

I do hope that you enjoy reading these carefully selected talks, and that they give you a sense of the range of forums and occasions where someone like me has been asked to speak and then the messages I have sought to share with the wide ranges of audiences. Maybe these talks will do for you what the audiences often assured me they did for them - to challenge, to make you think, to encourage and hopefully to inspire. If that is the case then I can carry on and whilst this is probably my last book, there are still more talks to plan, write and deliver for hopefully a few more years yet.

Very first talk! Looking back and looking forward with Alzheimer's Disease (AD) delivered to researcher (one person!) from Dementia UK - April 2011

Context: I had recently been diagnosed and brought to the attention of Dementia UK, and they wanted a person to express their thoughts about the diagnosis process and looking forward beyond this. My views were recorded by a researcher in an interview at my home.

Services used so far (all positive)

- Neurologist – gave initial diagnosis, blood tests, EEG scan
- GP – supportive – referrals for MRI
- Dementia clinic at St Martin's Hospital – tests, PET scan and invaluable support both in person and via email
- Admiral Nurse - Home visit and follow-up phone calls – we're so fortunate to have this/ her
- Alzheimer's Australia/ Flinders Centre for Aging Studies at Flinders University, Adelaide, South Australia – I attended a very good talk in Adelaide on Alzheimer's and the Association publish very good booklets, case studies, advice
- Attended an excellent course (two sessions) organised by staff from the dementia clinic at St Martins and the Admiral nurse for young sufferers of AD and their partners
- Some telephone support from Dementia UK (tends to be more for the carer) in London linked to me helping them with a research project they are undertaking nationally
- Doctors at Occupational Health at KCC supported me initially to stay in work and then to secure ill-health retirement when working was no longer possible. Senior Colleagues who were aware of my illness proved crucial in supporting me both initially and as the illness has developed

- A recently established support group in the Canterbury/ Whitstable area for Early Onset folk (many of whom are mid/ late 50s). This is co-ordinated by EKIDs (East Kent Independent Dementia Support)
- School – SLT were excellent

Services used so far (less useful)

- Alzheimer's Society – nothing personal available locally and 'Talking Point,' their website blog, was really quite depressing (their publications though are quite good). I have also attended their support group at Ashford, which was sold to me as an early onset group, which is true but all other members are around 65 and the group served to get carers and service users out of their house to chat together
- Not sure that the antidepressant medication prescribed by the Consultant at St Martin's is doing anything as I have not been depressed and have seen few changes in my symptoms (never took it)

What additional services would help me and others with AD in the future?

- Point 1 - Suffering from AD can be very isolating and I would hope that the course/ group organised by the dementia clinic could be maintained. Membership of this group should be dynamic as newly diagnosed people will be able to join and gain support quite quickly – delays and waiting add to people's stress and make symptoms worse for many
- Point 2 - Linked to this, provision of specialist therapies for both sufferers and carers – e.g. help with concentration/ memory activities, coffee mornings/ talks, respite breaks/ visits
- Point 3 - There is also, amongst myself and some local young sufferers and carers a desire to try and DO something within their varying capabilities in order to try and contribute. Some guidance and support from the Health Authority would help here

How could additional services be delivered?

- Point 1 above - It needs professional facilitation as many attendees have difficulty with communication skills and whilst members actively participate no member has the skills to ensure the group could function effectively
- Point 2 above - I base this on early less expensive intervention paying dividends in delaying the need for more expensive interventions later. Ideally this should be at a venue away from the hospital – e.g. a church hall in Whitstable - and would be coordinated and led by staff from the clinic
- Points 1 and 2 - Age UK runs many events for older sufferers but there is very little/ nothing for younger sufferers and a relatively small investment by the Health Authority would help delay some more severe symptoms
- Point 3 - In the case of fundraising and raising public awareness, some guidance and suggestions from the Health Trust would help direct any enthusiasm from sufferers and carers

Main symptoms I have experienced

- Significant deterioration in short term memory
- Significant problems with concentration – these symptoms describe drastic changes - I can only focus on one thing at a time, am easily distracted; processing information is difficult, I cannot absorb messages and signals unless clearly spelled out, all this is very frustrating as it is a complete change from previously
- Drastic reduction in energy levels
- Struggling to communicate at times – from being a strength this, over the past year, is now an area of significant concern to me and my wife
- Balance difficulties/ unexplained falling over

- Reduction in problem solving ability and previous problems viewed have become much larger
- At times I get disorientated especially in new settings
- Spatial awareness has never been great but has further deteriorated since my illness where now I am often banging myself or things I am holding
- I have become a creature of habit relying more on set routines
- Forward planning is very difficult and conversations such as we must have... if not done immediately, I am unable to do it. Breaking tasks into do-able chunks is difficult
- Experienced pains at the front of my head
- On more difficult days the colour drains from my face

Diagnosis came from

- Explaining symptoms to my GP, neurologists, clinical psychologists and consultant
- MRI scan – this showed problems at the front of my brain
- EEG scan – this showed that I wasn't suffering from epilepsy
- PET scan – this helped the consultant with the diagnosis
- Negative blood tests undertaken to try and find a cause other than AD
- Series of in depth memory and executive function tests which, whilst exhausting, were administered very thoughtfully and clearly confirmed areas where I am struggling (memory and processing information) and other areas where I am coping better (number/ spatial tests)

How I currently cope with the illness, how I feel and how I live with the illness

- I am fortunate in that I have always maintained a positive approach since being diagnosed
- I achieve this by keeping active mentally and physically. I read quite a lot, enjoy a range of long-standing hobbies – gardening, stamp

collecting, word puzzles, walking, travel – in the UK and in Australia. I have also recently developed an interest in completing jigsaw puzzles and tracing my family history

- I am keen to find out more about early onset of AD and to help raise public awareness about the disease, because I have encountered much ignorance and misunderstanding

- I not only keep a kitchen calendar and a diary I also keep a desk pad where I note and cross off jobs for each day – I do this on a weekly basis setting it out on a Friday for the week ahead

- I attend BodyWell in Canterbury which has helped through spinal adjustments, deep tissue massage and spinal/ balance exercises which help my balance, posture and supply of blood to the brain

- I have always wanted to know about the disease so I read both medical and personal accounts in books and through the associations online. I would hope that I can contribute to this from my own personal experience through my contacts in the local press, through the EKHA and through Dementia UK (registered with uniting carers and participating in a research project with Pfizers through Dementia UK)

- I have lost some immediacy in conversations, missing things people say to me, and I often have to pre-rehearse what I am going to say, subsequently it's often difficult following others' trail of discussion

- Symptoms were/ are often difficult to remember, especially the amount of time they last - so when the diagnosis was being investigated I kept a 'Health Log' with brief comments on how I was on that day which was helpful

- I enjoy watching films, but experience difficulty remembering plots and even what films I have seen so I have for the past seven months kept a log in which I complete key points from the film immediately after watching it

- My love of music is quite eclectic and I have developed a stronger attachment to music which 'touches my soul'

Fears and hopes for the future

- Whilst I certainly have a very positive attitude to my Alzheimer's at present I know there will be times when this will be challenged, sometimes quite severely. My key concern is to be able to live each day as it comes with my wife, supported by family and professional/ charity services thus enabling us to also plan some fun and enjoyable projects for the near future

- My wife and I have always had a very solid marriage and I now rely so much upon her; whilst this is a major concern it has resulted in us being even closer than previously

- I am about to begin medication which will target the Alzheimer's (Reminyl) whilst also treating symptoms of cardio-vascular disease (as there is a slight chance this could be the cause)

- I draw daily upon the skills and attitudes developed over many years as a teacher and as a headmaster. I sometimes see this as a reservoir from which I draw and realise that the reservoir sometimes needs re-filling – will I always be able to do so?

- I hope that the balance of self-help and support from the Health Authority and Dementia UK/ Admiral nurses will be dynamic. Currently my wife and I feel we can contribute as much as we draw out, we realise that AD is progressive and this will not always be the case and we hope that the crucial level of support we need will be there

- I hope that the current Government continues with the many positive proposals outlined in the previous Government's strategy 'Living Well with Dementia'

- The current 'interim' medication I am on will need to move to Alzheimer's medication and I'm reassured that this will be available and will hopefully work. One hopes that new medication to arrest the further onset of the disease will arrive in the near future

- We do hope that a support group for sufferers and carers can be established which is facilitated by a psychologist from the dementia clinic and the Admiral nurse – perhaps meeting monthly, away from St Martin's Hospital would probably allow people to relax more. Each session would have times when carers and sufferers would discuss things together and other times when the two groups discussed issues separately/ simultaneously

- Finances do concern me having ended my career as the sole main earner on a high salary and starting my retirement on just over a third of this level. Managing finances even with Power of Attorney which we are setting up is a concern because it's another example of me losing control

- I love reading for pleasure; reading for information has become difficult and whilst sometimes I lose my place when reading, or can't remember what I've read I have developed strategies to resolve this – ensure I'm reading something I am really enjoying and re-read sections. I would be very disappointed if I lost this ability to enjoy reading. I have tried audio but I couldn't absorb the text

- Having Alzheimer's is at times stressful and I no longer thrive as I used to on dealing with stress; my older friends with Alzheimer's don't realise they have Alzheimer's thinking it's just getting old – is that what the future holds...?

Conclusion

If, twelve months ago, someone had asked me what thoughts came to mind when dementia or Alzheimer's were mentioned I would have described an elderly person who was either being cared for in their own home by a devoted family member or in a residential or nursing home.

Since then I have experienced first-hand how misinformed this view is. I certainly was not really aware that it could affect younger people in their 50s (or younger) who are still striving to forge successful careers with much of their life still to live. I realise that currently I may be as well as I am going to be; consequently I am determined to focus my strong will and stubborn nature towards contributing to the raising of public awareness, and in turn to help dispel some of the myths and misconceptions around this disease.

Even illnesses such as Alzheimer's give rise to humour. Recently we were travelling to France by ferry for the weekend and the weather forecast for the crossing was to expect rough seas. I told my wife this, to which she replied 'I wish you hadn't told me that.' 'It's ok for me,' I replied, 'I shan't remember it in the morning!'

The best way to describe living with my illness to those who ask is to use the analogy of the weather, where some days the fog descends and nothing is clear and things are confused, on other days the cloud sometimes blocks out the sun causing me to think more carefully about what I am able to do, and fortunately for me in my world the climate is kind and for most days the sun shines and life is good.

Presentation to a Young Onset group with Elizabeth Field at Folkestone. Wednesday 11th July 2012

Context: one of three similar talks delivered with Elizabeth over the course of a year to groups of people recently diagnosed through a Memory Clinic in East Kent. The main aim was to show them that there is still life after diagnosis. Now this type of talk is delivered by others within the Forget Me Nots.

Introduction

Firstly, thank you to Elizabeth Field for inviting me along to speak with you this morning. I do feel privileged to be asked to share some thoughts and ideas I have developed since being diagnosed with Young Onset dementia 18 months ago. Whilst seldom a day passes that I don't consider the impact of the Alzheimer's Disease that I live with, I have always been determined to try my best to live as well and as positively as possible with whatever challenges the disease presents.

My teaching career concluded on April 1st 2011 when I took early retirement from a job that I loved as head teacher at Blean Primary School where I'd been in post for 11 years. I say this because initially when I was displaying symptoms at work and away from work I used the skills and experience I'd developed in my job to cope, and to screen from people the fact that I realised something was wrong. It is very possible to use positive thinking not just to cope but to continue to live life to the full. The doctors and professionals do give us some great support and advice but this talk is from someone who is really dealing with the issues and concerns which are perhaps worrying you – I have been there as well.

Coping strategies

- I do live each day as it comes, and whilst I do make some plans for the future I find it works best for me to live in the present and enjoy the moment. Whilst one door may close with the disease and diagnosis another can, and often does, open

- Keeping active physically and mentally. I read a lot both for recreation and for information, at times re-reading what doesn't go in. This did bother me at one time, now I am a bit more relaxed about this, as I try and remember the main details and the gist of something rather than details I'd previously have absorbed without much problem. I use highlighter pens and when I remember and really want to try and recall what I've read I'll talk to my wife about what I've read or record a message for myself on my mobile phone. I do read books about Young Onset in order to know what is happening to me and to better understand the disease, not perhaps for everyone but it does help me, however I only read for recreation after 7pm as serious reading was disturbing my sleep. (Show Christine Bryden book and explain why it is really positive and helpful.)

- It's important to keep up existing hobbies and ideally to start new ones or re-visit those one used to enjoy. In my case some of these re-visited hobbies hark back to childhood, e.g. I've become a bit of an eBayer/ collectors' fair attendee, searching for bubble gum cards and other 60s memorabilia. Often the press report research projects which endorse the view that doing puzzles can help slow down the progress of dementia. I do puzzles but tend to get a bit frustrated when they don't go right, but I find that leaving it and coming back to it later helps considerably.

- In-depth conversations whilst at times difficult and slow do, I feel, help to stimulate my brain and in turn raise my self-esteem by showing me that I can still engage in useful dialogue.

- Diet can help with both feeling good mentally and physically and there is some evidence to suggest that foods such as blueberries ('brainberries'), walnuts, green tea, dark chocolate, a glass of red wine, mackerel, water, avocado and spinach plus others rich in antioxidants help not only to stave off dementia but also to restore and maintain some brain function.

- Since not working, my wife and I have joined the University of the Third Age – basically a club for those who are retired and wish to choose from a range of activities and then engage in those one feels will be fun. Sometimes my wife and I attend things together and occasionally if I can get there easily we go to different things. I do commend this to you. I find the need to retain one's own self-worth and dignity important and, as I so miss the children and colleagues from school, I try and compensate for this by helping in a local primary school hearing children read one morning a week which I really enjoy, and which gives me an excuse to wear a tie and retain an element of professionalism. Listening to music is a good therapy for me and I try and enjoy a wide range of tastes. One day I am determined to pick up my guitar again but I'm concerned that I won't be able to play anywhere near as well as I used to (which even on a good day was ordinary at best!)

- Combining keeping physically and mentally active is my love of **travel** and this has been an excellent therapy. Over the past year we have been on three or four holidays, sometimes to familiar places which does give me a bit more independence but my wife and I have also travelled to some new places together which, with some extra preparation on my part, has been a positive adventure. It is important though to pace oneself during the trip and do some extra planning beforehand.

- With regards to staying **physically active** – because I don't drive, I do walk quite a bit and have made good use of my free bus pass which as someone with YOD one is entitled to. I do exercises most days to try and improve my balance and mobility, and as I need to record in order to remember, I write this down in an exercise book – this is also interesting to look back upon as I am quite competitive.

- Speaking of exercise books I enjoy films but couldn't remember what I'd seen or any details of the film, so to help with this I keep a little exercise book which notes the title and a very brief summary I write after watching the film. In the early days I kept a health diary where I again briefly recorded details of how I was feeling and any symptoms of the illness and medications. I enjoy gardening and have since being retired taken more time not only to labour in the garden but time taken to enjoy more the fruits of this labour; I use the phrase taking time to smell the roses, which I do every day when they are in bloom. I have tried cycling again but find this difficult because of balance and spatial awareness difficulties. I also pay for a weekly deep tissue massage and spinal adjustments which do help alongside the exercises.

- I am determined to use time available to **enjoy life with my family** and live life positively but also to raise public/ medical understanding of YOD through the media, conferences, lectures, talks, interviews etc with professionals and with other folk who, like you, are in a similar position to me.

- **Family support is crucial**, but one needs to be mindful of the stress and strain that living with someone who has YOD can place on others. Spending more quality time with my wife is so important and is something I'm more able to do now that I've retired. **Friends** also sometimes find relating to someone with YOD difficult. They may not know what to say, or are embarrassed about discussing the subject of your illness. I try to be as matter of fact and open as possible and this usually helps. I tell them that I am still me, and they are to try and treat me as a person and not a set of symptoms. Usually areas I find difficult become apparent or I explain them and then we continue to enjoy each other's company. Folk often have the same incorrect stereotypical image of dementia as the domain of the over 75s that I had 18 months ago and it can be uncomfortable for them to have this challenged.

- For me I do feel that my **medication of Galantamine** does help with the coping strategies.

- Trying to be **ultra-well-organised** – e.g. daily note pad, thorough preparation before making a decision/ trip/ activity, diary, pens on elastic, ablutions – **elaborate on how I do this and show my note pad**

and pens – 2 for £1 from Poundsavers. I know others use a wipe dry white board perhaps in the kitchen to help them with organisation.

- I have trialled a **tracker phone** which has great potential in order to allow us to retain our independence for as long as possible.
- I think it is crucial to retain networks and contact with other people going through a similar experience with regards to YOD, so support groups like **EKIDs** for service users and their carers, and possibly the Alzheimer's Society, are an essential component in dealing with the disease and realising you're not on your own – (hand out the EKIDs leaflets and explain)
- Be wary of some **internet websites** and books which can paint a bleaker picture than necessary.
- I think that it is so important to put one's house in order legally. Establishing **Lasting Power of Attorney** is essential, as is I feel updating any will one may have. Once these are done they give enormous peace of mind. We did our own LPA, and used Dominic McCully as our solicitor for our wills who was excellent and was introduced to us through a similar group to this one and the EKIDs group. (Give them Dominic's details)
- There are a number of **benefits** that one can try and access with a diagnosis of dementia – Disability Living Allowance (help from Age UK)/ council tax reduction, bus pass, half price membership of English Heritage/ National Trust, reduced ticket price at the theatre and cinema.
- Retaining a **sense of humour** helps in a variety of situations.
- Having said all of that one of the most important and sometimes difficult things to do is to take **rest periods** during the day when required. This is essential. I remember when going through my assessment my wife asked Elizabeth Field and her colleague why I was now getting so tired during the day, to be told that the brain is a hungry

organ and I think this is a good way to think of this. It's also like a reservoir that we keep drawing from and we then need to refill the reservoir to stop it running dry.

Conclusion

Finally, because I do know from my own experience what it is you are going through, I sincerely hope that you can take heart and strength from my story and thoughts. It may be that you share my frustrations around the need to raise the public understanding of Young Onset in order to show that dementia is not only the domain of the elderly and to try and attract additional resources from both local and national government (mention Iceland charity support for a second year) Everyone is different, and you will all deal with dementia in a range of ways, I just hope that from what I've said this morning there is cause for positive thinking and some strategies that may help you.

The best way I feel to describe to folk who ask what it is like to have dementia, is to tell them it is like the weather; some days are foggy and are a real challenge, others are cloudy and have bright/ dull spells, and then I love the sunshine, and I have to say most days in my world do have at least some sunshine.

Talk delivered to Occupational Therapy undergraduates at Canterbury Christ Church University, Friday 16th September 2016 (and previously as listed below)

Context: this talk is based upon one which has evolved into an annual event - previous versions, which are similar, were presented in Oct 2012, Sept 2013, Sept 2014 and Sept 2015 and forms a part of the OT degree for third year students in showing them service user involvement.

- Play *Won't Give In* by Sara Storer and explain why I chose this.
- Thank you to Pat for inviting me to speak to you today. I hope that you find it interesting, informative and thought provoking. When preparing my talk earlier this week my mind wandered to my later professional days before my encounter with Dr Alzheimer. I was sensing that I'd have to think of what I'd do after retiring. I was going well with an MA at Christ Church and had some thoughts of perhaps a little lecturing in primary education. Never did I think I'd be here talking about myself and the subject of dementia.
- As an opening task I'd like you to do something which Briony - who supported me on placement last year – has also done. Please write down one sentence about you from your past, one about you at present and one about hopes/ intentions for your future. I will refer back to this at the end of my talk. ME intro: Who I was.... Who I am.... Who I want to be...or will be...

Reasons for wanting to be involved with the OT course

- Realise the importance of the next generation of professionals having exposure to the thoughts/ experiences of service users.
- My teaching background and a desire to continue to want to work in areas which may have a useful impact - any of these skills which I still have – use it or lose it.
- I think it's important for OTs to know the person they are supporting as a person in order to help them with daily living skills. Person-centred care/ support - from service user perspective and from yours as a professional.
- Please help the person with dementia engage in activities that are meaningful to them – e.g. life story work, music, interests etc.
- Importance of talking to the person and not the symptoms.

- Be wary of talking to the carer only and also of talking with the carer in front of the person with dementia – they may well be taking in and affected more by what is being said than one might realise. Be wary of being patronising through being over-sympathetic and falling for the trap of trying to equate one's own memory flaws with those of the person with dementia.
- I hope that OTs are aware of the range of assistive technology available to support people with dementia, and are skilled in teaching these clients how to use them in order to retain their independence.
- Independence is important but so, too, is inter-dependence (explain more about this later).
- Teaching and reinforcing strategies to retain both independence and integrity are important – sometimes the service user will come up with ideas which you can help them reinforce and/ or develop further with your professional suggestions – use e.g. of my morning ablutions, e.g. shaving, teeth cleaning etc.

How do I attempt to challenge stereotypes?

I guess this is one of the reasons I'm talking to you today.

- By educating people in order to challenge widely held stereotypes, such as the idea that dementia solely affects the elderly, that it is a natural result of ageing, and that those with a diagnosis are at the end of their useful life and are unable to contribute to society. I do this by being myself and talking to individuals, groups or large audiences who are willing to listen – especially about living positively through a series of coping strategies.
- By positive example to both professionals who work with people who have dementia and those who are not involved – thus raising the other person's expectations of the people with dementia.

- By influence – e.g. through having a voice on Government initiatives e.g. PM's Dementia Strategy, through being a member of the Dementia Action Alliance and through being a part of a small review group set up by the Alzheimer's Society to place service users at the centre of their operations, policies and processes. Interviews - eg Medical Research Council - Dementia Research Institute. On committee of VALID project - OT (more later).
- Through working with the media – e.g. newspaper articles which portray a human story.
- Use of piece of music - *While I am Here* by Eric Bogle, then explain why chose this.

Describe early and subsequent symptoms

- Series of unexplained falls, feeling wobbly.
- Fatigue and problems with concentration both at work and at home.
- Wife also reported me being drained of colour and reported subtle changes in behaviour.
- Decline in concept of time/ date/ deadlines and inability to respond in person or on the phone.
- **Then** – marked decline in ability to multi task, difficulty to problem-solve and plan ahead, retaining and retrieving information – visual and auditory, decline in word retrieval/ conversation – becoming more inclined to use monologue rather than dialogue, orientation, decline in short-term memory, spatial difficulties especially in crowds and near traffic.
- **All** of this in context of previously being a high functioning individual/ professional which made the symptoms harder to bear and diagnose, but also gave me the platform and positive attitude to devise strategies for coping.

NB – whilst short-term memory is a problem the main issue is that the action, instruction, event etc never actually makes it into the memory store – it's often not that it's forgotten, it's more that it never went in in the first place. (Mask and saying 'yes, yes.')

Benefits of diagnosis:

Sometimes health professionals, especially GPs, argue that it's not always helpful to give a person a diagnosis of dementia. Here are my reasons for suggesting this is the wrong stance to take, especially with quality post diagnosis support such as OT.

Whilst no one would wish to be diagnosed with dementia, it should not be the source of such extreme fear and calamity that it is often projected as and can, as we've seen, lead people to wish to end their lives prematurely. The slide shows what for me are the major benefits of having a diagnosis:

- It provides an explanation to the person and loved ones as to what is causing some of the symptoms which are displayed.
- It provides access to whatever support is available both locally and nationally.
- Provides access to medication if appropriate.
- To have the opportunity to get one's financial and health affairs in order through Lasting Power of Attorney and a will.
- It gave me and a number of others the opportunity to help others going through a similar experience (Forget Me Nots)

What coping strategies do I use to live positively and maintain my health

- Live each day as it comes and make the most of each day.
- My wife and I decided that we would be as positive as possible and that as one door closes another door will open – (show new book cover artwork by Rosemary)
- I try and eat a healthy diet especially increasing post diagnosis my intake of antioxidants. I have reduced gluten - 'Grain Brain'.

- I take frequent walks, do regular balance, posture and physical exercises. Puzzles to exercise brain. Things I enjoy and get fulfilment from.

- I read a lot – when less well my reading diet narrows as I do find retaining what I read increasingly difficult. I avoid books relating to dementia after 7pm as I found that reading these at bed-time disturbed my sleep.

- I read *The 7 Habits of Highly Effective People* by Steven Covey and I use a couple of his ideas in my everyday life – these being the circles of influence and concern and his account of being dependant/ independent/ inter-dependant.

- My involvement with raising my own and others' awareness of dementia (especially (YOD) is, to me, an important coping strategy as I feel more in control of the illness with greater knowledge and have met some super people who I have helped who have helped me.

- I take rest and chill-out periods in each day and after 7pm (I very seldom go out after 5pm) pacing myself is important.

- Maintaining my interest in a range of hobbies.

- Enjoying travel both to new and favourite places always with my wife, and at times also with friends, is getting harder and I feel my world in a number of ways is shrinking - but I am resisting this.

- I am determined, driven to live as positively as possible, and see this period as a window of opportunity to use what skills I still have to help to make a difference. I have had 35 years of public service and see this time as a gift to contribute.

- Many people with dementia experience depression and aggression partly due to frustration, I have not had this and I am determined for as long as is possible to continue to avoid these consequences.

Explain the way I feel physically, emotionally, psychologically

- Metaphor of the weather - sun/ cloud/ fog days.
- Physical – exercises help with balance, core stability and mobility, weekly chiropractic spinal adjustment, fortnightly deep tissue massage and occasionally require a stick for support when walking. Need to pace myself – get physically tired more easily. Occasional headaches in areas where atrophy has occurred. Writing by hand/ computer much slower and harder.
- Emotional/ psychological - Some frustrations, e.g. word retrieval when speaking and holding a dialogue. Much more heightened emotions (not necessarily a bad thing). Sometimes feel isolated/ disengaged when in a group or on my own. Feel I'm letting people (and at times maybe myself) down. Find excluding background noise increasingly difficult. Cannot now multi-task. For past ten months had fortnightly therapy sessions from a psychotherapist through KMPT/NHS.

What negative triggers prompt difficult spells/days

- Frustration – e.g. difficulty following storyline on TV – can't remember repeats (every cloud has a silver lining!), e.g. – word retrieval when speaking, e.g. slow/ errors on the computer, e.g. physically not able to do what I could do prior to the illness.
- Sense of guilt - associated with my dementia.
- Encountering stigma, prejudice, lack of understanding and lack of empathy.
- Stress and fatigue (usually induced in my case by non-dementia activities.)
- Being thrown or knocked by something relatively trivial, and linked to this increasingly I find I've misplaced things and they sometimes turn up in surprising locations with no recall of putting them there.
- If I read anything serious or use the computer now after 7pm, then I have a very disturbed night which then impacts upon the next day.

I began my talk by talking about teaching and that's where I want to move to next. All of what you've heard so far has been my words and thoughts, I now want to share some thoughts about the work of the late, great Tom Kitwood.

Kitwood was a psychology professor at Bradford University who, in the 1970s and 1980s, felt that dementia care in the UK was of poor quality. His thinking and teaching revolutionised the field by focusing on person-centred care, and his work really came to prominence during the mid/ late 1990s, culminating in a number of publications produced by the Bradford Dementia Centre within the University, which became the UK's (some would argue the world's) best dementia centre.

Sadly Kitwood never lived to see the impact of his success as he died in 1998.

(Show the Kitwood flower and Malignant social psychology list)

I hope that you can see the relevancy of this to your studies and work. In 1990 he first wrote about 'malignant social psychology:'

- Disempowerment – doing too much for people with dementia, leads to lower confidence and reduced skills
- Deception – to comply with the wishes of others
- Infantilisation – way people speak to those with dementia
- Intimidation – professionals claiming to always know best
- Labelling – expected decline leads to a real decline
- Stigmatisation – consequence of labelling leads to real decline
- Outpacing – being left behind/ out of things often by those close
- Invalidation – being understood, valued and respected
- Banishment – being sent to Coventry – not involved
- Objectification – not being treated as a person

Taking this further in 1997 Kitwood wrote about 'indicators of well-being and ill-being.'

I would like to focus for a moment upon the VALID project (point to it on the slide). This stands for Valuing Active Life In Dementia and is a major £2 million plus OT project being run from 2012–2017 by University College London and NE London NHS Foundation Trust. It's based in London, Hull and Sheffield. I'm not sure what I can share about the project, so I really recommend that you visit their website which is www.ucl.ac.uk/valid where you'll see the enticing statement that this is an exciting time for occupational therapy relating to supporting people with dementia.

Talk delivered at Service User Network Meeting – Thanington Resource Centre, Canterbury. 16th November 2012

Context: this talk was delivered to six people with dementia, two students, an administrator and two psychologists at the inaugural meeting of the Kent Forget Me Nots in order to encourage and motivate those present.

Whilst much has been said over the past few weeks about dementia, today provides those of us with a diagnosis with a rare opportunity. We would all feel I'm sure, that we'd all much rather not have the difficulties which having dementia presents, however, that's the hand we've been dealt, and I'd like to make the point that we are indeed fortunate to have a diagnosis.

It's pretty alarming that nationally only 42% of those of us with dementia have a diagnosis, (the figure is slightly worse in Kent & Medway where it's 38%). You might like to note that Dorset is the lowest figure at 27%, and Scotland the highest at 62%.

Not only are we fortunate to have a diagnosis in order that we can understand the difficulties we face, but also so that we can consequently begin to put our affairs in order; that we can access support and services as they are, and that we can access medication if appropriate. Possibly as important is the opportunity now to make a difference for ourselves, for others with dementia and for those who will follow on from us.

Today can mark a watershed in the involvement with the NHS in Kent for those of us with dementia. If the service is to be effective in providing us the best possible care and support our voice needs to be heard, and more importantly what we're saying needs to be acted upon by those caring for us either as specialists or administrators.

I am very grateful to Janet Lloyd for her unstinting support for service user involvement, and who has made this group and much of my work possible.

Special thanks to Reinhard, who is a true champion for the cause of people with dementia and our involvement in shaping services.

Thanks also to Elizabeth and Nick, who are here this afternoon, and have for a very long time been trying to get their colleagues to hear our voice: now is the time.

For too long some in the NHS both locally and nationally have paid some lip service to the notion of involving service users – even this title is off-putting: we are people. The Alzheimer's Society is also currently undertaking a complete review of its operations in order to place people affected by dementia, i.e. those of us with a diagnosis or our carers, family and friends, at the centre of its operations. I am fortunate to be a part of this review and therefore I can take the views of this group and others back to them. It also means that some of what is happening there can be filtered into what Kent & Medway can achieve.

There are so many things we can do to help raise public awareness around dementia and reducing stigma, fear and misunderstanding. We can speak to audiences from two or three people to small/ large conferences. We can read and comment upon leaflets, documents and possible actions being introduced within the NHS locally. We can attend meetings and speak on behalf of others with dementia in order that professionals hear, and then if

necessary, take action. We can talk to students who are the next generation of professionals, and in whom the future lies. We can talk to those recently diagnosed and reassure them that they are not alone, and that there are services and help out there if you know where to look. We can take part in interviews held by the NHS to appoint new staff to help care for people with dementia, bringing to that and the other roles a unique perspective and experience. It can be really interesting and we can make a difference.

We have support at the highest possible level in Government with the Prime Minister's strategy for 2012-2015, which clearly sets out the Government's commitment to improving the lives of those of us touched by dementia. There are three main parts to this: spending a lot more money on research partly into finding a cause and a cure, but also research into projects which will make life better for all who are diagnosed; secondly to improving significantly the diagnosis rates from the current totally appalling rates – if that was the diagnosis rates for cancer then the NHS would rightly be besieged; thirdly, the element which fits directly closely with today is to create dementia friendly communities. These will never happen **FOR** us, but will happen **WITH** us; in other words, we need to help influence those who are leading these initiatives.

No matter what your politics might be, I applaud Cameron for trying to genuinely make a difference with this crisis which all western societies face.

Still thinking of politics, whilst the dust is just settling on the US presidential elections two quotes from former democrat presidents come to mind which are really relevant to what we should aim to achieve with this network. One is a message to those of you who, like me, wonder what we can do to help. The words of JFK come to mind when he said, 'Think not what your country can do for you, but what you can do for your country,' and to the NHS I use the words of Bill Clinton, (not regarding Monica Lewinsky!) But when he said, 'If you always carry on doing the same things, you get the same results' – Kent and Medway cannot afford the cost of getting the same results. Change is needed to make the good things that are happening even better, but also change through evolution – not revolution, which is why I guess I have the role of envoy rather than activist.

Whilst the label has its uses for professionals and possibly for us, we are not solely service users, we are people. People with dreams, hopes, stories and expectations from our past, and for our future. People with skills and abilities which although at times dimmed, still remain. Skills which we can bring to helping ourselves and others. As one person I can make a small difference, as a network of a number of people we can make a big difference with just a relatively small investment of effort and time.

Living with dementia – update on the work on DEEP: Talk delivered by Keith at Dementia Action Alliance, Westminster Hall, London on Wednesday 20th November 2013

Context: after being a member of the DAA for a year I now had the confidence to accept the invitation to deliver this talk at a big event in London - the first time I had done so. I had excellent support from Nada and Alex both before and at the event.

Good morning everyone. As a head teacher I was more used to saying that to a group of this size - the audience were aged 5-11, who responded with a chime of 'Good morning Mr. Oliver, Good morning everyone!'

I'm grateful to have been asked to speak this morning on behalf of a project which I think is making a fundamental positive difference to those living with dementia.

On New Year 's Eve 2010, my life changed when I received a confirmed diagnosis of AD at the age of 55. Consequently, with early retirement, a vacuum was created, part of which I'm pleased to say has been positively filled with involvement in a range of dementia-related projects, some of which I would like to share with you this morning.

Whilst as an individual I have been involved in a number of worthwhile causes and projects, I quickly realised that firstly this could be overwhelming and secondly, there would a greater impact by working together with other people with dementia supported by the expertise of professionals, some of whom, I'm delighted to say, are here in the audience today.

Exactly a year ago, eight people with dementia and two clinical psychologists met in a Canterbury community centre to discuss how we could collectively work to improve local attitudes to dementia, and increase effective provision for people with dementia by the NHS in Kent.

The group, which has now grown to 14 members, comes from all walks of life across East Kent, and, although linked by a common belief of wanting to help to make a difference, were previously unknown to each other. One of our successes has been a real sense of comradeship, and sharing. Members, who previously would have shrunk from speaking in public, now readily speak at a range of events within the region. We recognise the importance attached to the next generation of professionals coming into services to support those of us with dementia, and are very willing to become active participants on interview panels for staff appointments, and follow-up training. We live in an information-rich time, but the information is not always rich. The group has contributed towards making the good better, and consigned the bad to the bin.

Over the course of the year, the initial aims have been exceeded, and the group's influence has extended beyond the Kent border, which leads me now to speak about our links with DEEP.

DEEP stands for Dementia Engagement and Empowerment Project. It's generously funded by the Joseph Rowntree Foundation, and is about supporting groups of people with dementia across the country to share knowledge and experience, with an aim to creating a more collective voice.

With that in mind, we were delighted when contacted to be involved in two projects, which I want to give you a sense of this morning. The first involved a triad of DEEP, the British Psychological Society and the Forget Me Nots, which Reinhard will tell us more about after the break. I will though say, from a service-user perspective, the two meetings we had in the middle of August when one might have been tempted to be swimming in the sea on a blue-flag beach in Thanet were so engaging that a full attendance of Forget Me Nots was achieved, and the feedback from members was extremely positive. Thank you to Nada.

The second linked project involving Forget Me Nots and DEEP was the examination of the implementation of the Mental Capacity Act. The Forget Me Nots met to create written evidence for the House of Lords select committee with skilled facilitation from Nada and Reinhard, the ten people with dementia present (supported by six talented Kent University students on placement with the trust), were comfortable in commenting, at times emotionally, on the impact that the Mental Capacity Act is having upon them.

One of the main issues explored with the chairman of the House of Lords select committee, Lord Hardie, and his colleague Lord Swinfen, was Lasting Power of Attorney. It was quite alarming that the majority of people with dementia present, although diagnosed one or two years previously, had still not put their Power of Attorney in place, although this has subsequently heightened people's motivation to address this.

The written evidence has been submitted by DEEP to the committee, who will be publishing their report in the spring.

This is a good example of how a local group, such as the Forget Me Nots, can have a national impact.

I mentioned earlier my career coming to a close immediately after my diagnosis was confirmed. During the ten months of assessments, I was struggling to either maintain a 480 pupil school and manage 50 staff, or sign off sick. For me, the support of occupational health to secure early retirement was the correct option, and has allowed me, whilst still well enough to devote some of the energy previously used as a head teacher, to the dementia cause. This might not work for everyone.

Most of us are defined by the job that we do, rather than by our name, and so when one retires, particularly abruptly, this can lead to issues around self-esteem and direction. In my case, taking on a role needed to be voluntary, and I was encouraged to adopt a title. Meetings with the trust for the role description were straight forward, a title was problematic. They wanted 'champion,' which I felt uneasy with, as champion, to me, implies being the best at something. 'Ambassador' was taken by the Alzheimer's society, 'Advocate' has mental health act connotations, and we finally settled on the word activist. Fortunately, following a conversation with my son-in-law, who, when he had stopped laughing, said 'Keith, you cannot use that title, they'll ask where's his balaclava, and has he just come from the barricades?' So he and I came up with the label 'Envoy.' And it is with the label KMPT Dementia Service User Envoy, that I am part of the Dementia Action Alliance.

A few months ago, I met with Nada, Toby (from the Mental Health Foundation), Reinhard, Mike (from the Open Doors Project), and Cathy and Gill (from Greater Manchester West Mental Health NHS Trust) to discuss how employers could support people who develop dementia whilst working. It was brilliant to share experiences and knowledge on this very important issue, and I am delighted that DEEP have utilised some of this to produce an extremely useful guide (HOLD UP GUIDE)

This moves me on nicely to share with you a series of guides, which are now available from the Dementia Voices website. The guides have been created with different groups and individuals as part of DEEP. They are aimed at people with dementia themselves, groups, and organisations working with people with dementia. They cover issues from involving people with dementia, to creating dementia-friendly communities. If anyone wants to see draft copies, they are on the JRF stand in the exhibition hall.

People often ask why do I get involved in activities relating to dementia. For me, the answer is clear. Firstly, it's to try and make a difference, to make things better for others who have this diagnosis, and secondly, it's because of some of the wonderful people who I have been honoured to meet and work with, over the past three years, who make this wretched condition far more tolerable.

Talk written by Keith Oliver, Nada Savitch & Alexandra Bone

Public lecture given at Canterbury Christ Church University on Tuesday 17ᵗʰ September 2013

Context: The first, and at this time only public lecture I have delivered. I was nervous as I didn't know how many people would turn up and I was the sole speaker. It went very well.

(Play music as people come into lecture theatre: *Something Inside So Strong* by Labi Siffre)

Hopefully that's given us an inspiring start. Firstly, thank you very much to all for coming to hear me speak today, I really do appreciate your interest and support and I hope that I am able to provide some insight and thought provoking information. I can't promise a bundle of laughs but hopefully tissues won't be required. Also thank you to Jan and Katy for your support and faith in me providing the start for this season's programme of talks. Today's talk will have a little psychology, a smattering of sociology and LOTS of personology!

This is my plan for my talk today.

Over the past two years I've done many talks on a range of topics relating to dementia for health professionals, students here and at University of Kent, for the Alzheimer's Society, for care home staff with the Bradford Dementia Group, for post diagnosis groups with KMPT, but never have I had the challenge of tackling such a personal topic to such a diverse audience. I suspect I'll either satisfy all or none of you. I await your response at the end as my reading of body language and subtle signals is now beyond me. This is not an academic professional looking in from outside of the mind of someone with dementia but the scene from the inside based on my story and my opinions because everyone living with dementia is a unique person.

I hate the cliché of being on a journey – it reminds me of coach loads of children and sick buckets, and journeys usually have a positive conclusion of reaching somewhere you wish to be. That is NOT the case with dementia. Just before I launch into the first section I'd need to mention that, frustrating though it is for me, I do need to read from a script as I have much I want to say and fear my ability to remember information and express it without this prop is extremely difficult.

Whilst flattered and humbled by the award of Kent & Medway NHS Partnership Trust Volunteer of the Year for 2013, I accepted it on behalf of others with dementia as an illustration of what someone with this condition can achieve.

An opening task I often use on courses where I speak is to ask delegates to write down one sentence about themselves from their past, one about them at present and one about hopes/ intentions for their future. Often I'll do this before they know I have dementia – it can work better like this. Then I'll give them a potted life story and talk about my mother and her dementia, before they view a film which I'll show you shortly. I do this in order to challenge stereotypes and misunderstanding around dementia. Person-centred care is something which I support wholeheartedly and in order to understand my stance on this you need to get a sense of the person that's here in front of you today.

I am almost 58 years of age. I was born in the same house my father and grandfather had been born in, and brought up in Nottingham, living for the first seven years in a back-to-back terrace long since buried under a 1970s road system in a part of the city where no grass was to be seen with the rather unlikely name of 'The Meadows.' The name came from the area's pre-coalmining days.

We escaped the black and while world of Sillitoe's Nottingham of Saturday Night, Sunday Morning, when I was seven in 1962, moving to the colour of one of the country's largest council estates where we enjoyed the luxury of a garden, an indoor toilet, a bathroom and parks in which to kick a football and imagine I was playing for my beloved Nottingham Forest. Through education and the encouragement of mostly my mother I was able to go to university in Sheffield and, after graduating, to become a teacher.

Whilst as an only child I was able to do things with both parents, outside of football most of my childhood memories revolve around times spent doing things either with my mother or the hordes of other kids who seemed to live nearby. I was very close to my mother; in many ways I guess she lived her life through me. She was clever, fun, a bit nervous in company, loved travel and her work as a secretary in a busy office. Whilst she was supportive of me going to university she clearly took me leaving badly, and it coincided with a decline in her mental health about 38 years ago which moved from bad nerves, difficult menopause to diagnosis of bi-polar and then to have added to this Alzheimer's in her mid-70s. She now lives in a nursing home in Nottingham where we visit her.

I'm married with three grown up children and three grandchildren aged from five to 15. I've lived in the Canterbury area for the past 32 years having come down from Cheshire in 1981. Having graduated from Sheffield University in 1978, I began teaching in Cheshire. I taught at two primary schools in the Canterbury area, and was Deputy head of Swalecliffe Primary. In 1995 I left Swalecliffe for my first headship in Dover, followed in 2000 with promotion to the headship at Blean, midway between Canterbury and Whitstable (albeit with a two-year secondment as Canterbury's primary schools' adviser for KCC). I enjoyed a really fulfilling career, worked with some very talented people – some of whom are here today - and helped to positively influence thousands of young people, many of whom I am delighted to still see from time to time either in person or in the local media, one of whom is Dr Richard Brown - now a consultant within KMPT.

I think this is the point where I'd like to show you a short film which links into the next segment.

I am very proud of this little film which, whilst I found challenging and tiring to do, was, I think, brilliantly made by film maker Mycal Miller who sensitively supported me through two-and-a-half-days of filming to make an eight-minute film which we initially used as a training tool at courses designed for staff working for Kent County Council in libraries, art galleries, museums and Gateway services.

There were I feel a number of stages to the way the diagnosis period impacted upon me, my wife and my life.

Firstly the shock of starting off with thoughts around an ear and/ or another urinary infection, moving to the slight chance it was a brain tumour I was contending with through to the relief it wasn't but to the complete shock that I was being tested for and consequently diagnosed with Alzheimer's Disease.

Secondly, I really did appreciate the openness and honesty of firstly the neurologist who first mentioned the potential diagnosis of Alzheimer's and drew pictures for us to explain the scans, followed by Mary Aston and Elizabeth Field who completed my assessment with Jouko her assistant at St Martins. Whilst I fully support the drive to improve diagnosis rates for reasons I'll outline later, this needs to be done as sensitively as it was for me, with the needs of the person and the people closest to them, and not merely to hit targets or make the NHS look better.

My assessment took five months from start to finish, which I've subsequently learnt for cases of Young Onset (i.e. youngsters like me who haven't yet reached 65) is quite quick, of which the final three months were more intensive and exhausting. I used to attend assessments desperate to score as highly as possible and to be told at best I was performing as average and on many occasions my recall placed me in the bottom 5% of the population wasn't easy to hear.

Thirdly completing the diagnosis presented me with a 'cliff edge' moment. Whilst not frightened, I was in the dark, and felt a need to find out more and seek support. Promises of a course and meeting others were made by the Trust but no definite date or information was forthcoming.

I turned to the Alzheimer's Society, whose fact sheets were excellent as opposed to the lack of local support from them and their 'Talking Point' blog, which I only visited once, because I was really put off by the negative pleading comments there – it was being used as a pressure release for carers which I fully understood and appreciated but didn't want or need. To fill the vacuum, I read as much as I could about dementia, especially Young Onset, and was particularly inspired by the books *Dancing with Dementia* by Christine Bryden and *Still Alice* by Lisa Genova.

The press article you saw on the film was written and this gave me a sense that there was a void around public awareness which maybe I could help to fill by utilising the skills I retained from 33 years in education. I didn't want to begin my retirement (which had now begun) with no purpose in life, and I met with Reinhard Guss from KMPT who has become a friend, ally and confidant in trying to improve knowledge and understanding of what living with dementia is like.

So far all this talk has been my own words, now I'm going to share a quote from Martin Sheen's recent autobiography written with his eldest son Emilio Estevez and called *Along the Way*:

He quotes an old Irish story about a man who, when he died, met St Peter at the gates of heaven. St Peter asks the man to show him his scars before permitting his entry. The man replied that he had no scars, to which St Peter was a little dismayed and said, 'What a pity. Was there nothing worth fighting for?'

I leave that thought with you as I give my voice a rest now for a couple of minutes and play for you a song which inspires me and maybe will help provide some greater insight into my motivation as I move to the next section of my talk. It's called *While I am Here* and is performed by an Australian Scot named Eric Bogle.

The song means a terrific lot to me. I hope that you can understand why and see my reasons for sharing it.

Whilst no one would wish to be diagnosed with dementia, it should not be the source of such extreme fear and calamity that it is often projected as, and can as we've seen lead to people wishing to end their lives prematurely. The slide shows what, for me, are the major benefits of having a diagnosis:

- Provides an explanation to the person and loved ones as to what is causing some of the symptoms which are displayed
- Provides access to whatever support is available both locally and nationally
- Provides access to medication if appropriate
- To have the opportunity to get one's financial and health affairs in order through Lasting Power of Attorney and a will
- Gave me and a number of others the opportunity to help others going through a similar experience (Forget Me Nots)

There is a definite line for me from childhood through to University and on to teaching and being a head teacher and advisor (certainly not an inspector) on to my role now as Kent and Medway's Dementia Envoy. The common ground for me is drive and a desire to do something positive and, as Eric Bogle said in the song earlier, about leaving this place better than we found it, be it a school or something related to Dementia.

I would like to share with you the work of Stephen Covey

This influences my thinking now, and I'm indebted to Christian Farthing at the BodyWell Centre in Blean for both introducing me to Covey's work as I'd never have discovered it otherwise, and for his care for helping me to stay well through spinal adjustments, deep tissue massages, turning around our eating habits and introducing us to the wonders of juicing and encouraging a focus on wellness and not on sickness.

The phrase Experts by Experience and Service User Involvement are much used at present. Whilst all people with dementia are experts on their own experience I am determined to try and retain as wide a perspective as possible which became second nature as a teacher and head. Speaking for others has pitfalls and as you'll see from the job description my role, which is completely voluntary, is pretty comprehensive.

Picking out a few key points from the role which was much easier to write than the title – 'Champion' (not for me), 'Ambassador' (AS got it), 'Advocate' (Mental Health Act implications), so 'Activist' (story with Nick) In the role I've met some great people and many of you are here today which really motivates me to continue. The photo shows two key allies – Reinhard who I mentioned earlier and Ian Asquith who has been a brilliant supporter and friend for the past two years.

Here we are at the Alzheimer's Disease International Conference in London in March 2012 which was followed by a presentation delivered by us at the UK Dementia Congress in Brighton in November 2012. Since then I've given many talks and lectures on a range of dementia-related subjects both in Kent and in London. Next week I'm doing a conference with the Alzheimer's Society and on the 9th October I'm speaking at a major conference for the British Psychology Society. Every talk I do is written with the audience and occasion in mind – I guess one day I'll get it right! I am very much involved in working with a wide range of organisations and am part of the Dementia Action Alliance based in London and charged with the task of delivering the Prime Minister's Challenge. I am often asked to comment upon new books, TV programmes, research projects and a new curriculum for dementia studies. Many of these require calling upon my former skills which I try and refresh by going into Wincheap Primary School once a week and hearing children read which I really enjoy and gain far more from than I contribute. *(Hold up Wincheap mug)*

This reminds me of a story from the end of last term. One of the children here, Lewis, said to me one day, 'I saw you in a magazine!' *(Hold up Health magazine and mug)* 'Oh, did you?' I replied, not knowing what words on dementia were about to be forthcoming from him. He gave a big smile and said, 'Yes, and I know your first name!' Clearly the article had made a big impression on that nine-year-old.

Whilst I do this role for the satisfaction and desire to help to make a difference, the main positive for me is the fantastic people I've met either as professionals through societies such as the Alzheimer's Society, Age UK in Canterbury, EKIDS or Dementia UK. I get no pay for the consultancy roles or talks beyond travel expenses. Without support the role is at times every bit as isolating as that of a head teacher, and this alongside occasional over-load and blips in communication can bring down the fog.

When this isn't the case it's more like the season of 'mellow fruitfulness' and the sun shines as the role is very rewarding at these times. However, I do not find it enjoyable in the usual sense of the word: what I find enjoyable is the quality time I spend with my wife, Rosemary, and our family, plus the many interests and hobbies which I still do either with her or on my own. We both enjoy U3A activities which are so interesting and stimulating, I've a lifelong interest in studying the American Civil War, I collect British and Australian stamps, listen to a wide range of music from the 1950s through to Mumford and Sons and Adele. I enjoy travel, especially to friends in Australia and new places in the UK and Europe, although these days I need a little assistance from Rosemary, friends or airlines/ travel companies. As you'll have seen in the film we both enjoy gardening and are now taking more time to enjoy the fruits of our labours. I enjoy reading biographies and memoirs and have signed up again for a Christ Church course on reading and writing our own memoirs – perhaps something to do when I retire or wind down as Envoy. I enjoy films and television but do struggle to follow plots and storylines, so shows like Strictly Come Dancing are a real treat for me.

Having a positive impact is important to me and to those who wish to see greater service user involvement in dementia services. In order to achieve this Reinhard and Elizabeth from KMPT sat down with me six months ago and, with the support of the Trust, we set up a Network based in Canterbury of people who had been diagnosed in the past two years or so. The group has grown to about 14 people with dementia, three KMPT professionals and a number of Kent University psychology students on placement for a year with the Trust. Members are aged from 54 to 82, are male and female and live across a wide area in the east of Kent. We meet monthly and our two-hour meetings are a mix of social time and focused, deep debate and discussion around issues relating to dementia for us as individuals and across our county. There are also occasional additional meetings to meet and discuss specific issues with relevant professionals from outside Kent.

We read and feedback on draft literature – the good, the bad and the ugly! We've been on interview panels for KMPT posts. We've been involved in relevant research projects within the county and many of the group have given talks to other people who have recently been diagnosed and for whom seeing and hearing those who have been through it as well as the wisdom of the Trust staff is of enormous benefit.

When the group started some felt their situation was quite helpless, there was little for them or little they could do about their dementia – now this is far from the case and it has transformed their thinking initially and in turn is starting to transform thinking across the county.

The group has come to the attention of the national scene and as part of a national project called DEEP – Dementia Engagement and Empowerment Project - the group is now working on national guidelines for post diagnosis care and has been invited to meet with senior civil servants from the Prime Minister's cabinet office.

Whilst I am delighted with this innovation, and support 100% the notion that the more people involved the more potential for positive influence we have, the dementia world needs to recognise that involving people with dementia - whilst essential - needs careful management, support and encouragement and whilst carers are not part of this network by way of participating in meetings as we really wanted the diagnosed person to fully participate inter-dependently, carers are at the centre of the process by helping and encouraging the participation of their loved one. We are all carers and people affected by dementia, and I feel demarcating roles whilst understandable, especially as the disease progresses, is not always helpful.

So to conclude: (Show audience the Alz Soc book *Dementia Guide*) The Alzheimer's Society wanted someone smart, intelligent and good looking to advertise their excellent new Dementia Guide and... they got me. Despite that the guide is one of the best books around on Dementia and it's free from the Society.

We know dementia is currently affecting many millions of people, there are few families where its threads have not touched. At last the Government is giving society a lead on this, and through the Prime Minister's challenge, allied to media interest and a groundswell of movement from people touched by dementia and professionals there is more cause for optimism. The three areas of – dementia-friendly communities, improved diagnosis and (hopefully) post diagnosis support allied to greater spending on research means that it should be easier to live positively and well for longer with a diagnosis of dementia.

Thank you again to Jan and Katy, to Reinhard and Elizabeth for their encouragement, commitment and faith in me and in us to make things better for people with dementia in East Kent, to Ian for his help with the powerpoint and for being such a loyal friend, to all of you for supporting me today and for listening so intently – I do hope that it's been interesting and thought provoking, and saving the most important until last the biggest thank you goes to Rosemary for being a wonderful supporter, friend, confidant and wife – sure she's also my carer, but the fact is, we care for each other.

From now it should it be 'PERSON with dementia,' and not 'person with DEMENTIA,' I hope that I've conveyed that during this talk.

Whilst noting down these details to find out more about what you've heard today I'd like to play the third and final piece of music, called *Won't Give In,* which I used at my final assembly at Blean when I retired. It's written by the Finn brothers from Crowded House and sung by another Aussie favourite of mine – Sara Storer. (Play music – *Won't Give in)*

Christmas time (Talk given at the Alzheimer's Society's Carols by Candlelight on 4th December 2013)

Context: I include the following two talks in this way to illustrate that as they are two years apart they are different and yet similar - a bit like me really. Time had passed and the first one is quite secular, the second begins to illustrate the journey into faith which I am taking. Nearly all my life I have been seen as a 'rock' for other people; recently I have sought and needed a rock I can rely upon. In God I know I have found it. In writing this piece I drew from a piece I wrote for the Barton church newsletter, The Prodigal, published in September 2016.

As one gets older, time certainly appears to run away much quicker; one example of this being the speed at which the Christmas season approaches. Christmas is a special time, more so for children and for those sharing the time with them. Most people get wrapped up in the glow of Christmas.

Reflecting upon the magic of Christmas as a child, this was one of the highlights of being a primary school teacher and head. Once the nativities and plays were ready to be performed one really felt that the magic of Christmas had arrived. It always amazed me how quickly and professionally plays and nativities involving casts of hundreds were conceived, rehearsed and performed, usually without any hitch.

Teaching in a village school the Christmas plays took place in the church across the road from the school. This anecdote involves a child named Jamie who, as narrator, really shone in rehearsals. He was confident and word perfect well before any others in the cast. On the big night, the Wise Men were a little over excited, and jostled to have the honour of being first to deliver their cherished gift to the baby Jesus, and this may have distracted Jamie or maybe it was the atmosphere of the setting or just plain nerves, because his key lines came out as, 'The wise men arrived at the stable to deliver their gifts of gold, Frankenstein and mirth.' I wonder if he's shared this tale with his own children by now.

Some years later, at another school where I was by now a head, we had the grandchildren of the Archbishop of Canterbury (later Lord Carey). This particular Christmas, Year 6 were performing *Joseph and the Amazing Technicolour Dreamcoat,* and it was marvellous. Lord Carey was sitting in the audience next to me on the front row enjoying the show, laughing at the jokes and tapping his feet to the catchy tunes which were brilliantly sung by some very talented youngsters. One memorable scene was when Potiphar's wife – a tall 11-year-old in heavy make-up - did a great job of accosting the Archbishop to great applause and hilarity from a packed hall. He turned to his wife and I heard him whisper, 'I thought that was coming!' Fortunately, he took it in very good heart.

As a primary school teacher I always appreciated the Christmas cards which the children sent me and which initially decorated the classroom, or later, as a head, my office, and were then taken down on the final day of term, carried home and used to add additional colour to our lounge over the festive season. One card stands out in my memory from a child named Kirsty.

Kirsty was a very friendly, unassuming child who although she found learning difficult, would always try hard - and no one can ask more from a pupil. Her card sent in her final year before leaving for secondary school carried this message:

'To Mr. OlivER, the bEst teacher in the woRLd.' She really should have stopped there, but she went on to say 'You teached me good. Love Kirsty.'

I often thought I could use that as a reference for job applications!

In 1989, we discovered (during a year-long teacher exchange in Australia) how different an Antipodean Christmas is. We were also introduced to the music of a range of singer-song writers, many of whom I still listen to today. (Play *While I Am Here.*)

(Talk was written by Keith Oliver, supported by Sophie Razzel and Alexandra Bone, University of Kent placement students with KMPT.)

While I Am Here written by John Munro and performed by Eric Bogle is reproduced by kind permission from Eric Bogle and John, who I contacted while putting this manuscript together.

The Lion, The Sun and the Christmas Card: Reflections on Christmas (Talk given at the Alzheimer's Society Christmas Carol Service in Rochester, December 2015)

I am delighted and honoured to have been asked to speak with you tonight as someone who was diagnosed with Alzheimer's Disease five years ago, and to share with you some thoughts on this, alongside reflections on this most important time of the year.

Often Christmas is a time to live in, and enjoy the moment whilst also looking back and reflecting upon happy times in the past. Both of these aspects are so important for those people like myself who are affected by dementia.

How often do we say how stressful and hectic the lead up to the festive season is, and how much we still have to do rather than sit for a moment and reflect upon what we have achieved or have at our fingertips. Living with dementia can certainly exaggerate and complicate the difficulties one faces - busy shops, noise, over the top marketing, hustle and bustle.

This Christmas I am determined to try and take time to reflect more on what Christmas is really about.

Over the past year I have been fortunate to be involved in so many positive activities on behalf of the Alzheimer's Society, which I am proud to be associated with as an Ambassador. One of which is the *Welcome to our World* book which was written by eight people with dementia and which has a super intro by Jo Brand. Currently 1,450 books have been sold/ distributed and it's raised approximately £6,000 for the Alzheimer's Society. Can I say it's an ideal stocking filler at £5 with all the money going to the Alzheimer's Society.

I was blessed to enjoy a long and happy career in primary education, and Christmas was always the busiest but best time of the year in school. It was a special time for the children who we tried to wrap up in the magical warm glow of Christmas.

I loved reading to the children (and still do when I get the chance) and my favourite book was *The Lion, the Witch and the Wardrobe*, part of the world of Narnia series, set in a place where it is winter but never Christmas. Imagine! I know that for some people affected by dementia this is their reality today. But it need not be the case.

Recently I have, through a friend, re-visited these books with my eyes opened wide and have seen them in a totally different light. A light much brighter than I have seen before. There is so much wisdom and theology contained in the stories. Aslan, as I discovered, is an allegory for Jesus, and the *Last Battle* has a scene by the stable - not difficult to transpose this into considering and visualising the humble stable where our Lord Jesus was born in Bethlehem, an event we are here to celebrate this evening.

Often the perception (sometimes true, other times it needs to be challenged) is that people with dementia are not able to learn new things or to take on new activities. With sensitive support this is clearly wrong. I have experienced this first hand and seen it many times for others.

Also, one undoubted consequence of having dementia is that one's physical world DOES shrink, and to have this extension of my spiritual world has really helped me to live as well as possible this year.

To close I want to reflect upon the title of my talk. The **Lion**: the reference here is to Aslan and also to the thought that a lion is seen as brave; I know so many brave people living with dementia, or professionals supporting us through the Alzheimer's Society and the NHS. The **sun** we all crave for warmth and light, and through feeling the comfort given by warmth and the truth we see through God's light enables us to live as well as is possible; and, finally, the **Christmas card**; what better way to keep in touch with our family and friends who mean so much to us all.

Living well with Young Onset Dementia (KMPT Young Onset Dementia Conference talk in Ashford - 12th March 2014)

Context: A KMPT conference for health professionals. By now my confidence at such occasions had grown and this is reflected, I feel, in my talk.

(Show the YouTube film of Ravel's Bolero accompanying Torvill and Dean) Good morning. Thank you to Alex Bone for your help with this talk.

I guess you are wondering why I chose to open with that wonderful beginning. It could be because the winter Olympics and Paralympics are again in the public's attention - but it's not. Nor is it because Jayne Torvill and I both attended at the same time the same Primary School in Nottingham. Nor is it because the music prompts my mind to go back to when I was a naive 20-year-old watching Bo Derek in her role in the film, *10*. I tossed the coin and Torvill and Dean won – that will either please or disappoint you!

The reason is because of the music, The Bolero, which was composed by Ravel at around the time that he was starting to experience what would turn out to be Young Onset dementia. A splendid illustration of what can be achieved by someone despite all that this wretched condition throws at us.

There is considerable evidence to suggest that people with dementia continue to relate to, and enjoy, engagement with music. Alas, my own musical skills were never very good, and this hasn't been improved since having dementia. I do however enjoy an eclectic taste in music. I love listening to favourite pieces of music, particularly the genre of singer/ songwriters, one of whom is an Australian named Eric Bogle, and it is one of his songs entitled *While I am Here* which is going to support my talk this morning.

While I am here
I will make to you a promise from this simple man
That whatever I may do, I'll do the best I can
I will try to make a song that touches someone's heart

Though I may not do it all but I will make a start

I fully understand that the disease is progressive, and that I currently have a window of opportunity to deliver talks such as this one, so I am determined to make the most of this time. As an ex-head teacher, I recognise the importance of engaging with other people and utilising their skills and interests alongside my own, in order to get across an important message. In my abstract I refer to *Dancing with Dementia*, and I took this from the excellent book written by Christine Bryden. Last week, my wife and I returned from a winter hibernation in Australia during which we spent time with Kate Swaffer in Adelaide. Kate has taken the baton from Christine Bryden, and is leading an advocacy campaign internationally, to which I am eager to contribute in the UK.

Christine and I also use two useful metaphors – sunny/ foggy days and the swan looking serene and clam but paddling quite frantically below the surface to keep up

Don't know how long I can stay, but I'll do all that I can while I am here

While I am here, I have dues I have to pay

Only once to pass this way

This is my promise for the days

While I am here

Retiring from a profession to which I was fully committed and which I enjoyed, was hard. I needed to retain my self-esteem and feeling of self-worth, and engagement in public service through awareness-raising of what life can be like with Young Onset dementia is very important to me. I feel privileged to have the faith and support of the trust, as shown through my role in KMPT as the Dementia Service-User Envoy.

The role involves a range of activities, such as speaking at conferences, attending and sharing meetings, reading and commenting on literature, participating in staff interviews within the trust, and generally providing the trust with insight from the perspective of someone with dementia.

Whilst on my own one can have an impact, Reinhard and I felt that with the support of the trust, greater impact could be achieved through involving others with dementia in carrying out these activities. Consequently, in November 2012, KMPT Dementia service-user network, better known as the Forget Me Nots, came into being.

I could speak all day about the positive aspects of the Forget Me Nots which is a network, or group, we have established in East Kent which is part psycho-social intervention supporting people with a diagnosis who are in the early to mid-stages of the condition to have their voice heard, whilst also supporting KMPT in providing that unique insight only available from those who live everyday with dementia.

We read, discuss and comment upon a range of relevant literature produced both by the NHS and the voluntary sector, provide people with dementia to sit on KMPT appointment panels where we do not comment on the candidate's professional skills but are best placed to judge how we would feel to be in their potential care. We also provide speakers at dementia conferences around Kent and beyond, and it's great to have Chris Ryan speaking here with me today. Approx 50% of the group are below the age of 65. This is a model which I know other Trusts are considering.

Since being diagnosed, the most positive experience has been meeting some brilliant people who are fully engaged in supporting those of us who are trying to live as well as possible with dementia. One consequence of having dementia is that I no longer readily recall what people say to me, but I do take away from an exchange with someone the way they made me feel. If one imagines a balance between cognitive and emotional, previously in my case the cognitive would have weighed heavier. Now the reverse is true.

While I am here

I will recognise that weakness is my constant friend

I'll keep it to myself except for now and then
I will not become a shadow of my present self
A watcher with no words to offer someone else
Don't know how long I can stay, but I'll do all that I can
While I am here

Often we hear horrendous stories relating to people with Young Onset dementia and their route through diagnosis. Many are misdiagnosed, and fobbed off; large numbers struggle with their job, finances, and family commitments. One cannot overstate the anxiety associated with the early progression of dementia, and not achieving support, and the answers to one's questions.

My route through diagnosis was rather unusual. It started with a visit to the GP, because of a series of unexplained falls, diminishing concentration and increased fatigue. I thought this was caused perhaps by an ear infection. The GP prescribed antibiotics, but felt there was no infection, and told me to return if nothing improved. Unsurprisingly, nothing did improve, and I did return to see him. After some more tests in his surgery, he referred me for an MRI brain scan, and an appointment with a neurologist. He didn't tell me at the time, but he was looking to rule out the worst case scenario (in his view) of a brain tumour. I had the scan, and saw the neurologist, who on that bright, sunny May day in 2010, told my wife and I totally out of the blue, that the scan and some questions/ tests he asked, were suggestive of Alzheimer's. This was on no-one's radar, and came as a complete shock.

My perception of Alzheimer's was that it only affected the elderly, and certainly not someone aged 54, who despite these recent difficulties, was still functioning reasonably well. There then followed a period of four months, during which, with support from my wife and close colleagues at work, I was able to continue working whilst undergoing blood tests, further cognitive tests, and two more scans, one being a PET scan and one being a SPECT.

Following this, another consultation took place with the neurologist, who felt even more confidently that the diagnosis of Alzheimer's was correct, and he referred me to a Memory Clinic. Whilst the neurologist's approach was forthright, I did feel supported and welcomed his clear explanations: it all made sense.

Between September and New Year's Eve 2010, a series of assessments took place at the Memory Clinic, during which a clear picture of where my cognitive abilities were at best deemed to be around average, and at worst in the lowest fifth centile. I knew the implication of this with 95/100 scoring better than me on that test. The latter being particularly clear where stories or words were read to me, and I was asked to recall, which I couldn't do. Another area where I scored quite badly was around semantics. Words used to come easily, and on one of my sunny days, they generally still do so. On cloudy days, it's harder, and on the foggy days they never arrive.

A million miles may lie between the man I'd like to be
And how I live my life from day to day
I'll take my chance make my choice and look again to see
A million miles is just one step away

In order to live positively with dementia, it is important to live each day as it comes, whilst having something in the near future to look forward to. If one picks up the Daily Mail, or Daily Express and reads about dementia, invariably the article will focus either on a wonder drug (that may or may not be round the corner), or state that doing sudokus and crosswords will protect one from dementia. Unlikely. Quality psychosocial interventions, alongside caring support from family, friends and professionals (possibly allied to medication for those who can benefit from this) are, I feel, the best ways to cause the sun to emerge from behind the clouds.

I do not look back at what I could do or who I was previously, indeed I still see myself as the same person with a range of skills and interests and -

yes - many flaws which have always been there, but which are, with dementia, at times harder to conceal. My interest and engagement in hobbies does now come and go. I try and sustain an interest in gardening and in travel both of which I enjoy in the company of my wife. Also some solitary time can be positive when I'm keen to develop my Australian and British stamp collections or go walking with my thoughts and the company of favourite pieces of music playing on my iPod.

While I am here
I will always seek to love and be loved in return
I will never raise my hand, and never point a gun
I'll not spend too much time thinking of when I'll go
Leave it better than I found it, though no one may ever know
Don't know how long I can stay but I'll do all that I can
While I am here

I have gained an enormous amount of insight and inner strength from the work of Stephen Covey, especially his work in the book entitled *The 7 Habits of Highly Influential People,* where he explores thinking around circles of influence/ concern (explain) and being dependent – independent – interdependent.

CARER/CARED FOR/JOURNEY/SUFFERER - especially to do with young onset dementia

While I am here
I have dues I have to pay
Only once I have to pass this way
This is my promise for the days
While I am here

Towards the latter days of my career, occasionally I would consider the question, 'What will I do when I retire?' Never for one moment could I have anticipated how the last three years have unfurled. Looking back over this time, the biggest rewards have been to see a growing awareness within all sectors of dementia care, so that the person with a diagnosis can play a significant part in the services which we receive. It has been great to see a number of people who previously felt that there was no contribution they could make, and nothing they could do to help themselves or others, grow to speaking in front of large and small audiences with passion and conviction, and a real desire to help to make things better for all. Some say, once a teacher, always a teacher. Thank you for listening to me this morning.

Conference closing at the end of an excellent day - some final thoughts shared with the audience: From my background in education I have a real sense of the risks and benefits of attaching labels to people. In my past career I spent much time and energy supporting and challenging parents who used labels sometimes unwisely to describe their child. More recently I have been a part of many dementia projects which effectively brought people together with a wide range of interests, backgrounds, agendas and, yes, labels. I am actually comfortable with the use of 'carer' to describe this crucial role when applied positively – I do care for my wife, my grown up children and grandchildren, and my elderly mother who also has Alzheimer's, and they, including her, care for me.

And, finally from me, to be described as a youngster at the age of 58 is probably as good as it gets!

Talk delivered at a MSNAP Conference at the Royal College of Psychiatrists, London on Monday 29th September 2014

Context: The structure of my talk was suggested by Sophie Razzel and her idea worked so well. This was the first time Rosemary had attended a big event such as this, and the first time I had met and spoken after and with Alistair Burns.

The day began normally. The sun was shining. The BBC Breakfast weather girl predicted warm sunshine which pleased me as a trip in the sun is always better than in the rain. Dinner duty back at school awaited me, and it is much less hassle if the children are able to run around outside. Today, because it was so dry and warm would have the added bonus of them going on the field.

Rosemary and I arrived in good time. I hadn't been to this hospital before so I was more nervous about being late and not finding the right reception area, rather than nervous about receiving the results of my MRI scan. Why would I need an MRI scan if I had problems with my balance and ears? I only briefly dwelt upon this question.

I was relieved to be met by a friendly receptionist in a quiet, rather than crowded, foreboding waiting area. A promising start. What time is it... 10:15 - my deputy would be standing in for me and conducting the assembly today. I did chat to her before leaving school last night and we agreed the story and the hymn - a story about being positive, and the hymn, well it was *'One More Step Around the World I Go.'* That should go with a bounce as always, the children love that one.

Exactly on time the neurologist's nurse calls me in to have my weight and blood pressure checked. All very routine I'm assured. Back into the waiting room.

Break time back at school now, again thank goodness for the sunshine.

Thoughts of school were interrupted by 'Mr. Oliver, will you please come this way?' I was accompanied by Rosemary my wife across the waiting area to a typical doctor's consultation room. Square. Modern. Paperwork strewn across a table. Computer screen idling on the corner of a desk. NHS files much like the Dept for Education equivalents in my office. And there, centre stage, was the neurologist who - until this moment - was merely a name on an appointment letter. In the next few moments this was to change, but not only that, you could say my life was to change.

The consultant invited us to take a seat and asked a series of questions about my health, why I had gone to my GP a month or so previously, to which I explained about the falls, the tiredness, the inability to concentrate, the *petite mal* type phases recently experienced. He listened intently to what seemed like a long explanation but wasn't really. Then he embarked on a series of what I thought of as silly questions, what month is it, what season, who is the Prime Minister, count back from 70 in sevens - all very easy. Then onto him reading three words and asking me to repeat them - I hadn't a clue, where are we at this moment - can't remember the name of the hospital but it's in Margate, isn't that good enough? Then the three words/ objects again - still they didn't register. This prompted him to pause and turn his, and then our, attention to his computer screen.

'Well Mr. Oliver, I think that the results of your scan and what you have said to me today is consistent with early stages of Alzheimer's Disease.'

He went on to say that the GP had referred me for the scan to rule out a brain tumour. He assured me there was no tumour. Along with Alzheimer's this was the first time this had been mentioned.

I was speechless. My wife was speechless. He sensed this, and went on to explain that this was a suggested diagnosis and lots more tests and scans would be required in order for this to be confirmed. He then drew two helpful pictures, showing as he described it, a healthy 54-year-old brain; and then he drew mine based on the scan - he did try and explain the scan to us but it was too difficult to draw sense from it. The comparisons the drawings illustrated were helpful then, and subsequently as we came to terms with this and tried to explain it to friends and family. By now I was regaining some sense of the moment and the dialogue which was necessary I felt. The first question revolved around the subsequent tests and scans, then we moved to talk about carrying on working, which I wanted to do.

Next we raised the question of our forthcoming, long booked annual trip to Australia. We were alarmed by his response to this which was not to go. But everything is planned and paid for...? His advice remained the same. Subsequently, I reflected upon this. Determined with Rosemary's support to go ahead with the trip, albeit with a slightly amended itinerary, I wrote to the neurologist to say I felt with us visiting friends and having been many times before the benefits far outweighed any potential risks. Thankfully, he was kind enough to send a written reply stating that if I felt well enough then I should go.

It left me though with the thought which I've never forgotten which is, had I taken his advice (as many would have done in that situation) we would have missed a wonderful trip which has subsequently been followed by four more trips to South Australia, our beloved place in the sun.

The sun was still shining as we emerged from the confines of the hospital. I suggested to Rosemary, 'Let's have a walk on the beach nearby,' (a favourite spot of ours), 'to clear our heads and take stock, and I'll ring school to get someone to cover my lunch duty.' That's what we did, and I turned to Rosemary the moment we felt the sand under our feet, and I said, 'One door closes and one door will open.' I didn't know which door it would be, but I have been proved right.

That piece was taken from a new book entitled *Welcome to our World*, which I'm delighted to have written with seven other people with dementia. It has a wonderful foreword written for us by Jo Brand, and will be published just in time for us to launch it at Alzheimer's Europe in Glasgow and UK Dementia Congress in Brighton. This is the first book of life writing to be published by a collection of people with dementia.

After leaving the tender care of the neurologist I landed up soon after in Canterbury's Memory Clinic. My route through the continued assessment was complex because, despite my difficulties, the last thing I wanted was a confirmed diagnosis. I tackled each assessment as crucial and tried to retain a positive attitude, allied to a real determination to score as highly as possible.

I quickly developed screening strategies to protect myself from my difficulties - something I still do.

Over a period of three months I had a number of cognitive assessments, all of which I gave 100% towards, and came away from exhausted. I was extremely well supported and informed by the psychiatrist, the clinical psychologist and her assistant. Every assessment was scored, analysed, and reported back at each stage which built a gradual, comprehensive picture of areas where at best I was functioning at about the 40th centile, but at worst was performing in the bottom 5th centile. Alarming for someone who had, nine months earlier (despite worries at the back of my mind) been well on course for an MA in educational leadership; now even following Coronation Street was a challenge.

People know how dementia is portrayed in the media, and by large sections of the public, and are often frightened and can be depressed. Giving encouragement to live in the moment and to take each day as it comes is essential. Coping strategies to recover and retain one's own personhood, skills and enthusiasms is essential. Positive living requires the acceptance by the person and those close to them that not every day will be as clear as we would wish for.

The need for services which provide the opportunity for people to be interdependent, to be able to relate to others on a range of levels is essential. Some people like the dementia café-type model, some require something rather more such as provided by the FMNs - more of that before lunch. Some people want to live life without reference to dementia, others want to fight it, others to live with it and others alongside it.

Through the person-centred care I would like to see a range of therapies and activities made available to people which are local, interesting and accessible. Please keep people on the radar - what is rejected now might be extremely helpful and appealing later. A care-plan worthy of the name needs to be the key to dementia pathways which is written with the person and a clinician and reviewed at a relevant period, i.e. perhaps six-monthly, and which monitors the person's wellness in the light of the pathways they are following, not solely their medication. The emphasis needs to be on realistic positivity. I remember being offered on two occasions antidepressants because the neurologist felt I would need them - I never cashed the prescription and know others who have done the same. For some it might help. Resources - both in terms of people from a range of disciplines such as clinical psychologists, psychiatrists and OTs, need to be available for post-diagnosis groups which are currently run across the country but are inconsistent. The worst feeling is that sense of being on one's own and having little or no effective support from outside the immediate family/ social circle. Pathways has to address this. Some people are comfortable with the support of the GP, but many feel that the GP lacks knowledge and understanding of dementia.

We need to ensure that agencies work together, and that the person with dementia is at the centre of this collaboration - not each vested interest or agenda. Signposting and mutual support for professionals and the public needs to be far better. We MUST avoid the notion that the clinician's sole role is to diagnose and then hand over to the voluntary sector, some of the best post-diagnosis support I have received and others I know have received has been from clinical psychologists via the post-diagnosis groups and then the Forget Me Nots.

Often it is helpful to use metaphors to describe what it is like to live with dementia, and one of the most accurate is that of the weather - the foggy days which are challenging and difficult, the cloudy ones when some things are clearer than others, and the sunny days we crave: thank you for listening to me and consequently for making this a sunny day for me.

Talk delivered to Faculty of Psychology Older People at the British Psychology Society conference in London on 13th July 2015

Context: I delivered this talk twice, both times with Reinhard plus a student. I shared the role this time with Chris Ryan.

Good morning. Whilst I'm honoured and flattered to be asked to speak this morning, I'm also a little anxious. In order to support me I hope you understand I will have to read from a script.

When contemplating retirement from my career as a head teacher, I imagined myself sitting in my garden reading a book in the sunshine, although this choice of material (hold up two booklets) wasn't in my expectations at the time. However, my diagnosis of Alzheimer's at 55 and my wife's enjoyment from watching *Neighbours* at lunchtime has prompted me to read many books about dementia, and to be involved in the writing of a number, two of which are what I consider to be these extremely important publications, more of which I'll talk about as my presentation unfolds.

I'm delighted that these publications carry the endorsement of four organisations which I am proud to be involved with, these being the British Psychological Society, the Alzheimer's Society, the Dementia Action Alliance, and the Dementia Engagement and Empowerment Project.

Although widely accepted I make no apologies for saying that everyone with dementia is a unique individual, and I know from being a head teacher of a school with almost 500 unique individual children this can provide many challenges to those providing services which engage and support people's needs.

Whilst dementia has changed my life, and continues to do so, I am still underneath this veneer the same person with beliefs, interests, connections and flaws. I hate the analogy of being on a journey at the best of times, but get very cross when it's used to describe the progression of dementia. Having been on many journeys both for pleasure and with coach loads of children, each journey has a destination we wish to arrive at – often as soon as possible. With regards to dementia, this is not the case. We want to stop or get off the bus. Dementia pathway seems more fitting.

For everyone, life can be described as a journey, and our past has a bearing on our present. Before speaking in depth about my dementia experience, I think it worth explaining a little more about me as a person, and how I would wish to be defined. Firstly, I live in Canterbury with my wife and have three grown up children and three grandchildren. For 33 years I was a primary school teacher and a head teacher, and in the latter days of my career was Canterbury's primary school advisor. On New Year's Eve, 2010, I received a confirmed diagnosis of Alzheimer's disease, at the age of 55. So how would I define myself? Husband? Yes. Parent and grandparent? Yes. Ex- teacher, head teacher? Yes. Person with dementia? Yes. Because I am all of those things, and not just one. My experience is that so often it is the latter label by which one is judged.

Pre-diagnostic counselling and consent
There is no question that the early consultations between professional and service user are crucial in establishing trust and confidence in the process and the individuals, from the service user's perspective. A timely and accurate diagnosis is crucial, but needs to be delivered in a supportive manner.

In my case the diagnosis period took seven months, from the day where, totally out of the blue, it was suggested by a neurologist based on scans and an initial assessment that I had the early signs of Alzheimer's, through to confirmation at the Memory Clinic, I feel I was very well supported in an honest, clear and compassionate way, with information given that I could understand in a way that was meaningful to me. This was true person-centred care, and at all stages I was given the option of an opt-out clause, which of course I declined, because I wished to know what it was that was giving me these difficulties and confrontations in my life.

There was a little bit of discussion with the clinical psychologist and her assistant around the changes and challenges that I and my wife were confronting, but there was no signposting for further information and support. I tried to fill that vacuum by reading myself around the subject and by going to the Alzheimer's Society website. Books I read at the time included James Warner and Nori Graham's brilliant little guide (**Hold up book**) and *My Bonnie* by John Suchet.

The Alzheimer's Society website proved a mixed blessing. The factsheets were and continue to be a great source of accurate information and helped a lot. Because there was no person in East Kent available from the Society I could engage with, I was signposted to the Talking Point blog. That was not helpful. On the day I visited this, early in 2011, it appeared to be a resource for carers to share their horror stories, and to seek mutual support and reassurance. I have never been back there since.

The dialogue established during the pre-diagnosis phase is important because it builds the person's understanding of both the condition they are experiencing, the range of support that might be available, and the professionals who might be delivering that support. To a person with dementia whose ability to cognitively retain information is diminishing, the relationship that is being formed with the people caring for us is crucial, and the person with dementia will take from many of those appointments a sense that we are being looked after, or that we are being dumped.

Cognitive assessment/ Communicating a diagnosis

I guess like most, my cognitive assessment began with the beloved MMSE, which I've probably now encountered a few times. I can remember scoring well on that with the exception of remembering the three items, and every time that catches me out. Because, I guess, I am still able to operate fairly well intellectually, this provided a greater challenge to the psychologist and the psychiatrist doing my assessment. I desperately wanted to score highly, and I wanted them to tell me that I wasn't likely to get a diagnosis of dementia. The tests I was given were the RBANS, Weschler Memory Scale and Weschler Reading. In the case of the former, the memory test, I was in the 13th centile for one part, and the 7th and 5th centile for another. My overall score on delayed memory placed me in the 3rd centile.

Now from a lifetime in education, I understood what centiles meant, and this was quite an alarming realisation. I guess it would have bypassed many, because they wouldn't have understood the significance of centiles.

I was also given the D-KEFS. The report I received from the psychologist who carried out my test, which went into detail about what the tests showed, is perhaps untypical of the experience of most service users (HOLD UP REPORT) At each cognitive assessment appointment, time was also factored in for *me* to report back to the psychologist around how I was feeling, not just about the assessment, but about my health and circumstances at the time. This meant a great deal to me, as did having the phone number of an administrative clerk who I could speak with about concerns regarding appointments. The tests were exhausting, but also exhaustive, and gave a comprehensive assessment of my cognitive abilities.

Whether it was the psychiatrist, the psychologist or the assistant psychologist who was delivering the cognitive assessment, I had equal confidence in their professional and personal skills, and I found this enormously supportive, and it gave me the confidence in the service that was being provided, and the accuracy of the assessment.

During this time, my GP was quite supportive, and whilst I get along well with him, I am not at all confident that he would have the skills, experience, or understanding to deliver a diagnosis of dementia in the way that it was delivered for me, or indeed for most other cases of people I've come across.

Again, during my assessment, I referred to James Warner and Nori Graham's book, which was really helpful in understanding what scans and assessments were going to involve.

Going back to my point about everyone being different, right from day one, I wanted to know what I was confronting and what support was going to be available to me. The neurologist at the initial appointment drew me some illustrations of a healthy brain and my brain, which I found really helpful. The clinical psychologist at each assessment appointment held at the memory clinic, talked me through in some detail the previous assessment, outlining where I was performing better and areas I was finding more difficult. There was a little bit of advice around coping with the areas of difficulty. Now for other people, this might not be appropriate. When this issue is discussed within our Forget Me Not group, whilst there is a range of views expressed, by and large this group of people who are more accepting of their diagnosis are consequently keener to know more, and indeed made some significant contributions to the two books that we are here to discuss today.

Post-diagnostic support and psychosocial treatments

There is no question, there are a number of cliff-edge moments for people being diagnosed with dementia. One is the point of diagnosis, and another is often the realisation that, for them, they think there is nothing available to help. Whilst I think my medication of Galantamine is helping me - and since November 2014 I am now on the maximum dose - I know absolutely that good quality psychosocial support and interventions do work, do help, and do allow me to live as well as possible with dementia.

I am delighted that the four main organisations involved in these books are best placed to deliver quality post-diagnostic treatment and support. I know this through the personal experience of myself and many others who I meet with. I whole-heartedly commend to you today the Guide to Psychosocial Interventions in Early Stages of Dementia.

My endorsement of this book comes in part from my involvement, along with a number of other service users, when it was being compiled, and from accessing some of the therapies and programmes it advocates. We felt, as service users, that it was comprehensive, clearly set out and accessible, and would be useful for both providers and users of services. The partnership of professionals, academics and service users in its production are fundamentally at the root of its credibility. There was great optimism amongst the service users involved, which for many replaced previous feelings of distress and poor expectation of what was available.

For some, of course, there is no medication available due to the type of dementia which they live with. There is still a lack of understanding amongst politicians and some in the medical profession around the need to invest money and resources into this crucial area. The consequences of not doing so are greater distress for people with dementia, increased isolation and, in many cases, greater reliance upon hospitals and care homes. I get a sense that the NHS are looking to address the lack of effective care plans for people with dementia, because this is a key to making progress. Previously care plans solely seemed to record medication and its impact.

There seems to be an expectation that people with dementia will be depressed, and we are offered, in the early stages, medication to address this. I have always turned this down, but would never turn down the opportunity to engage with others, to enjoy the company of others, and to gain a sense of purposefulness and comradeship that often come from the interventions outlined in these books.

Everyone is unique and different, and there does need to be a range of treatment and support available from which people can choose. For some, the Forget Me Not model works well.

(HAND OVER TO CHRIS TO OUTLINE HOW FORGET ME NOTS WORKS)

For others, a dementia café fulfills their needs. I would like to see life story work being utilised more with people in the early and mid-stages, because at the moment, it strikes me that it is often left too late, and consequently the person with dementia is not able to be as fully engaged in its production and review as they perhaps should be.

There needs to be a much greater cross over working between agencies and departments, and a greater sharing of information. Again, these booklets will help with that, I'm sure.

I do a lot of training for the Alzheimer's Society, and I talk to staff there about evaluating treatments, services and programmes that they are delivering, and encourage them to do this in a robust and detailed way in order to ensure that the best standards are achieved. Simply saying to a service user, 'Did you like that?' is not good enough. Professionals should not underestimate the level of support required for people to engage effectively with these treatments and programmes. The best interventions I have seen, either through the Forget Me Nots, or elsewhere, have been where this support has been fundamental and readily available both before, during and after the intervention. (Plug *Welcome to our World.*)

Keith Oliver assisted by Lewis Slade

Have things improved in dementia care in the last ten years? Delivered at UK Dementia Congress, Telford. Tuesday 3rd November 2015

Context: This talk formed part of the opening debate for the National congress. I shared the podium with a number of professionals, including Reinhard, each of whom spoke for or against the question set by the organisers. Having Reinhard also on stage with me, and some familiar faces in the audience helped settle my nerves.

Whilst I am comfortable speaking for the motion, it won't surprise anyone who knows me that there are many mountains still to climb. Indeed climbing is a good analogy, as I used to do this quite a lot as a student, and would always be excited but frustrated when I thought I'd reached a peak only to see sometimes through fog (another analogy) that it soared up above enticing me to push on to the next stage.

Climbing mountains is always safer and more fun with others, and being isolated it's easy to feel less positive, but I am a glass-half-full kind of person, and working collectively over the past ten years, a great deal has been achieved. I rarely see myself lucky to have dementia, but I do see myself as lucky to have developed it in the past five years rather than ten years ago.

Great strides on service user involvement led by DEEP are to be applauded. Again with additional funding through Comic Relief who usually back a winner, it's pleasing that this project is to be built upon over the next few years. This country is being looked to as an exemplar of excellent practice around service user involvement. Groups linked to DEEP have grown from 12 to over 60 in just a few years. It's not just numbers, it's the excellent work being done which ten years ago would never have been envisaged.

Similarly, with the Carers' Call to Action moving now to its next stage as TIDE, thus giving a voice and a forum alongside numerous local outstanding carer's groups providing heaps for this crucial and vital group of people - vital to us as individuals and to society as a whole. Alongside this many areas now have the wonderful, growing service of Admiral nurses. Not enough I know but again, what was there ten years ago?

The DAA initiative is established in seeking cooperation and collaboration, and is a worthwhile network which should provide a firm basis for positive impact. I know as an active affiliate that the Alliance is well set to build upon gains and this is partly evidenced through the local alliances and the dementia friendly communities which, for some people, are making a real difference.

If we consider research where additional funding is now available, and I am delighted to see it being spent through the Alzheimer's Society's excellent Research Network, on both seeking a cure AND supporting care and well-being of those affected by dementia. I know it is from a low starting point, but the increase in spending by government, third sector and yes - the drugs companies - is both substantial and to be applauded. There is a real desire now to raise and spend even more and to develop sustained excellent researchers in larger numbers devoted to dementia research which wasn't previously the case.

Events such as UKDC illustrate some amazing work happening in our country. Central to this, over the past ten years, there has been much greater service user involvement, which has enriched the lives of those involved, both as users and providers of services.

For me the best thing about having dementia is the wonderful people I have met in the past five years, either as a person affected by dementia or as someone supporting or caring for us. They need and deserve the confidence and support we can all give them to know that their efforts are valued and that progress towards a situation we can all be justly proud of is attainable. It is tempting to seek (with the spirit of Kitwood watching over us) a replacement for the great man; this isn't, I feel, necessary, as there are many replacements and lots of them are here today. Let us build upon the successes of the past ten years as we all seek further improvements.

'From little things... Big things grow!' Talk with Tommy Dunne given at DAA annual meeting in London, 9th December 2015

Context: Invited to present a 'rallying speech' to endorse collaborative working within the DAA which is its main theme. Shared podium with fellow service user Tommy from Liverpool who is also a board member. This was the first time I met Richard Madeley, who chaired the event.

As new members of the DAA board, Tommy and I are both very pleased and honoured to have the opportunity to speak today. Although new to the Board I have been an active affiliate and member of the National Alliance since October 2011, and it is about the Alliance that I wish to speak this morning.

It's fair to say that in my first year or so I just listened, watched, thought and reflected upon the Alliance. I attended all the meetings and I learnt a lot from both the professionals and the other people affected by dementia who I got to know and came to see as friends. To be able to do this I needed support, and I got excellent support from Sarah, Simon, Renee, Reinhard and some Kent University psychology students on placement with the Kent & Medway NHS Partnership Trust.

As a former head teacher and primary school advisor I have always seen the potential benefits and also challenges involved in working collectively and in collaboration. This involves giving something in order to receive, and in order to see progress across a broad front. I remember the Labour Government's vision of a children's department where the child was at the centre of all relevant services and that education, health, local and national government, social services, the police etc. would all work together for the benefit of what we saw as the child, although other agencies sometimes saw them, instead, as the key 'stakeholder.'

First issue: we didn't always speak a common language. We didn't always understand the other professionals' perspective. Professionals didn't always want to share our knowledge or expertise, and rarely did folk want to share their budgets.

Now, if we replace the child with a person living with dementia and take education out of the picture and add the third sector, we have a parallel with regards to dementia care, which we think and know should be person-centred.

I see in the DAA an outstanding opportunity. An opportunity to bring together the best this country provides by way of service providers allied to a committed band of people affected by dementia in order to bring about the best services which can be provided for the maximum number of people.

The title of the DAA sums it up. Dementia needs to be first and foremost, as recognising and naming it is the first stage to addressing the issues it presents to all; action is next to make things significantly better and today's programme clearly shows this intention in a number of areas; in order to achieve this we do need to work closely together, and that is the idea of Alliance. One feature of today's conference is the desire for greater engagement of our membership and the board are keen to help facilitate and more importantly achieve this through a series of initiatives designed to achieve greater involvement of you all.

Recently I was asked by the Journal of Dementia Care to write about how I thought dementia care has improved over the past ten years, and we then took this to Congress for the debate. Clearly there has been much progress in SOME aspects, for example in service-user involvement - much of which is coordinated by DEEP and TIDE - and in some parts of the country, but there is still a long way to go. Improvements in diagnosis rates are to be commended. Although this does place extra pressure on the need to support the people affected by dementia.

There is some good quality post-diagnostic support and treatments - some delivered by professionals in the NHS and others by the third sector. Some of the best treatments I have benefited from have not come in a bottle but through some outstanding psycho-social interventions. Recently my consultant psychiatrist (who I taught for two years in primary school - I cared for him, now he cares for me) wrote my care plan - it took five years to get and ten minutes to write.

One of the best ways of achieving our goals of good quality care for everyone living with dementia is through working together, and one of the best vehicles to achieve this is the DAA.

Shared tribute to Peter Ashley at DAA Annual Conference (DB/KO) Wed 9th December 2015

Context: I was asked to co-present with Professor Dawn Brooker a tribute to Peter Ashley, who had recently passed away. Peter was an early advocate who also very much walked the walk and talked the talk, and I was proud and honoured to have been asked to write and say these words in his honour with his family and members of the DAA present.

Firstly, Peter always referred to people with dementia and their carers' as being the two sides of the same coin.

I am honoured and pleased, though rather humbled to have been asked to contribute to this tribute today to our dear friend Peter. I would like my piece to be seen as a thank you to him.

I have known Peter really well for four years, and I wish to express my thanks for his humour, intellect and wisdom which is always a powerful combination, especially when found in a friend and ally.

Secondly, to say thanks to him for asking the questions many of us thought about but lacked the confidence to ask, and for those questions which never occurred to us because we didn't have the benefits of his insight or experience.

Thirdly, thank you Peter for holding the professionals to the tasks they needed to address by teaching them what it really is like to live with a dementia. 'A,' though a short word was a big word when used by Peter, and he was A big star. A pioneer, an advocate in the truest sense of the word and the first to pick up the baton (hold up relay baton I will have from local primary school), move forward with it and as a part of his legacy to pass it on. Many aspire to leave the world a better place than when we arrived, although few achieve this. Thank you sincerely Peter for giving hope to us all who follow on from you that through your efforts and success, maybe we can also achieve this. I am proud that I am here along with George, Lorraine, Tommy, Trevor and Peter who are here today to pick it up and to build upon your lasting contribution.

Personal perspectives on living with dementia and cognitive decline (Talk delivered to Global Agenda Council on Ageing Symposium, London. 4th February 2016)

Context: Invited by Age UK to speak at this international event - second of three, first in Tokyo, third in Philadelphia. The aim was to speak to professionals about dementia and ageing.

Good morning. Whilst I'm honoured and flattered to be asked to speak today, I'm also a little anxious. waiting to speak I was drawn to my ID badge which says, 'If found please return to KMPT NHS offices in Maidstone.' I'm not sure if it means the badge or me! I've nothing against Maidstone, but I'd much rather be returned to my home in Canterbury!

In order to support me I hope you understand I will have to read from a script.

The main reason for needing a script is that for the past five years I have knowingly been increasingly sharing my brain with an unwelcome and unwanted guest, Dr. Alzheimer, as I was diagnosed at the age of 55 as a host to this insidious visitor on New Year's Eve 2010. Others who share my life are so much more welcome and friendly, amongst whom are my wife, my three adult children and my three grandchildren. Others who have entered my life over the past five years and have made such a positive impact upon me include other service users and some wonderful professionals working in the NHS and in the Third Sector. Speaking of the latter I want to acknowledge the outstanding support Rosemary and I have received from Age UK staff in the lead up to and during the course of this Symposium, especially from Celia and Lea, both of whom have been tremendous.

Like all good teachers I recognise the value of messages in stories, and here is a true one: I am now going to read an extract from this little book about a day which changed my life and that of my wife. (Read about the day I received my diagnosis on pp321-323)

After leaving the tender care of the neurologist I landed up soon after in Canterbury's Memory Clinic. My route through the continued assessment was complex because despite my difficulties the last thing I wanted was a confirmed diagnosis. I tackled each assessment as crucial and tried to retain a positive attitude allied to a real determination to score as highly as possible. I quickly developed screening strategies to protect myself from my difficulties - something I still do.

Over a period of three months I had a number of cognitive assessments all of which I gave 100% towards and came away from exhausted. I was extremely well supported and informed by the Psychiatrist, the clinical psychologist and her assistant. Every assessment was scored, analysed and reported back at each stage which built a gradual, comprehensive picture of how I was mentally functioning.

I wrote this talk on a day of appalling stories (19 Jan 2016) in the media around dementia particularly connected to hospitals. (Hold up and make reference to the newspaper articles)

Frustrating and worrying that the thing about having dementia is what frightens me and others the most is the failure or lack of appropriate person-centred care as portrayed in reality and in the press. How much better would life be for people with dementia if the Kitwood Flower was a consistent reality. Is this too much to ask for from one of the world's wealthiest countries in

340

2016? There is no question that as society we stigmatise the elderly, and those with dementia are further stigmatised. When you are a younger person with dementia because one doesn't conform to the stereotypical image people have of someone with dementia, the disbelief and difficulties are always different and are often greater.

Whilst it is often hard to find positives in having dementia, for me the most positive aspect has been the many outstanding people who have come into my life since I was diagnosed. Some of them are other people affected by dementia - with a diagnosis for themselves or their loved ones; some are professionals working in the NHS or psychology students who are the professionals of tomorrow, and amongst those who have had the biggest positive impact are those working in the third sector primarily at the Alzheimer's Society in London and at Age UK in Canterbury - especially Dementia Outreach Manager Judy Ayris, who was outstanding in her support for Rosemary and I when navigating the minefield of legal and financial matters in the early days, and who has since, as a professional friend encouraged us to attend relevant events in Canterbury.

Once our Powers of Attorney, wills, pensions and allowances were sorted we next turned to our banking arrangements. About two to three years ago we changed bank, and our new bank is so much more effective in meeting our banking needs. All their staff were trained as 'dementia-friends,' and many went beyond this. We were given a named member of staff who helped us with things like activating cards, maximising banking benefits in a clear person-centred way, gave us his work mobile number, and who was always friendly and helpful in answering any queries or letters we didn't understand. The bank sent us weekly texts with a mini-statement and a text if our account is getting low on funds. Whilst still able to use PIN we have looked at other options than PIN whilst maintaining maximum security for our account. Although our previous bank staff were efficient and friendly they could offer nothing like this.

Still, I live on, I try and live as well as possible with all the challenges that dementia presents. At one time I thought that I was 'bullet proof.' I was wrong; no one is. Treatments don't just come in a bottle, and support can mean intervention in order to help people to live as well as possible with dementia. My aspiration remains that tomorrow is better than today for others and myself.

I began with reading from this book which I co-authored. £5 available today - all proceeds to Alzheimer's Society (read bit from Jo Brand.)

It's been said that I inspire. I am very unsure of this. To inspire in my view means that positive change follows. We shall see.

Men's perspective on dementia (Talk delivered for the VERDE project conference in London. Thursday 2nd June 2016)

Context: potentially a tough one! A conference and project focusing on the needs of women and here I was, asked to give a man's perspective! I need not have worried. Delegates, many of whom I know, were interested and supportive of my views and reasoning. I handed over to Joy Watson's husband, Tony, who spoke from his perspective as a male carer for his wife.

Thank you Toby and Jo for asking me to speak to you today and for giving Rosemary and I the privilege of listening to some excellent talks. When thinking about today, I was tempted to come dressed as one of my heroes, Grayson Perry, but thankfully for everyone (not least Rosemary) I decided just to opt for the pink shirt and tie.

Coming from a background of home - wife, daughter, strong mother who also had Alzheimer's and work for 33 years in primary schools which has been 95% female focused, I do understand and support the issues being covered. Much of what we have heard and will hear is gender specific but a lot of it isn't; I think that also applies to parts of my talk.

I guess I am here with my friend Tony representing blokes, and as a fan of the late, great David Bowie, it will be good to show there is still life on Mars. Having said that I'm pleased not to come on to strains of Holst and Mars from the Planet suite, although there are times in groups I've been involved in when anger, frustration and pain shown by some men present might have made that very fitting. Thinking also of music, when Nada Googled Verde, it gave references to the composer Verdi, which set my thoughts onto another great classical composer - Ravel. I wonder if you knew that he composed the Bolero after developing Young Onset dementia in his 50s? Amazing and inspiring.

All my talks are written with the audience in mind, and this is a tough subject because, a) there is a dearth of information out there beyond my own personal experience, b) it is very personal and c) it is so easy to get it wrong and upset some people. I'll try my best to make it useful to you and avoid the last point.

As a panel and board member of the Alzheimer's Society Research Network I have yet to see, in the four years I've been involved, a project submitted from a UK University setting out to investigate the impact dementia has on men and ways men can try to live well if affected by it. My friend Alison Milne from Kent University pointed me to a tiny project called the 'World Cup Effect' carried out in 2010, which looked at a small group of men with dementia and how engaging them in watching football led to some well-being gains.

I also found a piece in the Daily Mail dated 22nd March 2013 which looked at early warning signs in men developing dementia with Lewey Bodies, and this was based on US research from Mayo Clinics in Minnesota and Florida and involved 75 men. These signs were around walking, talking and hitting out when asleep. Now I used to love football but am not so keen now, and as far as I know I have never sleep walked, or hit out, although Rosemary tells me that for the past year or two I have occasionally talked in my sleep - sometimes making more sense than when I'm awake!

Not much there for me to flex my limited biceps on!

One consequence of having dementia for me is that my previous strong cognitive engagement with people is now much less so and has been largely replaced with a more emotional engagement. I now no longer remember what people say to me, but I do remember how they made me feel. This is very different from how I was as a head or a teacher. I guess this is seen as a more female trait generally.

So, what is it about me that is maybe typical of how dementia affects a bloke who has it? Firstly, as a person with Young Onset I had to give up my career - one I was very successful in as a head teacher and adviser who was also well on course for an MA in Educational Leadership - that stopped too, as it became too hard to concentrate, learn and remember and write lengthy pieces.

I was the main bread winner and was comfortable in that role, seeing it as part of my 'husband' persona. I feared how the diagnosis would affect perceptions in my family of my role as father and granddad: I need not have worried, things on that front have remained very positive.

I seldom go to the GP - typical of men, and I would argue that there are many more men out there undiagnosed because they simply do not come forward, either to have concerns checked or to be part of the covert checking by GPs of the over 75 age group. I read a piece in the Independent recently about men in masculine jobs ignoring cancer symptoms. I am sure this is common to dementia as well.

I am a driven, a very independent sort of person, who tries to retain a sense of inter-dependence - more difficult I feel for men who are often, like me, less comfortable in social settings - dementia makes one act like a gawky teenager again at times, at others social inhibitions might get changed or lowered and one can easily get embarrassed or embarrass others. Often people have their driving licence revoked. My spatial awareness is much worse, so things like decorating are more challenging. Word retrieval which, for me, was never a problem is now difficult at times, and it's the same with writing and spelling - I find I miss out vowels and repeat significant consonants, e.g. when doing crosswords which we both do together to help our brains and because they are good fun.

Going back to the point about anger - I don't get angry but I do get frustrated. I have had a lifetime of dealing with anger in other people and have seen the pain it causes, but men do often get angry and show their anger at having dementia and not getting the support or the cure they crave; I understand this and try to help if I can. The book I am currently three quarters through reading is called something like *Totally Forgiving Yourself,* by an author I can't remember - I need your help and support to be able to, at times, forgive myself for my flaws and the occasional sense of guilt around having dementia.

Dementia from the Inside Out (Talk delivered in the main auditorium at Olympia for The Alzheimer's Show, Friday 10th June 2016)

Context: The organisers of this show heard me speak at the DAA in December and invited me to deliver a key note address at the Alzheimer's Show in London. I chose the theme of being inspired in the hope of inspiring maybe some of the audience which was a very mixed one - professionals, the public and people affected by dementia.

When approached last December and asked to speak today, words like 'inspired' and 'inspirational' were mentioned. Whilst this comment is well intended and made, and gratefully received, I am unsure how accurate it is in relation to my efforts. For anyone to be inspirational requires the inspired to take something significant from the experience and to either enhance and continue the good things they are doing or to amend or change practices to do them more effectively.

I am grateful and honoured to have been asked to speak to you today and I realise that you have invested time and expense to be here. I do hope that what I say will be interesting, thought- provoking, informative and maybe even a little inspiring! Please forgive that due to my dementia I will need to read from my notes.

The thread for my talk 'From the Inside Out' is this notion of inspiring. What inspires me to live as well as possible with dementia, and what can others take from this? Firstly, for me it is about people, and people with talents; one of these is the ability to engage through music. Now if I was to go to see my favourite singer-songwriter, Paul Simon, who has a new album out after a five-year gap, I would want to hear the old favourites alongside the new material. That is my plan for this new talk I've written for today, a mix of my old faithfuls and many new ideas and thoughts. I hope it works.

Often inspiring people cover the work of others and I will do the same, beginning with a quote from John Miles' hit from March 1976 entitled 'Music'

Music was my first love and it will be my last,

Music of the future and music of the past

There are important themes in those two lines which for me resonate on a number of levels connected to living with dementia. Looking back, looking forward; wistfully, happily, sadly, contemplating, recalling old times, friends, holidays, good times/ bad times. Music can inspire, and everyone's taste is, like all of us, unique and individual. My up to date choices on my iPod include Mumford and Sons whose first two albums I think are amongst my favourite ever and would come with me to a desert island, along with Johnny Cash's American recordings done in his later years with Rick Rubin, and two CDs of original songs written and recorded by Jennie Russell, a friend of mine whose music happily helped inspire my reconnection to the Christian faith.

The next point to make is that this isn't a talk about dementia (wait for audience to leave!) This is a talk about a person. A person who is trying to live well with dementia and who has done so with varying levels of support and success for the past five-and-a-half years. The majority of my support has been good, most has been exceptional. Some on-going, some too short- lived, and much missed when it ended. Some genuine, some tokenistic. Some freely given, and some at a cost to me either in time or emotion. Some genuinely focusing upon my needs, some purporting to be person-centred, but has been either process-centred or provider-centred. I could do a whole talk on my thoughts and experience of person centred care - remembering that I come from a background of striving to deliver this for children and often parents and staff, as well as in my role within our family.

The next inspiring person to mention is Tom Kitwood, who I never knew and who, alas, died back in the late 1990s. His 'Flower' model for me is crucial and I carry copies of this in my diary and in my CBT notebook which I take to sessions with the considerate and patient KMPT psychologist who is currently supporting me. The petals of the flower with love at its centre is precisely what care *should* be about, and whilst we are here today to focus upon dementia, I suggest this model works for far more aspects of life. Thank you, Tom, if you are looking down upon us today. I want to pause for a moment to allow us all to reflect upon what we see as the relevance of the words within this model. (PAUSE)

Reflecting further upon being inspired and inspiring others I noted down these thoughts which I would like to share with you and which I see as very relevant to this amazing event.

On my 50th birthday, my three kids joined together to buy me a new guitar and Rosemary bought me an amp. My previous one, bought when I was 17, was a bit past it. I treasured this new guitar and had lessons to be an even better musician. I loved playing it, and some people seemed to quite appreciate my efforts, but it was really for me. The last time it came out of its case was shortly before I was diagnosed. I haven't played it since. I have lost the confidence.

I'm telling you this because whilst I hope my talk is positive, there is no escape from the fact that Alzheimer's is a wretched condition and I would be living even better as a youthful, energetic, driven, bright(ish) 60-year-old if I didn't have it.

Confidence for me is now more fragile, I am thinner skinned and more easily hurt. Having said that, I feel that my emotional intelligence has now counter balanced deficits in my cognitive intelligence and I have done so many new things confidently which I wouldn't previously have considered, including going in a speed boat out into a choppy Thames estuary, loving swimming more than doing a couple of strokes, and standing in front of an audience talking about myself rather than in the second person about my school or others.

That's me engaging in an activity with others which I would have previously walked away from and not engaged with. This is a circle dance, and shows us responding to music and enjoying each other's company.

I am no different from others with dementia in enjoying inter-generational conversations and activities and some of these for me have revolved around music, including one psychology undergraduate who listed *The Sound of Silence* as a favourite song, and another who viewed Pink Floyd as one of his favourite bands. Numerous train trips to dementia events have been enriched for me by sharing musical tastes with these talented leading care professionals of tomorrow.

As a primary school teacher and head for 33 years I loved music, both listening and teaching it to the children. My choice of music for assemblies was wide and eclectic. For the assembly the day after my initial diagnosis I chose 'Time to Say Goodbye,' no-one but me and my senior staff knew the reasons. I held on for four more months before I knew the school door would need to close and a new one would open.

Other fundamental support I access to help me enjoy the best of health and live well includes weekly visits to my chiropractor who has taught me so much and has inspired me in ways I never thought possible. Their specialty is in the optimum function of the central nervous system with proactive methods to ensure my body is working at its very best, with spinal correction adjustments, deep tissue massages and a truly holistic approach, addressing my nutrition and mental wellness. I am convinced that Chiropractic care should be part of everyone's health plan. They have also provided me with inspiring reading including *The 7 Habits of Highly Effective People* by Steven Covey which has allowed me to understand dependence - independence - interdependence. A book that everyone here today should read. Oh, how I wish I had read that when I was working. Please don't seek just to make people with dementia independent but go further and encourage, support and seek ways to enhance inter-dependence as we are really social beings not best placed in isolation, albeit independent isolation.

The next musical inspiration is an Aussie singer-songwriter, Eric Bogle, I discovered his music when I taught in Australia. Before saying more about him, just to say Australia is a very special, inspiring place to my wife and I - partly due to the Aussie people and the music, but also the diverse and beautiful country. Those of you who have read our book *Welcome to our World* will know that when diagnosed the neurologist told us to cancel a planned trip Down Under - to be our 14th visit to Adelaide. I didn't take his advice and we have been back safely and happily with professional travel industry support five more times since and laid down even more happy memories of this amazing place and its people. One can draw from this the value of travel to living well.

Finally, and most importantly amongst people who inspire me are Rosemary, Gareth, Karon, James, Byron, Rhian and William - my family who share my life and whose love transcends the inspiration music provides, because at the end of the day music helps me to live well with dementia, but it is the people close to us who make the biggest difference.

I have learnt a lot with you today and have enjoyed planning, writing and delivering this talk for you all. I do hope you have found it inspiring because there are thousands of other people out there affected by dementia who need you to be inspired so that they, too, can live well with dementia.

Garden Talk at RHS Hampton Court Flower Show conference on Health & Horticulture. Monday 4th July 2016

As a person with dementia who loves gardening, I am honoured to have been asked by the RHS and the Dementia Engagement and Empowerment Project to speak to you today.

There are so many benefits I derive from gardening, and in order for my garden to thrive it needs good weather - lots of sunshine, some water and some love. There's a parallel with having dementia, where some days for me are 'sunny' and positive days, others are 'foggy,' when I am less able to live well. I need to be nourished and hydrated and this is something which often doesn't happen with people who have dementia. Unsurprisingly, love is fundamental, not only from those close to us personally, but professional love based upon person-centred care is also essential.

Benefits of gardening for someone with dementia include remaining physically, mentally, emotionally and spiritually well.

Exercise is relevant to all four areas. Key benefits alongside being active include being outdoors absorbing vitamin D from the lovely sunshine, thinking and problem-solving, enjoying the results of our efforts, feeling contented and relaxed, and recognising the importance of elements beyond our control. Benefits, though, come with challenges. Having dementia is more than poor memory. My balance, my thinking skills, my sense of smell, my spatial awareness and self-esteem all take hits on those foggy dementia days, and it is the benefits as well as the medication I take which restores the sun.

Dementia affects all in the family. My late friend, Peter Ashley, who had dementia, referred to him and his wife as being two sides of the same coin. He was right. Gardening is an activity my wife and I can still share, both by way of labour and rewards. However, like so many other things, dementia brings change, and we have had to adapt what roles and tasks we share within the garden.

Gardening can also be a shared activity within a group, and there are some, though not enough, gardening projects and clubs for people affected by dementia. The benefits I've mentioned earlier can have added to them that this shared activity has great social and well-being benefits. We're always keen to share our garden with visitors, and alongside human friends we are keen to encourage and share it with wildlife such as bees, hedgehogs, birds and butterflies all of which so enrich our experience and quality of life.

Moving from my current situation now, to a probable future, which could well be in a care home. I/we dread giving up our lovely garden, but when we do, I hope I can be in a home where there is a garden, and it is experienced and enjoyed by residents like me, and that staff encourage this. So often it's a sterile green space.

Finally, to close, I was recently asked, if I was a flower, which would I be? I chose daffodil quite quickly as it heralds Spring - more sun than fog, and also if I'm grown in the hills which I love, my sap can be used to produce Galantamine - the drug I am prescribed for my Alzheimer's. That way I can give my sap to help others with this same condition. Thank you for listening.

The next talk...

Context: Looking to the future.

As Eric Bogle sings in John Munro's song *While I am Here*: I know I won't be able to write and deliver talks for that much longer, but whilst I can I certainly want to, and this is looking to the future. Hopefully this section of the book will encourage and inspire others to Walk the Walk and TALK THE TALK.

Well, that closes this section of the book and brings the reader right up to date with my story, my work and my life. Looking to the future, I am scheduled to deliver a number of talks through until April 2017 including some old venues such as UK Dementia Congress in Brighton and some new ones - working with Dr James Warner on a project in the city of London.

As Reinhard Guss said at the start of the book he is *'looking forward to continuing with our professional friendship for many years to come.'* Now, whether or not I can carry on doing more talks for many years to come remains to be seen. This will depend upon a number of factors, many of which I have covered within this book, namely my health and the support I can receive from family and friends, especially the many professional friends who firstly patiently sat and listened to these talks and now have stamina and endurance to read them!

Thank you, dear reader and friend, and as John Lennon said on the Beatles final roof top gig, I hope I've passed the audition.
Keith Oliver (Canterbury, October 2016)

Glossary of terms, acronyms and abbreviations

AD - Alzheimer's Disease

ALWAYS project - Action on Living Well - Asking You

CBT - Cognitive Behaviour Therapy

CST - Cognitive Stimulation Therapy

CCCU - Canterbury Christ Church University

DAA - Dementia Action Alliance

DEEP - Dementia Engagement & Empowerment Project

D-KEFS – Memory/cognition assessment test

EKIDS - East Kent Independent Dementia Support

FMN - Forget Me Nots

IDEAL project - Improving the experience of Dementia & Enhancing Active Life

KCC - Kent County Council

KMPT - Kent & Medway NHS & Social care Partnership Trust

LPA - Lasting Power of Attorney

MMSE - Mini Mental State Examination

MRI scan - Magnetic Resonance Imaging

MSNAP - Memory Services National Accreditation Programme

OT - Occupational Therapy

PET scan - Positron Emission Topography scan

PREVENT - Midlife Prevention of Late Life Alzheimer's Disease Project

RBANS – Memory/cognition Assessment Test

RCP - Royal College of Psychiatrists

SLT - Senior Leadership Team

SU - Service User

TIDE - Together In Dementia Everyday - carers support

VERDe - Values, Equality, Rights and Dementia project

YOD - Young Onset Dementia

Acknowledgements

When first thinking about writing a book on my own I felt daunted and tried to walk away from the idea. It was only when sitting down and thinking about how I might tackle this project that I struck upon the idea of using family and friends to contribute in the way they have. Although it was never my intention, it could be said that I am getting others to write the book for me!

When compiling a list of people to ask inevitably I am going to miss someone out, and I am very sorry to those who would wish to have helped but did not get the opportunity. I have tried to get a range of experiences and perspectives, both on me, and on the world of dementia. I also wanted contributors to give the reader a sense of who the contributor is, and how they fit into my story.

Everyone asked exceeded my expectations and gave so generously of their time, energy, memory, wit and wisdom, and for all of that I am really a most fortunate person who is truly grateful to you all.

Thank you to all of these dear family and friends who have kindly contributed to this book...

Rosemary Oliver, James Oliver, Karon Branch, Liz Jennings, April Doyle, Nada Savitch, Dr Tim Beanland, Jane Cotton, Richard Madeley, Lisa Bogue, Reinhard Guss, Jocelyne Kenny, Jen Holland (Russell,) Adrian Bradley, Adrian "Tats" Taylor, Alexandra Bone, Amanda Drury, Amy Merritt, Anna Grinbergs-Saull, Angela Chandler, Bev Endersbee, Charles & Pauline Ryan, Charley Laity (Massingham), Chris Norris, Chris & Jayne Roberts, Christian Farthing, Colin & Anne Beech, Prof Dawn Brooker, Dave Holland, Dave Kerry, Dr Elizabeth Field,

Eric Bogle/John Munro, Eric Harmer, Frances James, Gaynor Smith, Gerry Warren, Hilary Burnage, Ian Asquith, Jacky Neale, Jenny Samuel, Jess Amos, Joy Wood, Julia Burton-Jones, Julie Reece, Kate Comfort, Katie Bennett, Laurence Ivil, Lewis Slade, Lyn Dourthe, Matt Murray, Melvyn Brooks, Michael Blackburn, Mycal Miller, Dr Pat Chung, Patricia Dale, Philly Hare, Rachael Litherland, Rachel Thompson, Dr Richard Brown, Sarah Tilsed, Steve Milton, Sumita Chauhan, Tanya Clover, Tess Reed, Toby Williamson, Tessa Gutteridge, Wendy Mitchell, Dr Yvette Kusel

Everyone's contributions to the book are amazing. Thank you. Special thanks need though to go to Rosemary, Liz and April (in April's role in Community Arts and Education at Canterbury Christ Church University) for being incredibly supportive in helping me put the book together, without the help and support of the three of you there would be no book.

Particular thanks also to Richard Madeley who, following a contact from Jane Cotton at the Alzheimer's Society, placed such confidence and trust in this book as illustrated in his foreword when the book was still being written. Pete Doyle from NXP Europe who has been so supportive to work with, Jen did such a skilful job of the back cover photo and Rosemary, despite her modesty around her artistic abilities, did a fantastic job with the front cover. Also special thanks to Nada and Tim for being the very first two people to have the faith in me with this book, and then to enable it to happen by giving me grants from each of the organisations which you both so admirably serve - I hope I can repay your trust.